Quick Die Change

By
David A. Smith

Philip E. Mitchell
Publication Administrator

Published by

Society of Manufacturing Engineers
Publications Development Department
One SME Drive
P.O. Box 930
Dearborn, Michigan 48121

Quick Die Change

Library of Congress Catalog Number: 90-062589
International Standard Book Number: 0-87263-393-4
Manufactured in the United States of America

PREFACE

Trade publications point out the necessity of setup cost reduction to implement just-in-time (JIT) manufacturing and the reduction of economic order quantities (EOQ). This is particularly true of Quick Die Change methods and its technology. The greatest benefit may be the reduction in process variability from the consistent setups and repeatable Quick Die Change methods.

For most stampers, a conservative approach to Quick Die Change is the correct one. Claims of the economic necessity for hardware-related Quick Die Change methods are just idle talk unless it can be shown that a payback actually exists.

For example, adoption of improved clamping methods for the elimination of straps and an adoption of a common tie-down height can reduce setup time for a straight-side press from 45 minutes to under 20 minutes. Adoption of common-load and shut-height can reduce this figure to under 10 minutes, with the major factor being the threading of the stock. All of these items are low in cost and can be a part of an ongoing standardization program. A careful study of economic order quantities and cost of press time may show that further expenditures are justified.

Employee teamwork is the central theme of Quick Die Change in shops that are successful in substantial setup time reductions. If Quick Die Change methods are to succeed, teamwork must be encouraged. A major portion of this book shows how to achieve teamwork in the shop.

Included is information on how to:

- Decide on the Quick Die Change technology that is appropriate for the plant.
- Institute Quick Die Change in the plant.
- Make simple diesetting improvements to reduce setup time such as common pass, shut, and clamp heights.
- Retrofit existing equipment with powered clamps, bolster rollers, and specialized die handling equipment.
- Choose new presses equipped with moving bolsters and automatic die clamps.
- Identify and eliminate the causes of stamping process variability.

The individuals and firms who have contributed to this work have recognized that there are many benefits to be gained from cooperation and mutual assistance. By donating time, talent and design examples, the contributors have provided the reader with a wealth of practical design and troubleshooting information.

Without their help, this work would not have been possible.

David Alkire Smith

PROLOGUE

Process repeatability ensures successful metal stamping. The cause of stamping process variation consists of the variables in the process.

Quick Die Changing guarantees setup repeatability. Every setup must be done in the same way according to explicit instructions. Developing teamwork and individual responsibility is the key to the successful implementation of a Quick Die Change program.

Following instructions and imparting an understanding of basic stamping skills is the key to training. This reduces process variables attributable to diesetting methods. Process variability results in poor quality stampings, causing problems during the assembly process of consumer goods.

This book goes beyond discussing why setup reduction is desirable and explains in a nuts-and-bolts fashion how to achieve Quick Die Change in any stamping facility. From the press operator, to the chief executive officer, this book should be required reading.

Robert W. Prucka
Stamping Manager
Wayne Integrated Stamping and Assembly Facility
Ford Motor Company
Wayne, Michigan

LIST OF CONTRIBUTORS

Ronald C. Anderson, Director Of Human Resources, Opdyke Stamping Incorporated, Oxford, Michigan

James J. Albrecht, Dayton Progress Corporation, Dayton, Ohio

John Andrick, Electrical Engineer, Opdyke Stamping Incorporated, Oxford, Michigan

James G. Barrett, Jr., President, Link Systems, Nashville, Tennessee

C. Sean Battles, Executive Consultant, Strategic Manufacturing Planning, Deere Technical Services, Moline, Illinois

Ashok Bhide, Data Instruments, Acton, Massachusetts

Rollin Bondar, President, MPD Welding, Incorporated, Troy, Michigan

Ted Boop, Press Consulting Engineer, Elkhart, Indiana

John A. Borns, President, Benchmark Technologies Corporation, Toledo, Ohio

Dennis J. Boerger, StamTec, Minster, Ohio

Roscoe Brumback, Quality Control Manager, W. C. McCurdy Company, Troy, Michigan

Robert R. Campbell, President, Robert R. Campbell, Incorporated, Lansing, Michigan

Steve Cool, Facility Engineer, Wayne Integrated Stamping and Assembly Facility, Ford Motor Company, Wayne, Michigan

Gary Cousins, UAW Uptime Coordinator, B-O-C Lansing Fabrication, General Motors Corporation, Lansing, Michigan

Larry Crainich, President, Design Standards Corporation, Bridgeport, Connecticut

Rod Denton, President, Sun Steel Treating Incorporated, South Lyon, Michigan

C. R. Fait, Plant Manager, W. C. McCurdy Company, Troy, Michigan

Larry Falk, Operations Manager, Siemens Energy and Automation, Incorporated, I-T-E Circuit Protection Division, Bellefontaine, Ohio

David S. Fletcher, MC^2 Automotive Sensors Group, Broadview Heights, Ohio

Nicholas Fischer, Metalworking Machinery Systems, Incorporated, Elkhart, Indiana

Jeff Fredline, Operations Manager, Campbell Incorporated, Lansing, Michigan

Leo Geenens, Corporate Quality Control Manager, Midway Products Corporation, Monroe, Michigan

Wendell J. Geiger, President W. J. Geiger Incorporated, Ferndale, Michigan

Mike Gelbke, Facilities Engineer, Mazda Motor Manufacturing (USA) Corporation, Flat Rock, Michigan

Phillip A. Gibson, District Manager, Atlas Automation Division, Automated Manufacturing Systems, Incorporated, Atlanta, Georgia

Barry Goldsmith, Process Manager, Harris Semiconductor Division, Findlay, Ohio

Todd Gonzales, General Manager, Product Application Center, National Steel Corporation, Livonia, Michigan

Jeffrey Gordish, Manager, Maintenance Management Consulting, Management Technologies Incorporated, Troy, Michigan

Chuck Gregoire, Metallurgist, Product Application Center, National Steel Corporation, Livonia, Michigan

Paul Griglio, Stamping Special Programs Manager, Chrysler Corporation, Detroit, Michigan

A. L. Hall, Manager, Stamping Engineering, Ford Motor Company, Dearborn, Michigan

Ray Hedding, Stamping Manager, Mazda Motor Manufacturing (USA) Corporation, Flat Rock, Michigan

Michael R. Herderich, Senior Project Engineer, The Budd Company Technical Center, Auburn Hills, Michigan

Joseph Hladik, Tool Designer, Western Electric Company, Columbus, Ohio

Jack O. Hoenig, Press Equipment Corporation, Toledo, Ohio

David M. Holley, Chief Engineer, Dadco, Incorporated, Detroit, Michigan

Joseph Ivaska, Vice President of Engineering, Tower Oil and Technology Company, Chicago, Illinois

Norbert Izworski, Product Development Engineer, Body and Assembly Division, Ford Motor Company, Dearborn, Michigan

Art C. Jernberg, Manufacturing Manager, Siemens Energy and Automation, Incorporated, I-T-E Circuit Protection Division, Bellefontaine, Ohio

Ed Jewell, Machine Shop Foreman, Detail Machine, Oxford, Michigan

Robert I. Johnson, Director of Manufacturing Engineering, B-O-C Lansing Fabrication, General Motors Corporation, Lansing, Michigan

Dr. Stuart P. Keeler, Manager, Metallurgy and Sheet Metal Technology, The Budd Company Technical Center, Auburn Hills, Michigan

George Keremedjiev, Consultant, Tecknow Educational Service, Bozeman, Montana

Karl A. Keyes, President, Feinblanking Limited, Fairfield, Ohio

Steven A. Kontney, Project Engineer, Arvin, Arvinal Division, Columbus, Indiana

Roman J. Krygier, Stamping Operations Manager, Body and Assembly Division, Ford Motor Company, Dearborn, Michigan

Philip E. Laven, Director of Manufacturing, Trumark, Incorporated, Lansing, Michigan

John Lay, Manager, Process and Quality Engineering, Webster Industries, Incorporated, Tiffin, Ohio

Dan Leighton, Atlas Automation Division, Automated Manufacturing Systems, Incorporated, Fenton, Michigan

Cecil Lewis, Director of Manufacturing and Engineering, Midway Products Corporation, Monroe, Michigan

Robert G. Lown, Vice President, Greenard Press and Machine Company, Nashua, New Hampshire

Larry Lucas, Maintenance Manager, Webster Manufacturing Company, Tiffin, Ohio

Gary Maddock, Product Metallurgist, Crucible Specialty Metals, Syracuse, New York

Albert A. Manduzzi, Supervisor, Die Design and Standards, Ford Motor Company, Dearborn, Michigan

Michael R. Martin, Application Specialist, Darnell and Diebolt Company, Detroit, Michigan

John McCurdy, President, W. C. McCurdy Company, Troy, Michigan

Alex McNeilly, Commercial Artist, Southgate, Michigan

Dr. Anthony E. Melonakos, M.D., Monroe, Michigan

Ralph Meyers, General Foreman, Maintenance and Machine, Commercial Intertech Corporation, Youngstown, Ohio

Arnold Miedema, President, Capitol Engineering Company, Wyoming, Michigan

Dr. James Miller, D.O., Monroe, Michigan

Mike Moran, Vice President, Hilma Corporation, Acton, Massachusetts

Wayne Morey, Engineering, Manager, Opdyke Stamping Incorporated, Oxford, Michigan

Danny A. Morgan, Superintendent, Tooling and Maintenance, Siemens Energy and Automation, Incorporated, I-T-E Circuit Protection Division, Bellefontaine, Ohio

Eugene J. Narbut, Specialist, Stamping Manufacturing, Mazda Motor Manufacturing (USA) Corporation, Flat Rock, Michigan

Gil Novak, Manager, Capacity and Facility Planning, Body and Assembly Division, Dearborn, Michigan

Russ I. Peddle, Production, Manager, VME Equipment of Canada, Limited, Guelph, Ontario

Gerald A. Pool, Senior Manufacturing Engineer, Cadillac Motor Car Division, General Motors Corporation, Troy, Michigan

Angleo Piccinini, Die Design and Die Standards Supervisor, Chrysler Corporation, Detroit, Michigan

Robert. W. Prucka, Stamping Manager, Wayne Integrated Stamping and Assembly Facility, Ford Motor Company, Wayne, Michigan

Anthony Rante, Manager, Mechanical Engineering, Danly Machine, Chicago, Illinois

Thomas D. Ready, Attorney, Monroe, Michigan

William S. Roorda, Alcona Associates, Harrison, Michigan

Anthony J. Rotondo, Stanley-Vidmar, Allentown, Pennsylvania

Aniese Seed, President, (retired) Toledo Transducers Incorporated, Toledo, Ohio

Mr. Dennis Shirk, Vice President, Hydra-Fab, Incorporated, East Detroit, Michigan

Mr. Richard Shirk, President, Hydra-Fab, Incorporated, East Detroit, Michigan

Gary L. Smotherman, President, UAW Local 1892, Ford Motor Company, Maumee, Ohio

George Sondergeld, Estimator, Detail Machine, Oxford, Michigan

Fredric Spurck, President, Webster Industries Incorporated, Tiffin, Ohio

Philip D. Stang, Vice President, Professionals for Technology, Palm Beach Gardens, Florida

Robert Storer, President, Toledo Transducers Incorporated, Toledo, Ohio

Dr. S. E. Swanson, M.D., Ypsilanti, Michigan

Nick Tarkany, Director of Research and Education, Dayton Progress Corporation, Dayton, Ohio

Eric Theis, Vice President, Herr-Voss Corporation, Callery, Pennsylvania

Jack L. Thompson, Vice President of Manufacturing, Walker Manufacturing Division of Tenneco Automotive, Grass Lake, Michigan

George Tolford, Executive Vice President, Webster Industries, Incorporated, Tiffin, Ohio

Ismael Vicens, Project Manager, Lightlier, Division of Genlyte, Edison, New Jersey

Andy Wadson, Manufacturing Manager, W. C. McCurdy Company, Troy, Michigan

Robert L. Wagner, Regional Manager, Helm Instrument Company, Maumee, Ohio

Maurice Wayne, Director, Corporate Quality Statistical Systems, Opdyke Stamping, Oxford, Michigan

Bernard J. Wallis, Chairman of the Board, Livernois Engineering Corporation, Dearborn, Michigan

James H. Wilber, Production Superintendent, Siemens Energy and Automation, Incorporated, Circuit Protection and Controls Division, Urbana, Ohio

Donald Wilhelm, President, Helm Instrument Company, Maumee, Ohio

Richard T. Wilhelm, General Manager, Helm Instrument Company, Maumee, Ohio

Kimball Williams, Electromagnetic Interference Specialist, Eaton Corporation, Southfield, Michigan

Ron Wilson, Production Superintendent, Calsonic Yorozu Corporation, Morrison, Tennessee

Terry Wireman, Keith Stevens Company, Eden Prairie, Minnesota

Joseph L. Wise, Punch Press and Metals Treating Manager, Webster Manufacturing Company, Tiffin, Ohio

Samuel O. Wolock, Marwol Metals Limited, Southfield, Michigan

James H. Woodard, Manager, Tooling and Equipment, Inter-City Products, Lewisburg, Tennessee

Mike Young, President, Vibro-Dynamics, Broadview, Illinois

TABLE OF CONTENTS

Chapter

1

INTRODUCTION

HISTORY OF QUICK DIE CHANGE

History, the record of human progress, teaches that credit for authorship of important concepts is often clouded and uncertain. One of the best places to settle questions about the invention origin is at the patent office.

The acronym QDC, short for quick die change is a registered trademark of Danly Machine of Chicago, Illinois. Application for this trademark was made on June 29, 1961 and granted October 23, 1962. Patent application for the Danly QDC system was made by inventor Vasil Georgeff on August 16, 1956 and granted in 1961. This system featured dual moving bolsters that permitted exchanges of large stamping dies in under 10 minutes.

The Danly QDC system, which together with developments by USI-Clearing and others, is considered to be the basis for many automatic die changing systems that employ moving bolsters and automatic clamping systems. This is also clear from existing licensing agreements.

The Great Lakes Basin of North America was a natural location for the development of quick die change. Chicago is the home of both the telephone and the coin machine industry. The production volume of electromechanical relay parts demanded that a number of dies producing the same part be in operation simultaneously. To change them quickly, they were made and maintained at identical dimensions.

The next logical step was to build different dies to the same standard dimensions in order to facilitate quickly changing dies. Exchanging dies by automatic means and producing a different product in under 10 minutes was the following step.

Over a quarter of a century ago, the Western Electric Company had a boltless system of automatically exchanged dies that could change over in less than a minute. These dies punched the holes in standard relay rack panels. An almost endless variety of panel configurations were produced from a few standardized blank channels. Today, we would recognize this as an automated work cell for flexible manufacturing.

The Western Electric Companies' Chicago, Illinois Hawthorne Works is gone. It was replaced by a shopping mall. What remains is one of the best organized systems of manufacturing standards in the world: A pioneering computerized preventive maintenance system, a legacy of systematic industrial motion picture time and motion studies and the basis for the Science of Human Relations; The Hawthorne Experiment.

1

WHY WE FAILED

Starting in the late 1950s, Danly and USI—Clearing made presses equipped with moving bolsters, standard locating pins and automatic die clamps that were installed in a number of American and Japanese automotive stamping plants.

In many of the American plants, the automatic clamps were soon removed and replaced with manual bolts. This was due in large measure to a failure of the die room to get the locating pin holes in the correct location so the clamps would line-up with the clamping slots in the upper die.

When the bolster failed to move for any reason, the cause was seldom found and corrected. Instead a fork-lift truck was used to batter it into position. To remove the die from the press, die cushion pins were inserted into the tapped holes in the bolster that were intended for handling hooks. The bridge crane chain slings then jerked the die and bolster out of the press. This practice resulted in the threaded holes being ruined as well as serious accidents.

The Japanese succeeded in getting their equipment to work as intended. Perhaps some day a historian will document exactly why we failed. Several factors may have been:

1. A severe shortage of qualified skilled workers.
2. The entry of untrained persons into the skilled trades ranks.
3. Intense unrest within the skilled trades ranks as evidenced by a rival union, The International Society of Skilled Trades seeking to represent the UAW skilled workers.
4. Numerous wildcat strikes and acts of sabotage.
5. The ripple effect of the social unrest generated by the Vietnam war.
6. Some "experts" claim that the lackadaisical style of management that was prevalent during the era could have been a factor.

WHY WE MAKE IT WORK NOW

On February 2, 1988, the writer had the pleasure of presenting a paper at a SME Flexible Metal Stamping Operations Clinic in Southfield, Michigan.[1]

While showing slides of a die change on a double ram clearing Hitatchi transfer press at Woodhaven (Michigan) Stamping Plant, the question was raised as to how long it took to change dies. The reply was, "About two hours." There were murmurs in the audience. Someone finally said, "it's only supposed to take five minutes." The reply was, "Yes, I know. Do you have any idea how proud we were when we got it down to one day from three days."

As was explained, a dedicated team of operators, die setters, skilled tradesmen and management representatives would stop the die set whenever there was an indication of trouble and correct the root cause before proceeding further.

The Logic Behind the New Method

Simply put, it makes a lot of sense to find the root cause of a problem that delays a die set and fix it once and for all rather than to continue to be plagued by it on every future changeover.

REASONS FOR ADOPTING QUICK DIE CHANGE METHODS

There are a number of benefits that quick die change can be expected to provide.

Increased Capacity

The time expended setting up a stamping press is essentially idle press time. Setup time reduction is the most cost-effective means to increase the capacity of a stamping plant. The required capital expenditure is low compared to the cost of increased floor space and additional presses.

Scrap Reduction

The goal of quick die change is to quickly change from one standardized setup to another and produce top-quality parts when production resumes. The setup repeatability that quick die change requires insures that the first hit produces a good part. Trial-and-error adjustments usually produce unavoidable scrap. Eliminating these adjustments will eliminate the scrap.

Job Security

Metal stamping is a very competitive business. Staying in business depends upon making a profit. The term ''world-class'' means the ability to meet the challenge of any shop in the world in terms of deliverable quality, actual productivity, and real profitability. Backing away from the challenge simply means that ultimate defeat and insolvency has been accepted.

Safety

Conversion to quick die change provides an opportunity to improve die clamping methods. For example, if strap clamps are being currently used in conjunction with poor setup blocks, the quick die change conversion is an opportunity to adopt more secure clamping methods.

Die and Press Maintenance Costs

A very large percentage of the total die and press damage occurs when diesetting.

Shut height errors are a common source of difficulty. These will no longer be a problem if a common shut height is established. Quick die change requires secure die handling methods. Secure die handling will insure that dies are not accidentally dropped.

Reduced Inventory

The increased press "up-time" and productivity made possible by quick die change can cause the warehouse to overflow rather quickly. The reduced setup cost and increased setup confidence makes possible low economic order quantities (EOQ) and short production runs. JIT is now a realistic goal.

Improved Quality

Quick die change techniques require exact duplication of a standardized setup. Examples of this are positive die location and common shut heights. The elimination of trial-and-error techniques practically guarantees repeatability. Quick die change will reduce process variability.

REFERENCES

1. Smith, D. A., "How to Improve Hit-to-hit Time With a Tonnage Monitor", SME Technical Paper TE88-780, Society of Manufacturing Engineers, Dearborn, Michigan, 1989.

2

BASIC GOOD DIESETTING PRACTICES

Success in any activity requires that most, if not all, tasks be done correctly. In metal stamping, everything from poor quality to catastrophic die and press damage has often had the cause traced to a poor diesetting practice.

Examples of both good and bad practices are throughout this book. It is very important that the good practices that are appropriate be the ones that are used.

DIESETTERS ARE METALWORKING PROFESSIONALS

Avoid Shortcuts

Diesetters are the elite among pressroom employees. They are chosen for the position based upon their knowledge, experience, and the desire to accept the challenge of being a key person upon whom the safety and productivity of the shop depends. Professionalism in any field requires continuous improvement of knowledge and work habits. There is no substitute for good diesetting work habits.

Shortcuts that are intended to make the job easier soon become bad habits which may cause catastrophic damage to dies and presses and even result in serious injury. The safe and proper way is usually the easiest in the long run.

The Diesetter Helps the Operator

In many pressrooms, the diesetter is expected to help train the operator to efficiently produce quality stampings and to use safe operating practices. This may include:
1. How to start the strip into a progressive die correctly.
2. How often to inspect the part for defects.
3. What to look for when inspecting parts for defects.
4. The type and quantity of lubricant to use.
5. How the lubricant is to be applied.
6. Where, and how often to check for proper scrap ejection.
7. How to pack the parts in containers.
8. What to do when parts baskets or scrap tubs need changing.
9. How to identify irregular operation of the press and die.
10. How to keep the area clean.
11. The correct way to fill out job tickets and time sheets.
12. Where the operator may find the diesetter in case of difficulty.

BASIC GOOD PRACTICES

Basic diesetting skills apply to all diesetting situations. It doesn't matter if the assignment is to set a die weighing less than 50 lbs. in an OBI press, or to exchange dies weighing many tons each in a multi-slide transfer press. Checking for mechanical interference with a simple tape measure is often required to avoid difficulty.

Making Shut Height

This is the most basic task that the diesetter must do. Simply stated, the closed height of the die must not be greater than the shut height (at bottom dead center) of the press. Never guess, instead carefully double-check with a *tape measure*.

There are usually enough problems with roof leaks without trying to launch press parts into outer space through the roof *Figure 2-1*.

The procedure to make shut-height is:

1. Measure and note the die shut (closed) height.
2. Inch the press on bottom dead center.
3. Measure the opening—make sure that there is enough room.

The tape measure is as important to a good diesetter as a wrench.

Keep the Bolster Clean

Slugs are a frequent source of problems to the diesetter. The best plan is to have sufficient chutes of good design and construction to convey all scrap and slugs to the scrap bin or conveyor. Frequently a few slugs will still remain.

Slugs Cause Problems. A slug between the bolster and the lower die shoe is illustrated in *Figure 2-2A* . During the run, the slug will become imbedded in both the die shoe and bolster (*B*). Even if the slug is removed with the corner of a scale or scriber, the damage continues to cause an out-of-parallel condition (*C*).

For general presswork, the accepted maximum tolerance for slide to bolster parallelism is 0.001 in. (0.025 mm) per foot (305 mm). Precision dies for cutting silicon steel laminations require an even more precise out-of-parallel tolerance. A single 0.030 in. (0.76 mm) slug under one end of a three foot (914 mm) long die shoe will cause an out-of-parallel condition that will exceed the generally accepted tolerance by a factor of 10. *Figure 2-3* is an exaggerated view of a slug under a die shoe.

Slugs Are a Safety Hazard. When the slug becomes embedded in the die shoe and bolster, the die clamps will loosen. Slugs underfoot are a slipping hazard. All slugs must be cleaned up before proceeding with setting a new die.

Slugs Can Damage Dies. The out-of-parallel condition caused by slugs under a die can result in die damage. *Figure 2-4* illustrates a type of damage that can occur to cutting dies. The damage is not confined to cutting edges.

Setup blocks can literally be buried into the die shoe. *Figure 2-5* illustrates how this occurs. In *A* the setup block is making normal light contact with the

Figure 2-1. *The moon shot.* (*Alex McNeilly*)

upper die shoe. *B* illustrates the block mushroomed-out and buried into the upper die shoe. The lower shoe is damaged as well. The displaced metal in the shoes will spoil the precision line bored fit of the guide pin and bushing holes.

7

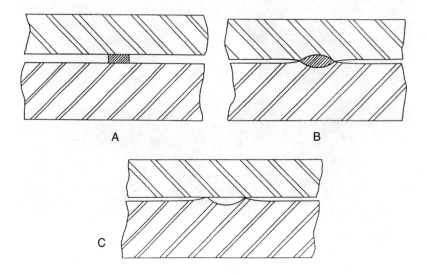

Figure 2-2. *A slug between the lower die shoe and the bolster: (A) before the run; (B) during production; (C) the damage remains after the next dieset.*

Slugs Affect the Process. A single slug can cause a drastic change in the die clearances that determine the quality of the product produced. SPC data is an excellent source of information on the process changes because of poor diesetting practices. Chapter 15 has detailed information on many of the causes of stamping process variability.

Repairing a Slug Mark. Setting dies on slugs and the resultant slug marks greatly accelerate bolster plate wear. Care in avoiding slug marks will greatly extend the intervals between required bolster plate resurfacing.

In the event that a slug becomes embedded in the bolster plate, it should be picked out with a pointed tool, and the upset metal peened down with a hammer. The area is then finished flat with a file. This procedure minimizes the amount of metal removed and the size of the remaining depressed area.

Figure 2-3. *A slug under the die shoe forces the slide to change position and become out-of-parallel with the bolster.*

8

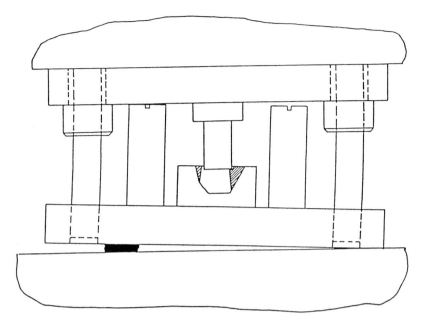

Figure 2-4. *Example of damage to a cutting die caused by an out-of- parallel condition from a slug under the die shoe.*

Avoiding Slug Problems. The best cure for any problem is prevention. Proper slug chutes are a necessity for top quality pressworking.

Scrap Chutes

In some shops, the diesetters are expected to fabricate the required scrap chutes. Often large stamping plants have a millwright or tinsmith who makes the needed chutes. This may also be a responsibility of the diemaker or die maintenance person.

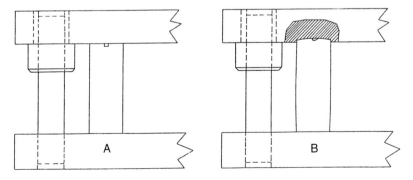

Figure 2-5. *Setup block damage caused by a large slug under the die. (A) before the run; (B) damage after the run.*

Tools Required For Chute Construction. Good chute construction requires that proper tools be available. The tools needed are a function of the sheet metal thickness used in chute construction. The usual range of thicknesses is from 11 to 16 gage. Purchasing a sheet metal shear and brake capable of working the heaviest gage metal formed is actually an investment in good housekeeping.

The alternative is to form poorly fitting chutes from whatever coil stock is on hand.

Keeping Slugs Out Of The Tee Slots. A few slugs always seem to bounce out of the finest of chutes and find their way into the tee slots. *Figure 2-6* illustrates the insertion of inexpensive rubber hose into a tee-slot to prevent a buildup of stray slugs.

Chute Storage. Keeping scrap and slug chutes in top condition requires everyone's cooperation. It does little good to be able to change dies quickly if several additional hours are required to construct replacements for chutes that were lost, damaged beyond repair while in storage, or cannibalized for another job.

A designated storage procedure is required for all chutes. Often the chutes can be left with the die provided it is possible to transport the die to and from the storage rack without damaging the chutes.

If wall space is available, it can provide an excellent place to hang chutes for storage. Painting an outline of each chute together with the appropriate job or die number on both the chute and the wall is a very good method. Visitors to the shop can be expected to make favorable comments about such a system.

Other systems such as storage in racks and tubs also can be used. Some highly automated stamping plants even have automated storage and retrieval systems which operate with computer control to store change-over items that cannot be stored with the dies.

As a metalworking professional, the diesetter has a responsibility to help insure that all chutes and production aids are stored correctly. Helping management devise good storage systems is a natural outlet for a good diesetter's talents.

Centering the Load in the Press

Maintaining correct die clearances is a basic requirement for producing

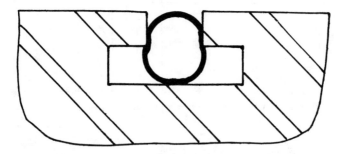

Figure 2-6. *Rubber hose inserted into an unused tee slot to keep out stray slugs.*

high-quality stampings. If the load is not centered in the press, critical die clearances will be changed.

How Off Center Loading Affects the Process. Off center loading results in an out-of-level condition much like that caused by setting a die on a slug. This is because the press must deflect to develop tonnage. If the load is centered the deflection is uniform and the slide remains parallel to the bolster. If the load is not centered, the greatest deflection occurs in the side of the press with the greatest load resulting in an out-of-parallel condition.

Cutting Clearances Are Changed. In the case of cutting dies, too little clearance between the punch and die will result in excessive cutting pressures which will break down the cutting edges quickly. Too much clearance will result with an excessive burr.

Press Deflection Should be Balanced. *Figure 2-7A* illustrates an exaggerated view of the press deflection that is a normal result of developing the tonnage. Just as a spring must change shape or deflect to develop pressure, a press must deflect to develop tonnage.

The illustration shows a rather small die centered in the press. Not all of the press tonnage capacity is available under such circumstances. As a general rule, at least 70% of the press bed should be occupied with a centrally placed die shoe if full press tonnage capacity is to be developed. Developing full tonnage with a small die can result in damage to the press slide and bed due to excessive localized deflection.

Reasons For Offsetting Dies. The most common reason for setting dies offset from the center of the press is for the loading convenience of the operator. The operator does not have to reach or bend as far to place and remove parts from the die.

Another reason is the lack of a proper stock guide or production aid needed to place the stock into the die with ease. *Figure 2-7B* illustrates a die offset to one side of the press for operator or setup convenience.

The Effect of Unbalanced Loading. The result of unequal loading is shown in *Figure 2-7C*. The result is an out-of-parallel condition when press deflection occurs.

The short-term effect in press misalignment under pressure is similar to that of a slug under the die shoe. The quality of work and the number of pieces produced between die sharpenings will be lower than if the load were centered.

The long-term effect is uneven press wear. Bearings will not wear evenly, resulting in an out-of-parallel condition in the future. The gibbing will be subjected to high localized pressures resulting in rapid uneven wear and scoring.

Solutions to Off-center Die Placement. A good solution usually requires a careful analysis of all factors. These may include:

1. Is a smaller press available so the operator will not need to reach as far to place the blank?
2. Can a production aid be constructed to permit the part to slide into correct location by gravity?
3. Is it possible to operate two dies in the same press to balance the loading?

11

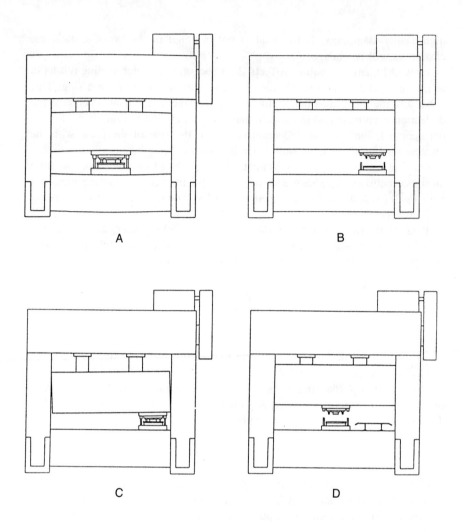

Figure 2-7. *An exaggerated view (A) of the press deflection that is a normal result of developing the tonnage needed to do presswork; the die offset to one side of the press (B) for operator or setup convenience; unequal loading results in an out-of-parallel condition (C) when press deflection occurs; to correct off-center loading of a press, a simple production aid or stock guide (D) may be all that is required.*

4. Is the placement of nitrogen cylinders on one side of the press to balance the load practical?
5. Will the addition of die or press automation be a cost effective solution?
6. Is there a good reason for offset loading such as placing a progressive die to one side to balance tonnage developed by the press?

Figure 2-7D illustrates a simple stock guide used to correct the problem. A detailed analysis of this problem is conducted in Chapters 11 and 15.

Mis-hit Damage

Many dies are designed with balanced cutting action. This is done to avoid side thrust which can change die clearances. If the part design or stock layout will not permit balanced cutting action, very large guide pins or heel blocks are required to limit the side-movement to an acceptable amount.

Mis-positioned stock can damage the die. The unbalanced loading can be so severe that the stock is flanged rather than cut. *Figure 2-8* illustrates this concept.

Out-of-location stock (A) is flanged into a large cutting die opening due to the unbalanced cutting action resulting from mislocated stock (B). Because the cutting clearance is only 10% of the stock thickness, the side displacement is so great that the punch and die cutting edges hit upon die closure and are damaged (C).

It is very important that the diesetter make the operator aware of how this type of damage occurs and how it may be avoided.

Honest reporting of any damage of this type is important. The damage shown in *Figure 2-6C* could be reported as a broken punch. Replacing the small punch in the press would not fix the damage to the other sta-

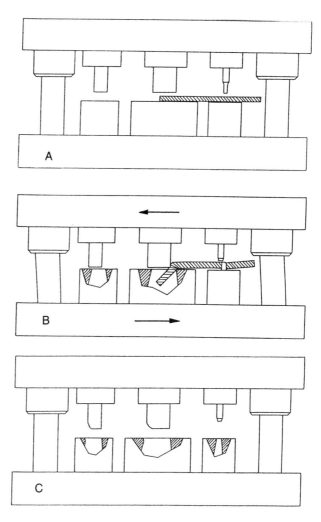

Figure 2-8. *Out-of-location stock can cause die damage: (A) out-of-location stock in a die; (B) a partial cut results in the stock being flanged into a die opening causing the die shoes to be displaced sideways; (C) the damage that results.*

tions. Press time should not be wasted. A die damaged like this should be taken to the dieroom for extensive repair.

TRICKS TO IMPROVE DIE ALIGNMENT

Most the diesetting is accomplished under less than ideal circumstances. In some shops, die shoes with guide pins and bushings are considered a luxury. For many punching, forming, embossing, and drawing applications, the punch is fastened to the press slide and the die fastened to the bolster after careful alignment. Exact alignment requires considerable diesetting skills.

Floating the Lower Die

This procedure involves a controlled side movement of the lower die before it is tightly clamped in place. This practice is usually necessary when tooling is not mounted in a dieset. Usually a part is in place when this procedure is followed. The lower die is permitted to "float" into position while the press is carefully inched to bottom. The lower die is then tightened into position.

Compensating for Alignment Problems

The floating technique is also of value when problems such as a worn guide bushing, press wear or poor alignment result in loose burrs on one side of a trim panel or uneven sidewall thinning in deep drawing operations. At best, it is a stop-gap measure because floating does not address the cause of the problem.

DIE LOCATING METHODS

A precise repeatable die locating method is essential if quick die changing and setup repeatability are to be achieved. Accurate die locating should not depend upon complicated measuring or trial and error methods. Adjustments with forklift trucks, bumpers, or pry bars are often not correct.

The following methods represent several popular locating methods:

"V" Locators

Figure 2-9A illustrates a very common method of locating dies and die subplates on the bolster. A "V" locator and machined flat pocket engage pins in the bolster that are spaced at standardized locations. To accommodate differing die widths in the same press, several pairs of pin holes may be bored in the bolster and the pins moved to the appropriate pair of holes for the die being set.

Figure 18-3 is another example of this locating system in which hardened inserts are used to avoid wear problems.

14

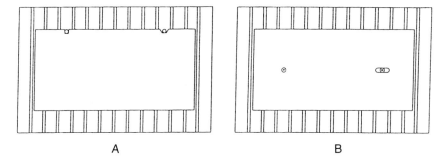

A   B

Figure 2-9. *Common methods of locating die sub-plates on the bolster. (A) a "V" locator and machined flat pocket engage pins in the bolster; (B) round locating pins located on the centerline of the bolster engage a hole and slot on the centerline of the die subplate.*

Pin Locators

Locating pins fitted into bored holes on the centerline of the press bolster are illustrated in *Figure 2-9B*. This is a very common method of locating dies on moving bolsters. The die bottom shoe has one round and one slotted hole machined on standard locations. Several pairs of bored holes may be provided on the centerline of the bolster to accommodate dies of various lengths.

For large dies, a typical pin diameter is 3 in. (76.2 mm). A conical point is provided on the pin to permit ease of engagement as the die is lowered with a crane.

Generally 0.060 in. (1.524 mm) clearance is provided to prevent binding and pin breakage as the die is lifted off the bolster. For this reason, the "V" locator system can provide more precise location and may be favored for moving as well as fixed bolster applications.

Tee-Slot Key Locators For Knee and OBI Presses

Figure 2-10 illustrates keys used to provide front-to-back location in a knee or OBI press. If the optional stem is used, only one key is needed and precise left-to-right location also is assured.

Locating Dies Front-to-back in Straightside Presses

Figure 2-11 illustrates a system of locating a die front-to-back by means of a keyway milled in the bolster *(D1)*. A wider keyway is milled in the lower die parallel *(D2)* to permit easy engagement of the key *(D3)* when the die is placed in the press with a fork lift truck. A standard practice is to shove the die toward the rear of the press to insure that the center of the stock path is lined up with the center of the bolster for progressive die operations.

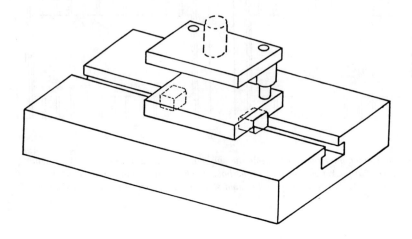

Figure 2-10. *Locating a die front-to-back in an OBI press. If the optional stem is used, only one key is needed and precise left-to-right location also is assured.*

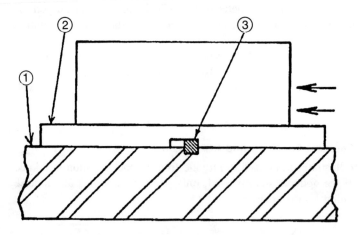

Figure. 2-11. *Locating a die front-to-back by means of a keyway milled in the bolster (D1): a wider keyway is milled in the lower die parallel (D2) to permit easy engagement of the key (D3) when the die is placed in the press with a fork lift truck.*

3

SETTING PROGRESSIVE DIES
QUICKLY AND SAFELY*

In addition to the good practices discussed in Chapter two, when setting progressive dies, the diesetter must perform additional tasks quickly and safely. These include:

- Adjusting the decoiler.
- Adjusting the stock straightener.
- Setting the feeder to the correct pitch.
- Assuring that the press, feeder, and decoiler are aligned properly.
- Compensating for stock camber if necessary.
- Starting the strip into the die correctly.
- Installing chutes, scrap conveyors, air blow-off devices and containers.
- Cam limit switches.
- Activating and adjusting die protection devices.
- Installing point-of-operation protection.
- Bottoming the die correctly.
- Running sample parts.
- Securing quality control approval.
- Instructing the operator if necessary.

Work Assignments Vary from Shop to Shop

Depending upon shop practices, the diesetter may work with other diesetters as a team. In addition, other persons such as the press operator may serve on the team during the dieset. In some shops, the function of operator and diesetter are combined.

PRESS FEEDERS, STRAIGHTENERS AND DECOILERS[1,2]

There is a great variety of available coil handling, decoiling, straightening, and feeding equipment used in blanking and progressive die operations. The equipment available from many manufacturers can be used interchangeably in many different configurations. *Figure 3-1* illustrates one such system.

*Arnold Miedema, President, Capitol Engineering, and Edwin A. Stouten, Retired Vice President, Capitol Engineering, contributed to this chapter.

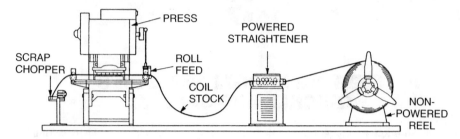

Figure 3-1. *Coil line containing a nonpowered reel, powered stock straightener, roll feeder, press and scrap chopper. (Cooper-Weymouth-Peterson)*[2]

BASIC FUNCTIONAL REQUIREMENTS

Decoiling System

The stock must be decoiled (unwound) from the stock reel in a smooth manner. Uneven stop-go operation may cause kinks in the coil stock that can cause variations in the parts produced. Both power and nonpower driven systems are used. Powered systems should incorporate controls to insure smooth actuation of starting and stopping functions. When the use of unpowered decoilers result in kinked stock or overloads the pulling capacity of the stock straightener or feeder, the need for a powered decoiler is indicated.

Quick Die Change Considerations. There should be a rapid means to band and remove a partial coil of stock left over from the job being removed. The new coil should be at the line ready to insert. If a cradle type of decoiler is used, the correct settings should be known in advance. If *shoes* or inserts are needed to change the diameter of a decoiler with a spindle or expanding mandrel, these should be ready as part of the pre-staging or external dieset function.

If the decoiler is movable on ways or a track to center the coil feed path, a means to achieve the correct positioning without trial-and-error adjustments is desirable.

Stock Straightener

When the stock is unwound by the decoiler, there remains a normal curvature or *coil set* in the stock. The coil set is often removed by a stock straightener for smooth feeding in the stock guides of progressive dies; as an aid in producing uniform parts; for other coil defects such as the bowing of the stock and kinks. This is done by subjecting the stock to a series of up and down bends as it passes through a series of rollers. The bending action must be severe enough to exceed the yield point of the stock as the outer fibers of the metal are alternately stretched and compressed.

Figure 3-2 illustrates the principle of operation of a powered stock straightener. The first pair of powered feed rolls *(D1)* feeds the stock into a series of seven straightening rollers *(D2)*. A second set of powered rollers *(D3)* operating

18

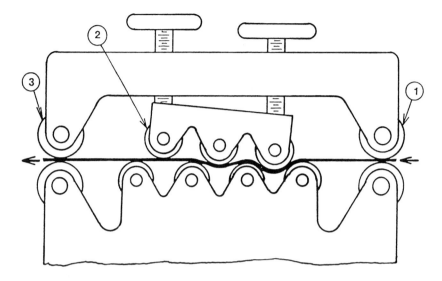

Figure 3-2. *The principle of operation of a powered stock straightener; the first pair of powered feed rolls (D1) feeds the stock into a series of seven straightening rollers (D2); a second set of powered rollers (D3) operating in synchronism with the first set (D1) acts to pull the stock through the straightener.*

in synchronism with the first set *(D1)* act to pull the stock through the straightener.

Depending upon the application, a greater number of straightening rollers may be used. For normal operation, the straightening rollers on the entry end of the machine are set to bend the stock more severely than those on the exit end. When correctly adjusted, the stock will exit the machine with an equal amount of *residual stress* on both sides of the *neutral axis* and be very straight.

Stock straighteners incorporating simple leveling rolls cannot correct problems such as stock camber or thickness variations. Specialized leveling equipment that incorporate adjustable back-up rolls is required for such applications.

Quick Die Change Considerations. A rapid means to set the stock straightener feed roll pressures and straightening roll positions to the correct values for the job being set is an important way to reduce setup time. The adjusting mechanisms should have built-in means to repeat the correct settings such as position scales, turn counters and pressure gages.

The setup settings can be kept at the press or in the pressroom in a file cabinet for ready reference. An increasingly popular way of maintaining this important data is to print it directly onto a diesetting work order from a centralized computerized database. If the job runs well in more than one press, the settings for the press can be printed automatically when the scheduling department issues the work order.

19

Roll Feeds

Roll feeds frequently advance the stock into progressive dies. Normally, the stock is momentarily released upon pilot entry to permit it to correctly align the stock. A slight overfeed is often helpful when using the pilot release feeders as it is usually easier for it to shove the stock back than to pull it forward.

Commonly, a single pair of rolls as illustrated in *Figure 3-3* feed stock into the die. Some specialized applications employ two pairs of synchronized rolls (*Figure 3-1*) with one pair pushing and the other pair pulling the stock across the die.

Roll feeders driven by the press crankshaft usually require some trial-and-error adjustment of the feed mechanism to achieve the correct pitch setting.

Quick Die Change Considerations. The latest roll feed designs include types powered by brushless direct current motors that provide very precise control. The feed pitch can be pre-programmed and stored as a job number in an on-board computer that can also preset press functions such as counterbalance pressure, shut-height, and tonnage limits. The correct information for setup of both the press and feeder can be done by such means as inputting bar-coded information from the die or dieset work order.

Measuring-type feeders have material-measuring rolls that are separate from the main feeding rolls so that accurate feed lengths can be maintained even though the material may slip occasionally on the feed rolls. The measuring rolls turn a digital pulse generator. As the preselected length is reached, the digital control initiates the slowdown and stopping action of the main feed rolls. Close feed accuracies and excellent repeatability can be obtained.

It is important to mark the correct pitch setting on the die itself as a check in case the figure from the quick die change database is in error.

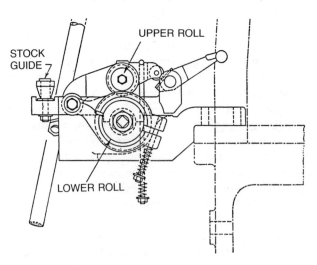

Figure 3-3. *A single roll feed attached to the press.*[1,2] *(E. W. Bliss Co.)*

20

Combining Roll Feeding and Straightening

Unless economy and space limitations dictate otherwise, the best feeding practice is to separate the straightening rolls from the feeding rolls. Feeding is naturally an intermittent operation. Removing coil curvature in a straightening machine will require less power and will do a better job of straightening if the machine runs at a uniform velocity. This is accomplished by providing space for a material storage loop (*Figure 3-1*) that maintains a relatively constant supply of material between the feeding and the straightening operations.

Progressive die operations that require a pilot release work best if the feeding and straightening operations are separate. Upper feed rolls are easily and automatically lifted to allow pilot pins to shift the material. The material may not have the desired flatness when the upper straightening rolls are lifted after each progression of the material.

A combined rolled feeder and powered stock straightener works on the same principle of the powered stock straightener as illustrated in *Figure 3-2*. The feeding rolls operate intermittently, and advance the stock a fixed amount called the *pitch* or amount of progression per stroke.

Hitch Feeds

Press Powered Hitch Feed. This type of hitch feed has a reciprocating head having a gripper unit. There is a similar stationary unit. On the downstroke of the press, a cam attached to the press slide contacts the cam roller on the reciprocating head. The continued downward motion of the press slide pushes the reciprocating head outward, compressing a spring. During the downward press stroke, the gripper plate on the stationary head prevents the stock from moving backward. On the upward stroke of the press, the stock is held by the gripper plate as the head moves inward propelled by the compressed spring. The amount of feed advance is set by a feed-length adjustment nut.

Air Powered Hitch Feeds. A feature of this type of feed is a large air cylinder that powers the back-and-forth feed motion while smaller cylinders actuate both the stationary and moving grippers. Usually the gripper has a provision for a pilot release that can be actuated by either a press-slide mounted limit switch or a programmable rotary-limit switch.

Quick Setup of Hitch Feeds. A proven technique for quickly adjusting the correct pitch setting of air-driven hitch feeders is to use a measuring bar equal to the pitch length required for the device adjustment. Power to the device (usually compressed air) is first locked out and residual air drained. The reciprocating member is then moved by hand between the adjustable stops and the correct adjustment of the stops made.

An excellent way to store the measuring bar is to bolt it to the die shoe.

ALIGNING A COIL FEEDING SYSTEM

The state-of-the-art method of aligning press coil handling machinery is to use laser sighting equipment. This is not necessary. A taut length of music wire stretched from the press through the feeder and decoiler provides an excellent straight-line reference. Conventional hand tools such as squares and scales are then used to verify alignment.

CAMBER COMPENSATION

The ability to compensate for some coil camber or sweep is necessary in most blanking and progressive die operations. *Figure 13-2, Figure 13-3*, and *Figure 13-4* illustrate the cause of the problem which is also discussed in Chapter 13.

Commercial steel standards established by the American Society for Testing and Materials (ASTM) provide for a slight amount of camber in slit coiled steel products. One method is to cut either a single or double pitch notch as is illustrated in *Figure 3-5*. A disadvantage is that the practice wastes material.

Traditional Camber Compensation Methods

The most common technique is to move the position of the die by trial-and-error until the strip feeds smoothly. Since the amount and direction of camber can vary both from coil to coil and within a coil, this procedure may need to be repeated many times during a run.

Providing for Quick Camber Compensation

A number of clever methods to permit rapid camber compensation within reasonable limits have been developed by pressroom personnel over the years. It is very common to see all manner of improvised devices forcing the lateral

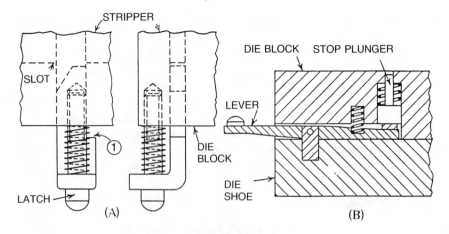

Figure 3-4. *A starting stop, (A) used to position stock as it is initially fed to a die incorporating a latch; the starting stop shown at view (B) incorporates a lever mounted between the die shoe and die block.* [3]

movement of the strip at the feeder. These include pieces of pipe, blocks of iron, mop handles, and wooden wedges. Clearly some means of providing a way to *force* the stock laterally at the feeder is needed since camber-free stock does not exist in the real world.

Proven methods include:
- Providing hardened steel rollers at the input of the feeder to force the stock to one side.
- Mounting the feeder on a platform provided with a screw adjustment mechanism to permit rapid adjustment.

A scale with a fixed pointer or other readout device should be provided to permit a quick return to the true centerline of the feed path if the feeder is fitted with a position adjust mechanism.

STARTING STRIPS IN PROGRESSIVE DIES

A major portion of the mis-hit damage to progressive dies occurs during the starting of the strip or coil of the stock. A correctly designed progressive die has a sight stop mark or mechanical starting stop to permit the operator or diesetter to position the incoming end of the stock for the first hit. The stock must be carefully advanced until the strip is correctly started for automatic operation.[3,4]

In some cases, the production of loose scrap pieces cannot be avoided on the first hit. A stick or a set of tongs should be used to clear or retrieve the scrap. The use of magnets on the end of a stick may result in magnetization of die sections which can cause slug retention. Avoid the use of magnetic pickup devices.

Starting Stops

A starting stop, used to position stock as it is initially fed to a die, is shown in *Figure 3-4* view A. Mounted on the stripper plate, it incorporates a latch which is pushed inward by the operator or diesetter until its shoulder (*D1*) contacts the stripper plate. The latch is positioned to engage the edge of the incoming stock; the first die operation is completed, and the latch released. The stop will not be used again until a new strip is fed into the die.

The starting stop shown at view *B*, is mounted between the die shoe and die block. The lever actuates a spring-loaded stop plunger to position the stock for the first hit *(Figure 3-5)*.

Pitch Notch Stops

These stops, which are also known as trimming or notching stops, bear against edges previously cut out of sides of the strip. Trimming punches cut the strip on both sides to the desired pitch plus a slight additional amount to permit exact location by the pilot pins upon release of the strip by the feeder.

Providing For Strip Removal

A solid pitch stop block will not permit the progression strip to be withdrawn

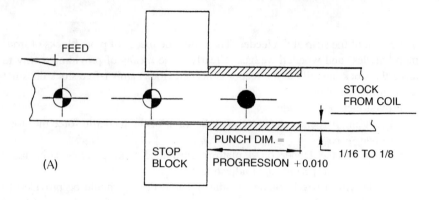

Figure 3-5. *Function of a pitch stop: (A) stock is cut from one or both sides of the strip the same length as the progression plus 0.010 in. (0.254 mm) to provide a slight overfeed; pilot action returns the stock to the correct location upon pilot release of the feeder.[3,4] (Capitol Engineering Co.)*

from the end of the die where the parts exit. In some cases, the strip cannot be withdrawn from the other end because the partly formed parts jam in the stock guides. The swing-away stop illustrated in *Figure 3-6* permits the strip to be withdrawn from the parts discharge end of the die.

Specialized Stops

There are a number of specialized stop designs used in hand-fed dies. Stops employing triggered levers and other specialized stops replace the function of pilot pins in many such operations.

In some manually fed operations, the strip is reversed after feeding through the die and parts cut from the other side. The function of many unique stop designs is explained in detail in references 3 and 4.

Plan a Good Starting Sequence

It is important to plan the starting sequence of a strip or coil to avoid damage. In some cases when a partial cut is made, excessive punch deflection caused by an unbalanced load results in a sheared die section. View *A* of *Figure 3-7* illustrates an acceptable starting sequence. The stock is first positioned against a stop pin (*D1*) and the press cycled to pierce the pilot hole (*D2*). The second hit does not produce loose pieces of scrap. The production of a loose piece of scrap is shown at *B*.

A few progressive dies cannot be started with stock having a square end without causing unacceptable deflections due to a less than optimal design. In such cases, the end of the coil may need an area cut out to permit safe starting of the stock. A plasma torch is a good tool for the job. A template to permit scribing the proper pattern on the stock should be stored captive to the die shoe.

24

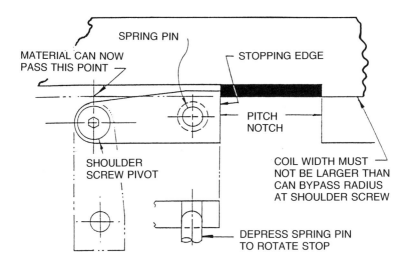

Figure 3-6. *Swing-away pitch stop to facilitate strip removal.[3,4] (Capitol Engineering Co.)*

Joining Coils by Welding

In the case of jobs that are especially difficult to start, it may be cost-effective to purchase specialized welding equipment specifically designed for joining coil ends at the press.

CHUTES, CONVEYORS, CONTAINERS AND OTHER EQUIPMENT

Chute and Conveyor Placement

To set jobs quickly, all required chutes and conveyors should be at the press in advance of the actual dieset. A written plan should be followed. No randomly conceived setup techniques should be permitted. Any chutes that do not remain with the die should attach without the use of tools.

Part and Scrap Containers

The exact type of container as well as its exact placement should be included in the written instructions for each job. The manner in which the parts are to be packaged in boxes and other shipping containers is very important in many cases to prevent shipping damage. Some parts can be damaged by simply permitting them to fall several feet (1 m) into a tub.

Many shops require the operators to inspect the parts run. This is a reasonable expectation, especially if the press and die has sensors for mis-hit protection. Increasingly, employees take pride in their work and are willing to certify both the quality and amount of parts in every container. The correct bar code information should be on the container and is often an operator responsibility.

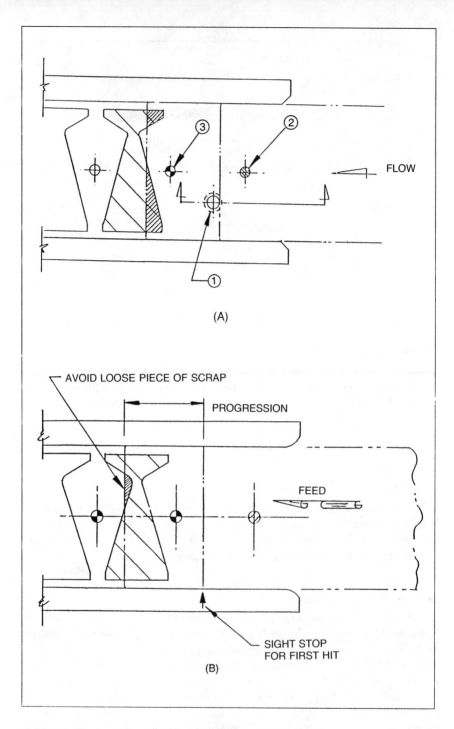

Figure 3-7. *The location of the first hit is important: (A) the first hit located against a starting pin (D1) does produce pieces of scrap; (B) the production of a loose piece of scrap.*[3.4] *(Capitol Engineering Co.)*

Lubrication

In progressive die operations, lubricants are usually applied by automatic means. The correct equipment must be in place and timed to provide the right amount of lubricant as needed. The type of lubricant used can be very detrimental to the storage and service life of the stamping as well as subsequent operations. Detailed information is contained in reference 5*.

Air Blow Off

If used, the air blow off should be connected and positioned properly. Generally a timed blast is more effective than a continuous one. The savings in compressed air can repay the cost of installing a good electronic cam limit switch in a few months.

Cam Limit Switches

Cam limit switches must be set correctly for the job to provide functions which may include the following:
- Timed application of lubricant.
- Air blow-off operation.
- Correct stopping at the top of stroke.
- Tonnage meter re-zeroing.
- Proper look windows for die protection.

While many mechanical cam switches remain in use, the trend is to use microprocessor-based electronic cam switches. Features to look for in a good system are: a non-optical brushless resolver, multi-channel memory function, and non-volatile memory that does not depend on battery backup.

DIE PROTECTION SYSTEMS

Pitch Stop Limit Switch

The pitch stop shown in *Figure 3-8* pivots a small amount to permit actuation of a limit switch when the feed advance is completed. It is important to provide a long beveled lead on the stop edge to avoid shearing the pitch notching punch when the press is cycled because of a short feed or no feed.

Detecting Both Under and Over Feed

The stop shown in *Figure 3-9* has several advantages when compared to a conventional pitch stop. The small semi-circular cut-out on the edge of the strip saves stock, and both under and over feeds are detected. The stop acts as a detent

---

*Joseph Ivaska, Vice President of Engineering, Tower Oil and Technology Company, contributed the information to reference 5 which is a recommended source of information on pressworking lubricants.

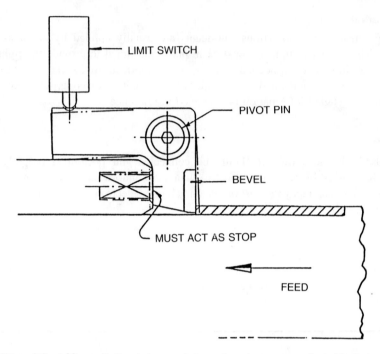

Figure 3-8. *Adding a limit switch to a pitch notch to detect proper feed. (Capitol Engineering Co.)*

to retain the stock in position. Another advantage to this type of protection system is that a mis-feed is detected much sooner than is possible with a pilot-actuated limit switch.

Additional Sensing Protection

In progressive die operation, the stock can feed properly to the pitch notch or other mis-feed detector and still be mis-hit in subsequent stations. Minimum protection should include the following:

- A detection system to make sure that the part(s) left the die.
- A sensor to be sure that the last part fed into and remained in the correct position of the last station.
- An end-of-coil shut-off sensor.
- A tonnage meter wired to stop the press.

Additional information on die protection systems is included in Chapters 26 and 28 as well as reference 6.

POINT-OF-OPERATION PROTECTION

The diesetter is usually responsible for all aspects of a safe and production worthy setup. This usually includes making sure that all required point of operation protection equipment is in good working order and installed correctly.

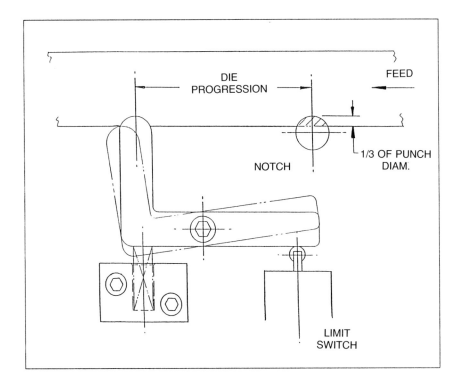

Figure 3-9. *Checking for both short and over feed. (Capitol Engineering Co.)*

BOTTOMING THE DIE

The most common method of bottoming dies correctly is to take a *lead check* on the bottoming or setup blocks. The block is provided with a groove such as that illustrated in *Figure 3-5* view *A*. A short piece of lead wire is placed in the groove and the press cycled. The deformation of the wire is then measured with a micrometer.

One company uses the following standard stop block groove configuration. The groove is 0.040 in (1.016 mm) deep. Lead wire 0.060 in. (1.524 mm) in diameter is placed in the groove. The correct spacing of the stop block from the upper die shoe is 0.010 in. (0.254 mm). Therefore, the micrometer reading of the wire should be 0.050 in. (1.27 mm).

A check should be performed on all four corners where close work is involved. It will detect any problems with out-of-parallelism. The test results often vary depending upon whether or not stock is present and also stock thickness variations. This is a normal result of the influence of press deflection on the stamping process and is discussed in many later chapters.

Other bottoming methods include correlating lead wire readings with tonnage meter readings and bottoming for proper gage fit where critical flanges and "U" bends are involved.

OTHER DIESETTER RESPONSIBILITIES

As an elite pressroom professional worker, the diesetter is expected to have many other duties which can include tasks such as running sample parts, securing quality control approval, and instructing the operator.

Never view an added task as an imposition, but as a way to improve your job skills and future employability.

REFERENCES

1. David A. Smith, *Die Design Handbook*, Section 23, Society of Manufacturing Engineers, Dearborn, Michigan 1990.
2. C. J. Wick, J.W. Benedict, and R. F. Veilleux: *Tool and Manufacturing Engineers Handbook*, Volume 2, Chapter 5, Society of Manufacturing Engineers, Dearborn, Michigan, 1984.
3. David A. Smith, *Die Design Handbook*, Section 16, Society of Manufacturing Engineers, Dearborn, Michigan 1990.
4. Arnold Miedema, Reference Guide for the videotape training course "Progressive Dies," Society of Manufacturing Engineers, Dearborn, Michigan, 1988.
5. David A. Smith, *Die Design Handbook*, Section 25, Society of Manufacturing Engineers, Dearborn, Michigan 1990.
6. David A. Smith, *Die Design Handbook*, Section 26, Society of Manufacturing Engineers, Dearborn, Michigan 1990.

4

DIE CLAMPING METHODS

SAFETY AND SECURITY

The primary requirement of any die clamping system is that it retains the press die in a safe and secure manner. Serious injuries and catastrophic damage to equipment have occurred because dies were not adequately secured in presses.

When considering any means of securing a die in a press, be sure to consult current safety rules. In the United States, Occupational Safety and Health Administration (OSHA) promulgates and enforces power press safety rules which are subject to change.

THREADED FASTENER MATERIALS

When threaded fasteners are used, they should be SAE grade 8 or ISO metric class 10.9. If the fasteners are plated, care must be taken to avoid hydrogen embrittlement.

The number of applied fasteners depends upon many factors, and is often covered by the individual company's die design and manufacturing engineering standards. A primary concern is adequate fatigue strength if the fasteners are subjected to shock loading.

Any shock should be reduced or eliminated where feasible. In an actual case study, the shock resulting from the impact of a 6,500-pound (2950-kg) pressure pad caused the failure of some one-inch (25.4-mm) diameter bolts used to attach the upper die shoe to the press slide. As many as 12 of the 15 total bolts had broken during production runs. The impact was eliminated by the installation of automotive-type pull-rod shock absorbers in the die.[1,2]

General Considerations

Good clamping methods help insure consistent setups, which in turn reduce stamping process variability. Poor clamping methods can result in product inconsistency and endangerment of personnel and equipment. Proper die fastening methods with special attention given to safety are an absolute necessity.

Tee nuts. The use of the popular tee-slot nuts and threaded rod should be discouraged. There is always a danger that the threaded rod is not fully engaged in the nut and may strip out under load. The tee nuts are just one more item to inventory (and another important item that cannot be found when needed.)

A further disadvantage is that the threaded rod used with the tee nuts is often purchased as needed from a nearby hardware store or industrial jobber. The mechanical properties of the material are often uncertain.

Figure 4-1 A illustrates fastening a die by using a hex head bolt with a tee-slot nut. This is an acceptable practice under some circumstances, although, all things being equal, much greater strength is provided by tee-slot bolts. The specification of the tee-slot nut is apt to be SAE grade five material, while heavy-duty hex diesetting nuts are available in SAE grade eight material.

For example, when tee-slot nuts are used in standard JIC 1 in. (25.4 mm) wide-tee slots, a 0.750 in. (19.0 mm) diameter thread per inch (TPI) (25.4 mm) bolt is the largest fastener that can be used. With tee-slot bolts, 1 in. (25.4 mm) diameter 8 TPI (25.4 mm) fasteners can be used. The ultimate strength of the larger fastener is over twice that of the smaller one. An added advantage is that the nut tightens 25% faster on the larger fastener. Substantially more torque is required to secure it, however.

Tee-slot Bolts. Square-headed bolts especially designed for use in press tee-slots are available from several suppliers. Properly cared for, bolts of this kind will provide decades of dependable service. *Figure 4-1 B* illustrates a square-headed tee-slot bolt used with a high-strength nut.

The threads should be protected from damage. Racks near the press or on a die cart can store the bolts by hanging them by the heads, thus protecting the threads from the damage that might occur if they were stored in a bin.

Modification of any die fastening bolt by welding should be strictly forbidden. There is uncertainty as to the exact alloy composition, and the risk of embrittlement next to the weld area that could cause failure.

If a very long bolt is needed for die testing purposes, or a special short-run setup, long coupling nuts are available for use in conjunction with threaded rod. Any such setup should be examined carefully to be sure that it is secure before cycling the press. Some safety rules forbid this practice.

Every press room should be equipped with good clamping equipment so that

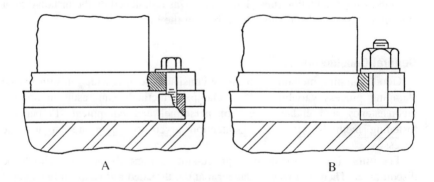

A   B

Figure 4-1. *Fastening a die by means of the use of a hex-head bolt (A) with a tee-slot nut; a square headed tee-slot bolt (B) used with a high strength nut.*

the diesetters will not resort to unsafe fastening methods to get their job done.

EXAMPLES OF POOR CLAMPING METHODS

Bad diesetting practices are everywhere. To institute good clamping practices in the plant, it is necessary to:

1. Provide enough proper clamping equipment.
2. Provide proper storage for the equipment when not in use.
3. Train the diesetters in the proper use of the equipment.

Figure 4-2 illustrates 10 bad die securing practices. Nearly all shops strictly forbid these practices as do many insurance inspectors and government enforcement officers. None of the illustrated practices should be permitted in any stamping shop.

Strap Installed Backwards. *A* illustrates a toe clamp or strap installed backwards. Nearly all of the holding force is used to hold the setup block instead of the die shoe.

The Use of a Nut for a Spacer. Good alloy steel nuts intended for diesetting applications (*B*) may cost $5.00 each. They are not suited for use as spacer blocks and the practice must be forbidden.

Hole in Clamp Too Large. The hole in a good clamp should be only slightly larger than the bolt. A washer will deform and permit the clamp to loosen (*C*) if the hole is too large.

Drilled Hole in Die Shoe Too Large. The same problem as shown at *C* will result if a flat washer is used over an excessively large bolt hole (*D*) in a die shoe. A steel strap of sufficient thickness to avoid deformation in service should be used to bridge the opening.

Hardened Steel Die Section for a Setup Block. *E* illustrates the use of a hardened steel section as a setup block. Such a practice invites bad housekeeping and the use of important interchangeable details as diesetting aids. Also, hardened blocks have been known to shatter causing injury when struck to determine that the clamp is secure. The importance of avoiding the practice of using hardened steel should be stressed, as the likelihood of injury may not be obvious unless explained to new diesetters.

Nuts and Extra Washers to Permit a Long Bolt Usage. Always use the shortest bolt that will permit proper thread engagement. Good setup bolts are expensive, and the cost rises with the length. Longer than necessary bolts (*F*) can create a pinch-point for the operator. Further, they are not as secure as a proper length fastener.

Improper Spacer Blocks. *G* and *H* illustrate the use of incorrect height spacer blocks resulting in an unsafe setup. The spacer block shown at *G* is too short; while the block shown at *H* is too long. To hold securely, the spacer block height must be the same height as that of the die surface being clamped.

Always Make Sure that the Bolt is Tight. Another evil of a bolt that is too long is that the nut may bottom on the end of the threads and not actually hold the clamp in place, as is illustrated at *I*.

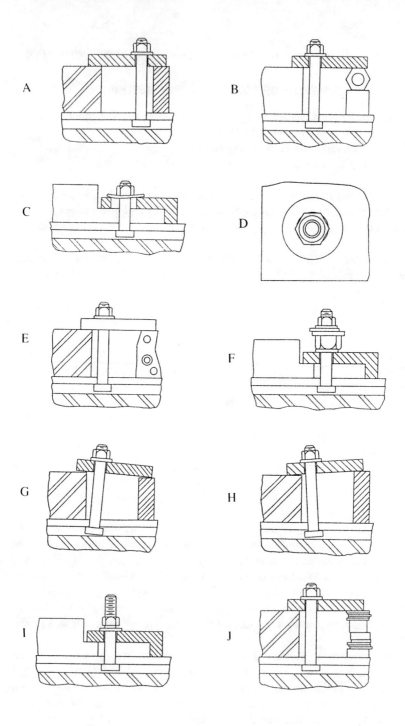

Figure 4-2. *Ten examples (A through J) of improper die clamping.*

34

Never Use Slugs and Washers. The use of slugs and washers to make up the required spacer block height are illustrated in *J*. This does not provide a secure setup. Slugs and washers are seldom perfectly flat and normally have some burrs that will compress and cause the clamp to loosen.

GOOD METHODS OF SECURING DIES WITH THREADED FASTENERS

Wrenches

Only proper heavy-duty wrenches designed for diesetting should be used. Light-weight automotive and adjustable wrenches are not suitable. Heavy-duty ratchet wrenches are suitable provided that they are of very robust construction.

Pneumatic impact wrenches are a good way to increase the diesetting rate and reduce fatigue. Special impact wrench sockets are required because automotive-socket wrenches are apt to split under impact. A method is needed that will insure that proper torque values are reached. Diesetters should check the final tightening with a torque wrench periodically to be sure that the tool is operating properly. In critical applications, final hand tightening is advisable.

Checking Clamping Security

Tap the spacer block or clamp with a wrench or hammer after tightening. Double-checking the clamping security is a required practice in many shops. When properly tightened, the clamp will emit a clear ring when the spacer block is struck. Even if the spacer block or clamp is not dislodged when tapped, a dull sound will alert the diesetter that the clamp is not properly tightened.

Common Clamping Height is Important

To change dies quickly, it is important to make the distance from the bolster surface or from the ram to the surface, a constant clamping dimension from job to job. This is true whether the die is fastened with straps and setup blocks or hydraulic clamps.

Figure 4-3 illustrates three simple methods of correcting differing die shoe thicknesses to a constant clamp height. In the case of a shoe that is too thick (*A*), small pockets can be milled to provide a common clamping height. If the shoe is too thick (*B*), the correct thickness spacers are attached to the edge of the die shoe to provide the correct dimension. In some cases, tack welds can be used, but screws are preferable to avoid warping the die shoe. In cases where tee bolts and washers are used (*C*), differing heights can be corrected by milling, or attaching a horseshoe-shaped spacer as shown.

Another obvious improvement for quick die change is to place a spring on the bolt to hold the clamp up in the position to be attached. A further improvement

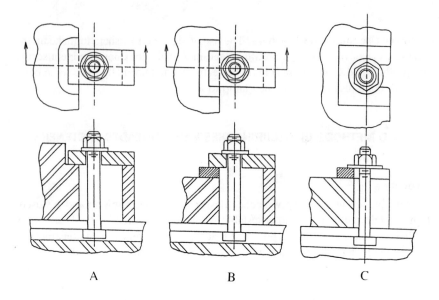

Figure 4-3. *Three simple ways to adapt to a constant clamp height: (A) Pockets milled to provide a common height; (B), Spacers attached to the edge of the die shoe; (C), Attaching a horseshoe-shaped spacer.*

is to weld the strap shown in *A* and *B* to the setup block to make a one-piece assembly.

Common Die Clamping Methods Using Threaded Fasteners

Figure 4-4 illustrates nine examples of commonly used die clamping methods. Depending on shop rules, shock loading, and changing government regulations, not all of these methods may be suitable for a given application.

Number of Spacer Blocks. The use of two spacer blocks to obtain proper height (*A*) may be an acceptable practice depending upon circumstances and applicable rules. A single spacer block (*B*) is a better practice.

One-piece Clamp. This type of clamp can be fabricated in-house from steel bar-stock cut to size with a powersaw. Drilling a single hole assures that the bolt is always in the correct position. The welding required is not critical because the assembly is held in compression. Cold-rolled steel is commonly used, but less expensive merchant-quality hot-rolled bar-stock will serve as well.

Constant Height Clamping Ledges. The basic requirement for any rapid clamping system used when changing dies is that a constant clamp height be employed. This can be as simple as providing a protruding ledge on a parallel (*D*) although a recessed ledge (*E*) is less apt to be damaged during die handling operations. If a parallel attached to a die shoe runs the length of the die shoe (*F*), the ledge can be milled the full length of the parallel if versatility of clamp

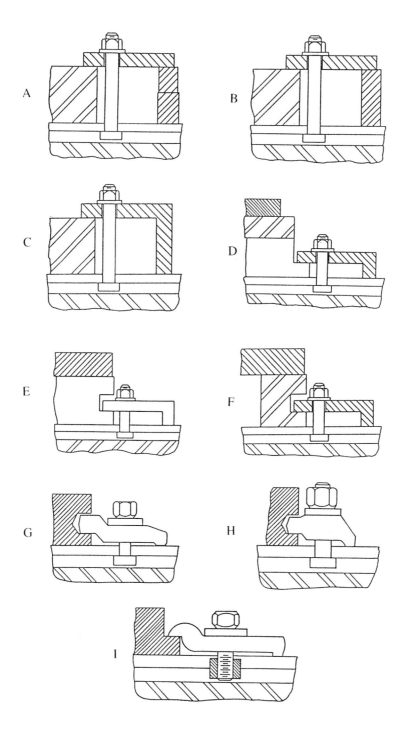

Figure 4-4. *Nine examples (A through I) of die clamping methods.*

37

location is a requirement.

Forged Steel Clamps. A number of styles of versatile forged steel clamps are commercially available from diemaker suppliers. The offset type clamp illustrated in *Figure 4-4 G* engages a drilled hole in the die shoe. The offset design has a low profile to permit ease of scrap shedding. A straight type clamp is illustrated at *G*. A forged goose neck clamp that engages a ledge on a die shoe or parallel is illustrated at *I*. All of the clamps shown are used with swivel washers and either swivel head capscrews or swivel nuts.

AUTOMATICALLY ACTUATED CLAMPS

Automatic die change requires some type of power-actuated die clamping system. The clamps can be actuated by electrical energy, compressed air or hydraulic pressure.

Some clamps actuated by electric motors are in use, although they are uncommon. The required gear reduction and electrical control systems tend to be complex and expensive.

Clamps powered by compressed air and hydraulic pressure have been in use for many years. Many good designs feature toggle or eccentric mechanisms to provide a large clamping force in the *locked* position.

Hydraulic clamps are by far the most popular for most new installations. *Figure 21-4* illustrates a complex automatic die clamping system attached to a press slide. An electric motor with a gearhead drives the mechanism which positions the clamp.

Safety Considerations

All automatic systems should be of fail-safe design where the die cannot become detached or shift position on the ram or bolster during press operation. This could occur due to a failure of the clamping power source or by an unclamp command while the press is in motion. To avoid this occurring, good designs incorporate some or all of these safety features:

- Hydraulic power sources across diagonal corners of the machine, much like the dual-brake system on automobiles.
- Pressure switches to detect a loss of pressure.
- Automatic machine shut-down in the event of the loss of pressure.
- Over-center toggle locking mechanisms that will hold in the event of a loss of pressure.
- Hydraulic clamps with check valves to prevent the release of fluid because of a pressure failure – these require a second hydraulic line to release the pilot-operated check valve.
- Limit switches to detect proper clamp position.

Chapter 19 discusses pressworking lubricant considerations and the possible effect on limit switch performance.

REPRESENTATIVE DESIGNS

Hollow Piston Cylinder Clamp

Figure 4-5 A illustrates a type of clamp that is essentially a hydraulically powered nut. The clamp (*D1*) screws onto a standard tee-slot bolt (*D4*). The

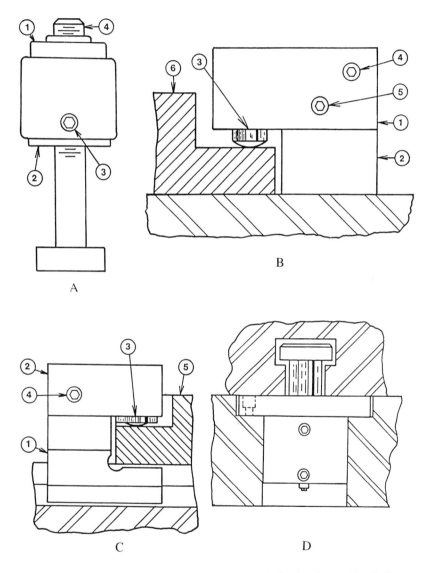

Figure 4-5. *Simplified drawings of four popular types of hydraulic clamps: (A), Hollow piston cylinder for use with a standard tee bolt; (B), Ledge type clamp; (C), Sliding clamp for use in tee slots; (D), Double-acting pull-in type clamp installed in a press bolster. (Hilma Corp. of America)*

piston (*D2*) applies pressure to the die clamping surface (not shown) just as a conventional nut does when tightened. Hydraulic pressure is supplied by a hose which is attached to the hydraulic port (*D3*).

This design is popular in quick die change retrofit applications. A major advantage is that the clamp can be adapted to a wide variety of clamping heights in the same manner as a nut.

Hydraulic Ledge Clamps

Figure 4-5 B illustrates an end-view of a type of hydraulic ledge clamp. The clamp body (*D1*) and user-supplied spacer block (*D2*) are fastened directly to the press ram or bolster by socket-head capscrews (not shown).

Up to six or more individual spring-return pistons (*D3*) are available in this design. The pistons are supplied with hydraulic pressure by means of internal drilled passages. For safety, this design can be supplied as a split system supplied by two individual pressure sources, with hydraulically controlled check valves, both applied to the hydraulic ports (*D4* and *D5*).

The clamping surface on the die shoe or subplate (*D6*) must be of a standard height.

Sliding Clamp for Use in a Conventional Tee-Slot

Figure 4-5 C illustrates a type of clamp that is popular for retrofitting existing presses for hydraulic clamping. *D1* is a tee-slot adapter that is made for several standard types of tee slots. The clamping block (*D2*) is attached to the tee-slot adaptor with screws. The hydraulic piston (*D3*) is of the single-acting spring-return type. Hydraulic pressure is applied through a port (*D4*). An optional design employs a second port and a hydraulically controlled check valve to prevent the release of holding force in the event of a line failure.

The clamping surface on the die shoe or subplate (*D5*) must be of a standard height to permit die interchangeability using this type of clamp.

Pull-in Type Clamp

Figure 4-5 D illustrates a double-acting pull-in type clamp installed in a press bolster. A clamp of this type features up-down motion for unclamping and clamping in a slot cut in a die shoe or subplate. It is shown in the unclamped position with a tee-slot cut in a die shoe. In this position, the die shoe can slide in or out of either side of the press.

The cylinder body is fastened into a bored and countersunk hole in the bolster. Two inductive proximity switches inside the cylinder sense proper piston position at either end of the travel. These switches provide an electrical signal by an electrical connector on the bottom of the cylinder. This is a safety feature and can be interlocked with the press controls to permit proper sequencing of automatic die movement.

Specialized Pull-in Type Clamps

Other types of clamp movement can be achieved in the same basic type of clamp body. By the addition of a second hydraulic actuator, and additional proximity switches, the head can be made to lift and swing 90 degrees, or lift and swing 90 degrees and then sink below the bolster surface. These features permit the clamp to engage a slot, or in the case of the swing-sink clamp engage an elongated hole in a die shoe or subplate.

REFERENCES

1. David A. Smith, *Die Design Handbook,* Section 13, Society of Manufacturing Engineers, Dearborn, Michigan 1990.
2. Ford Motor Company, ''Die Design Standards for North American Operations,'' Body and Assembly Division, Dearborn, Michigan.

5

ADVANCED DIESETTING TOPICS

OPERATING DIES ON PARALLELS

Setting dies on parallels or risers is a very common practice in many shops. Parallels often are used under the die to provide for a proper pass height and to provide a means of getting rid of scrap. Often parallels are placed on top of the die to build the die to either a required minimum or to a common shut height. It is important that enough parallels be used to avoid excessive die shoe deflection during operation.

Parallel Materials. Commonly used die-parallel materials include cold-rolled steel bar, hot-rolled steel bar, hot-rolled steel plate, and cast iron.

Cold-Rolled Steel. Rectangular cold-rolled steel bar is a popular material for die parallel applications. It is readily available from steel suppliers and can be quickly cut to length with a power saw. The top to bottom dimensional accuracy is often close enough for many non-critical applications if the bar stock is selected and matched with care.

The minus dimensional tolerance of cold finished steel bars ranges from 0.004 in. (0.1 mm) for stock up to 0.75 in. (19 mm) wide to 0.014 in. (0.36 mm) for thicknesses over 6 in. (152 mm). This is generally not close enough for high-quality presswork. The commonly specified parallelism requirement for the alignment of the press slide to the bed is 0.001 in. (0.025 mm) per foot (305 mm).

Hot-Rolled Steel Bar. Generally hot-rolled material is less expensive than cold-finished bar stock. Another advantage is that hot-finished bar stock has fewer residual stresses than cold-finished material, so warpage during machining is reduced.

Normally, only the top and bottom of the parallels requires machining. If a large number of parallels are to be sized to a common dimension, rotary-table grinding is often the most economical method.

Hot Finished Steel Plate. This material is excellent for the construction of large irregularly shaped parallels and die risers. The usual method of fabrication is to flame cut the shape on a plate burning table and then machine the finished dimensions by milling or grinding. To insure dimensional stability, the plate should be normalized after being flame-cut.

Useful sources of low-cost steel plate for parallel fabrication are obsolete die shoes and subplates. Usually the holes in such scrap steel are not objectionable if it does not cause excessive interruptions of the cutting flame when burning out the desired shape.

Cast Iron. Die risers or parallels requiring lightening holes, reinforcing webs

43

and feet are most often economically made of cast iron. Common grey iron has good compressive strength. The tensile strength is usually adequate in the large sections commonly used for die parallels. Irons with better tensile properties are available at a higher cost than that of common grey iron.

REDUCING PROCESS VARIABILITY CAUSED BY OPERATION ON PARALLELS

Parallel Height Variation

A common problem in many press shops is that there are a great many parallels of the same nominal dimension that are not of the same *exact* dimension. The cause of unacceptable variation, when using cold finished steel bar stock for parallels, is that the commercial tolerance for the material greatly exceeds the close parallel-size tolerance required for high-quality stamping. It is feasible to maintain the height variation of parallels to ± 0.001 in. (0.025 mm) or better.

Selecting and Maintaining Existing Parallels

A short-term solution to the parallel-height variation problem is to sort and select them for uniform height. *Figure 5-1 A* illustrates how they can be compared and selected by testing with a straight-edge.

Many experienced diesetters are in the habit of carefully feeling the parallels for burrs and removing any burrs that are found with a file. Slight differences in height can be detected by feel when parallels are placed side-by-side on a flat surface.

Resizing Parallels to Standard Undersized Dimensions

To eliminate any process variability problems caused by die-parallel height variation, resize parallels to standard undersized dimensions. A good action plan is needed before the standardization process is begun. It is a very poor idea to send random groups of parallels out to be ground for minimum cleanup.

A good action plan is to:
1. Measure and group all parallels according to nominal and actual dimensions.
2. Grind all parallels that are slightly oversized to the exact nominal dimension.
3. Group all undersized parallels to be ground to a standard undersized dimensions; e.g. 0.040, 0.080 in. (1, 2 mm).
4. Clearly identify the amount of undersize by a stamped designation, a color code, or both.
5. Check and standardize any new parallels introduced into the system.
6. Periodically inspect parallels, correct any dimension and straightness problems.

44

A

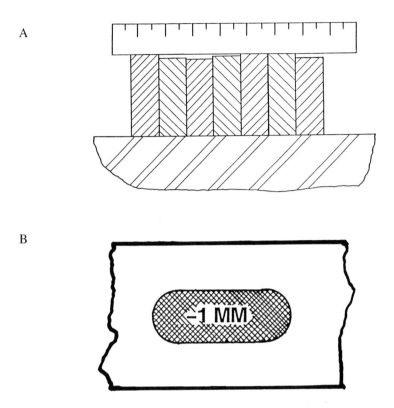

B

Figure 5-1. *(A) Checking parallels for height differences with a straight edge: (B) Identifying undersized parallels with a stamped marking in a milled pocket.*

When grinding parallels made of cold-finished steel, it is important to turn them over during the grinding process. The material removed has residual compressive stresses present. The same amount should be removed from each side if the parallel is to remain straight after grinding. Turning and checking the work also affords an opportunity to take an exact thickness measurement of the work in progress.

Identifying Undersized Parallels

It is very important to identify and segregate parallels by both nominal and exact size. Milling a shallow pocket in the side of the parallel and stamping the amount of undersize, if any, in the pocket (as shown in *Figure 5-1 B*) accomplishes this task. Rapid identification can be provided by color coding with a light coating of spray paint in the pocket and ends of the parallel.

A suggested color coding scheme is: if the amount of undersize is 0.80 in. (2mm) the color is red; if the amount of the undersize is 0.040 in. (1mm) the color is yellow; if there is no undersize, the color is green.

By identifying non-undersized parallels as well as undersized parallels, the diesetter is assured that no oversight in identification has occurred.

Relationship of Parallels to Clamps

The clamping method should not introduce deflection into the die shoes.

Clamp Over Parallels. *Figure 5-2 A* illustrates a die clamped midway between two of the parallels that can induce die shoe deflection. The result is an undesired deflection as shown in *Figure 5-2 B*. This deflection results in changing critical die clearances which, in turn, affects the geometry of the finished part. The maintenance of correct die clearances is a must if the stamping process is to be stable.

Figure 5-2 C illustrates a simple solution. By placing the clamp on the die shoe at the locations where it is supported by parallels, both an improvement in clamping security and the elimination of a process variable are accomplished. Both the shoe and parallel are held tightly in compression and no shoe deflection results.

Use Parallels That Are Long Enough. Shoe deflection also can result from using parallels that are too short. *Figure 5-3 A* illustrates a die shoe set on a short parallel or spacer block. This results in die shoe deflection when the clamps are tightened. Again, critical die clearances are changed affecting the process and the dimensions of the end product.

Figure 5-3 B illustrates a simple solution. The parallels must be long enough to insure that the clamp holds the shoe and parallel in compression.

Analysis of the Causes of Variation

Placing the clamps on the die shoe when running dies on parallels can result in an undesired process variation due to many factors. Some are:

1. The parallels may not always be placed in the same location, resulting in varying deflections of the die shoe during different runs.
2. Exact parallel to parallel height may vary, slightly changing the exact deflection of the die shoe.
3. It is difficult to place the clamps in exactly the same place each time resulting in slight variations in shoe deflection.

All of these root causes of process variability can be eliminated by making the parallels captive to the die and clamping to the parallels.

Fastening the Parallel to the Die Shoe

A number of requirements must be met in any good system of fastening the parallels to the die shoe. The primary requirement is, of course, safety. The type, number, and size of fasteners must be sufficient to equal or exceed the strength and impact resistance of the fasteners used to fasten the parallel to the press bolster or slide.

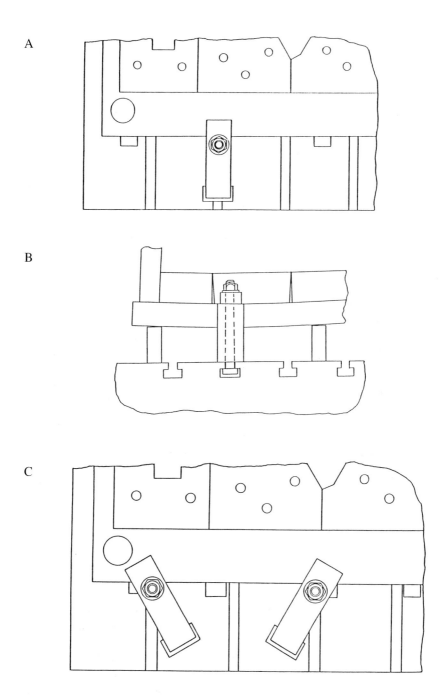

Figure 5-2. *Improper clamping of a die shoe placed on parallels will result in die shoe deflection: (A) view of clamp installed midway between two parallels; (B) the lower shoe deflection that results; (C) clamping directly over parallels places the parallel in compression, provides secure clamping and avoids die shoe deflection.*

47

A

B

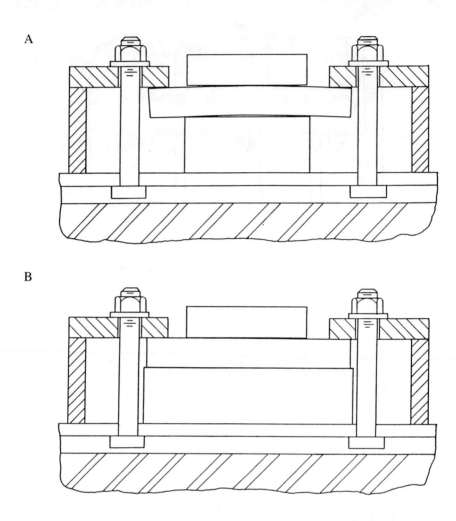

Figure 5-3. *Setting the die on short parallels or spacer blocks (A), results in die shoe deflection when the clamps are tightened. The parallels must be long enough (B) to insure that the clamp holds the shoe and parallel securely in compression.*

Many stamping shops set their own internal standards for die and diesetting fasteners based upon the nature of the work performed; particularly the amount of shock loading encountered.

The choice of attaching the parallels by screws going through the die shoe or by screws threaded into the die shoe is largely based upon individual circumstances. Where possible, a standard hole pattern should be adopted to facilitate the reuse of the parallels removed from obsolete dies.

It is important to remove the parallels quickly in the event that the die must be adapted to run in a different press than the one for which it was adapted.

Clamping to Parallels

A basic requirement for any rapid clamping system used when changing dies is that a consistent clamp height be employed. All of the following examples employ a constant clamp height and use simple one-piece die clamps.

When deciding upon a standard height for clamping ledges, it is wise to choose a height that will work with mechanical and power clamps.

EXAMPLES OF PARALLELS ATTACHED TO THE DIE SHOE

Chapter 4 has many examples of clamping to a standard-height ledge on a parallel or die shoe. It cannot be overstated that a basic requirement for quick die change is a standard clamp height.

Figure 5-4 illustrates a standard parallel having a keyway for locating the die in the center of the bolster. The parallel is made in standard increments of length to facilitate salvage and reuse when the die becomes obsolete.

Figure 5-5 illustrates a lower die parallel (*D1*) attached to a mounting foot (*D2*) having a locating keyway. The same socket head capscrews that attach the parallel to the die shoe also attach the foot to the parallel.

If the base of the parallel illustrated in *Figure 5-5* is permitted to extend past the edge of the die shoe as shown in *Figure 5-6 A*, it is subject to damage during handling and storage. This can be avoided by either making the base no

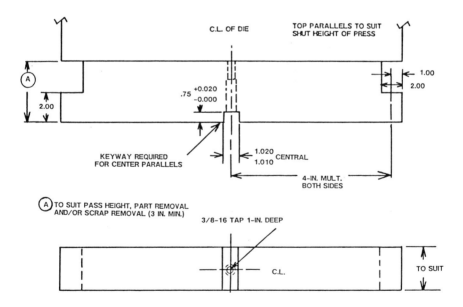

Figure 5-4. *A standard parallel with a keyway for locating the die in the center of the bolster. (W. C. McCurdy Co.)*

49

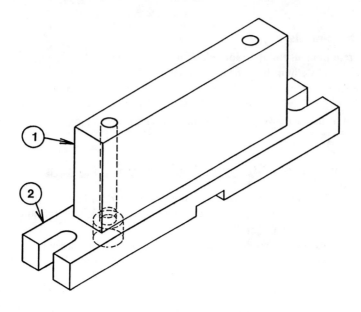

Figure 5-5. *A lower die parallel (D1) attached to a mounting foot (D2) with a locating keyway; the same socket head capscrews that attach the parallel to the die shoe also attach the foot to the parallel.*

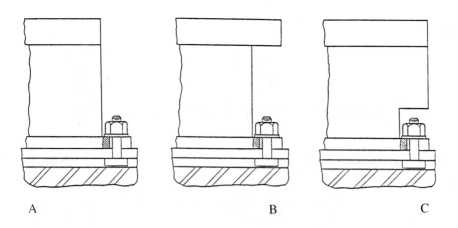

A   B   C

Figure 5-6. *If the base of the parallel illustrated in Figure 5-5 is permitted to extend past the edge of the die shoe (A), it is subject to damage during handling and storage: this can be avoided by either making the base no longer than the shoe width (B); or by making a recess (C) for the bolt in cases where maximum support of the shoe is required.*

longer than the shoe width (*B*); or by making a recess (*C*) for the bolt in cases where maximum support of the shoe is required. A very robust parallel made of flame-cut hot-rolled steel is illustrated in *Figure 5-7*. The plate is first cut to shape and then turned upright to permit the tie-down slots to be flame-cut. The top and bottom surfaces are ground and the keyway and tie-down surface machined to standard dimensions.

Figure 5-8 illustrates a bad design for die parallel feet with tie-down slots. In the event of a large stripping load, such as is often encountered in a mis-hit, the offset condition will tend to bend the parallel and attaching screws. *D1* protrudes past the edge of the die shoe and is subject to damage during die handling operations. *D2* is a better design and is conditionally acceptable if large fasteners are used.

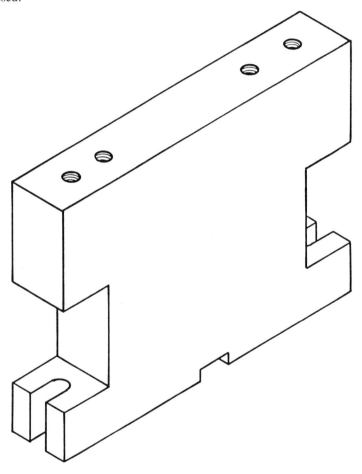

Figure 5-7. *A parallel made of flame-cut hot-rolled steel: the tie down slots can also be flame-cut by turning the parallel upright on the flame-cutting table after the basic shape is cut-out.*

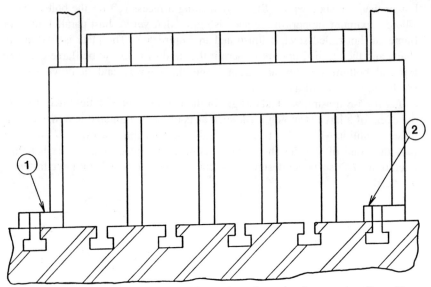

Figure 5-8. *A bad design for die parallel feet with tie-down slots because the offset will tend to bend the parallel and attaching screws in the event of a large stripping load: (D1) protrudes past the edge of the die shoe; (D2) is a better design and is conditionally acceptable if large fasteners are used.*

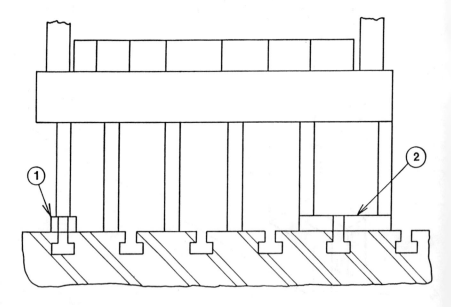

Figure 5-9. *Die parallel feet with tie-down slots that have balanced loading that will not deflect sideways in the event of a large stripping load: D1 is centered on the parallel; D2 bridges two parallels.*

The foot design illustrated in *Figure 5-9* avoids the problems shown in *Figure 5-8*. No side deflection is developed in the event of a large stripping load. *D1* is a standard design similar to the parallel illustrated in *Figure 5-5*. *D2* is a good design for use when the parallels cannot be placed directly over a tee slot.

Figure 5-10 illustrates a double parallel system designed to accommodate a scrap conveyor used in progressive die operation. The conveyor runs the length of a press bolster. The lower parallel is designed to provide room for the scrap conveyor, while the upper parallel is sized to provide a uniform load or pass height to avoid readjustment of the stock feeder when changing dies. A shim is tack welded to the die shoe to provide a common tie down height for the tee bolt.

An important consideration when running dies on parallels is the shoe thickness required to maintain deflection within acceptable limits. Engineering formulas determine the shoe thickness needed.

REQUIRED SHOE THICKNESS[1]

The thickness requirement of a die shoe for a given allowable deflection can be computed from engineering formulas provided that the loading and parallel spacing are known.

Example of Calculation. For this example, assume a lower shoe to be a simply supported beam with a concentrated load of 40,000 lbf (178 kN) at the center. The distance between the parallels is 10 in. (254 mm), the width of the lower shoe is 20 in. (508 mm), and there is a maximum deflection of 0.001 in. (0.0254 mm), which would cause the die clearances to decrease.

The formula is:

$$\delta = \frac{FL^3}{48EI} = \frac{FL^3}{48Ebh^3/12}$$

For a steel shoe, $E = 30 \times 10^6$ psi

$$h^3 = \frac{FL^3}{48Eb\,\delta/12} = \frac{40,000 \times 10^3 \times 12}{48 \times 30 \times 10^6 \times 20 \times 0.001} = 16.67$$

$$h = 2.55 \text{ in.}$$

For a cast-iron shoe, $E = 20 \times 10^6$

$$h^3 = 25$$
$$h = 2.92 \text{ in.}$$

The lower rigidity of cast iron necessitates the use of a thicker shoe. The die forces can be estimated from standard engineering calculations for metalworking operations.

A listing of lower-shoe thicknesses for central loading is found in *Table 5-1*.

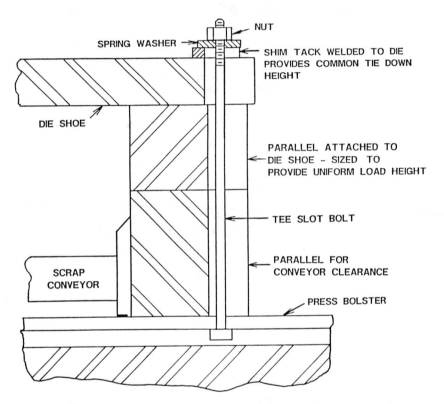

Figure 5-10. *Stacked parallel system that provides both conveyor clearance and a common pass height. (W. C. McCurdy Co.)*

If a distributed load is assumed, the correct formula to use is:

$$\delta_{\mathbb{C}} = \frac{5FL^3}{384EI} = \frac{FL^3}{76.8EI}$$

TABLE 5-1. REQUIRED THICKNESS OF STEEL DIE SHOES ON PARALLELS HAVING A CENTRALLY APPLIED LOAD.[1]

Load, tons	Shoe Width, in.	Distance Between Parallels, in.						
		5	10	15	20	25	30	40
10	10	1.30	2.60	3.80				
20	10	1.60	3.20	4.80				
30	10	1.80	3.70	5.50				
40	10	2.00	4.10	6.10				
50	20	1.70	3.50	5.20	6.90			
60	20	1.80	3.70	5.50	7.40			
70	20	1.90	3.90	5.80	7.80			
80	20	2.00	4.10	6.10	8.10			
90	30	1.80	3.70	5.50	7.40	9.20	11.00	
100	30	1.90	3.80	5.70	7.60	9.50	11.50	
150	30	2.20	4.40	6.50	8.70	10.90	13.10	
200	40	2.20	4.40	6.50	8.70	10.90	13.10	17.50
250	40	2.40	4.60	7.00	9.40	11.80	14.10	18.80
300	40	2.50	5.00	7.50	10.00	12.50	15.00	20.00
350	50	2.40	4.80	7.40	9.80	12.20	14.70	19.60
400	50	2.60	5.10	7.70	10.20	12.80	15.30	20.40
450	50	2.70	5.30	8.00	10.60	13.30	16.00	21.30
500	50	2.80	5.50	8.30	11.00	13.80	16.50	22.00

- Calculations are based on a deflection of 0.001 in.
- To obtain thicknesses for cast-iron shoes, multiply table values by 1.15.
- For an allowable deflection of 0.002 in. (0.05 mm), multiply table values by 0.785. For 0.005-in. (0.13 mm) deflection, multiply by 0.580.
- If parallels are not used beneath the lower shoe, the value may be the combined thickness of the shoe and bolster.

SCRAP AND PART REMOVAL

Holes in the Press Bolster

Dropping scrap through the press bed is the most economical and foolproof system of scrap removal. The scrap is then removed by a centralized conveyor system or a scrap tub in the basement.

It is important to have standardized hole locations in the bolster and that the dies be designed around these locations if possible. Care must be taken not to weaken the bolster excessively.

Generally, it is not possible to drop scrap through the press bed if die cushions are used, although some cushions have been designed with built-in slug tubes.

Required Chute Angle

It is desirable to have a minimum angle of 20 or more degrees, although there is no absolute minimum angle rule. If the operation involves a lot of shock or snap through energy release, the resulting vibration will assist scrap shedding. Some factors that hinder scrap removal are insufficient fall, heavy metalworking lubricants on the scrap, and rusted or painted chutes.

Chute Vibrators

Small air-powered vibrators can be attached to the under-side of the chute to assist scrap removal. The effectiveness of vibrators is greatly enhanced by suspending the chute on springs or rubber. Rubber-automotive exhaust-hangers are often a useful suspension device.

Chute Shakers

Reciprocating air-powered chute shakers operate on the principle of a slow forward motion followed by a very rapid return motion. During the return stroke, the inertia of the scrap causes it to remain in place while the chute moves under it. These devices can actually convey scrap up a slight incline if necessary.

Slug Boxes

Catching small slugs in boxes that are periodically emptied is an excellent system when operating dies on parallels. Small slugs tend to create housekeeping problems even with the best of scrap chutes.

The weight of the slugs produced per stroke can be calculated based upon their volume. The actual volume occupied by the slugs will be greater, so a safety factor of at least two should be used when designing the box. The frequency of emptying the box also can be determined in advance based upon weight and cubic volume.

The side box should not extend any closer to the lower die shoe than necessary, or be equipped with a clear plastic inspection window to permit a visual check of the contents of the box. It is important that the operator be instructed how frequently to empty the box.

Air Blow-Off

Compressed air blow off devices are used for both part and scrap ejection. A timed blast should be used rather than a continuous one. Not only will this help reduce the over-all noise level in the shop, it is more effective and the savings in compressed air is sufficient to pay back the cost of equipping a press with an electronic cam limit switch in a few months' time.

Conveyors

Installing conveyors in dies is often a last resort when other methods cannot be used. Conveyors can be expensive to maintain.

Conveyors with metal flights generally work better than those having metal mesh or rubberized fabric belts.

HIGH-PRESSURE NITROGEN SYSTEMS

When setting dies with a piped or manifold-type nitrogen pressure system, it is important to be sure that the system is charged to the correct pressure. This information should be marked on the die. It is convenient to place a small mark of paint or fingernail polish on the gage located on the charging console. The correct pressure is critical in many cases. *Figure 5-11* illustrates a combined up and down flanging operation where the nitrogen pressure adjustment is critical to obtain the correct sequence of events.

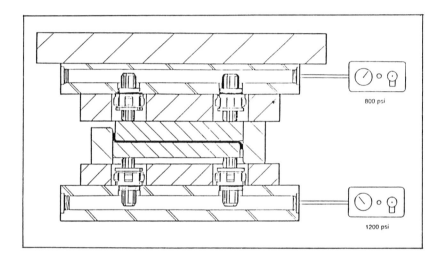

Figure 5-11. *Nitrogen pressure adjustment is critical on many jobs such as this combined up and down flanging operation in order to obtain the correct sequence of events. (Forward Industries)*

Charging the nitrogen system(s) should be done as part of the external dieset where possible. There are a few operations that must be charged in the press to avoid cocking the die.

The four-bottle nitrogen charging wagon illustrated in *Figure 5-12* was developed specifically for quick die change applications. A four-position valve *Figure 5-13* permits rapid sequencing between the tanks. To make the most efficient use of the available nitrogen, filling is started with the tank having the least pressure and sequenced to the next lowest until the desired pressure is reached.

The regulator is permanently shock mounted to the wagon. To permit rapid exchange of tanks without the use of tools, a special handwheel type connector

Figure 5-12. *A four-bottle nitrogen charging wagon developed specifically for quick die change applications.*

(Figure 5-14) is used. All fittings and piping are generic hydraulic components rated well in excess of maximum tank pressure. *Figure 5-15* illustrates the use of a quick snap-on nitrogen fitting and female fill-fitting with a shut-off valve. This special fitting can be hand-connected at full system pressure.

OPERATING DIES ON DIE CUSHIONS

When a single-action press is used for drawing operations, the manner in which the blankholder pressure is applied to control the flow of the metal blank is important. The application of pressure to a blankholder is one of the features of a double-action press. Single-action presses lack this feature and therefore require supplementary blankholding equipment.

58

Figure 5-13. *A four-position valve permits rapid sequencing between the tanks; the regulator is permanently shock mounted to the wagon.*

Dies are sometimes built with a blankholder using compression springs, air cylinders, or high-pressure nitrogen cylinders to supply the holding pressure. This greatly increases the cost of the die. A press cushion can serve every die with this requirement, lowering the cost of tooling.

Pneumatic Die Cushion

This type of die cushion is supplied with shop air pressure. A pneumatic-die-cushion design normally uses either one or two pistons and cylinders. The recommended capacity of a die cushion is about 15% to 20% of the rated press tonnage. The size of the press-bed opening limits the size, type, and capacity of the cushion.

Figure 5-14. *A special handwheel type connector is used to permit rapid exchange of tanks without the use of tools,*

A schematic arrangement of a pneumatic die cushion is shown in *Figure 5-16*. This illustration shows an inverted-type cushion in which the downward movement of the blankholder, through pressure pins, forces the cylinder against a cushion of air inside the cylinder, and moves the air back into the surge tank (not shown). The external components such as the surge tank, regulator, and pressure gage are essentially identical in function to a press counterbalance system illustrated in *Figure 17-2*. On the upstroke, the air in the surge tank returns the cylinder. Other designs function without surge tanks.

It is very important to load the cushion evenly to avoid premature wear and cushion failure. The die designer should incorporate equalizing pins in the lower shoe if required to accomplish loading equalization. Often these can be actuated by the upper heel blocks. In some cases, special pin drivers made of structural

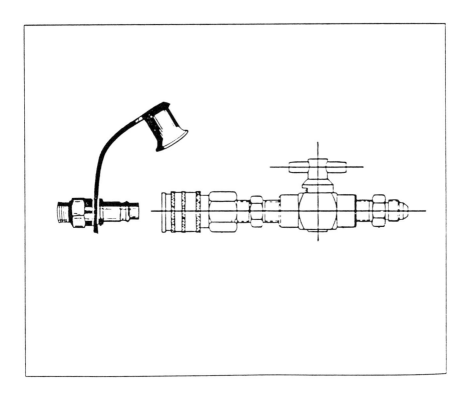

Figure 5-15. *Quick snap-on nitrogen fitting and female fill fitting with a shut off valve. (Dadco Inc.)*

tubing may be attached to the slide to actuate equalizing pins. Operator safety must be considered when doing this operation because additional pinch points are created.

Troubleshooting Cushion Systems

It is of extreme importance that the correct length pins be used. In drawing and other critical operations, a pin that is 0.06 in. (1.5 mm) longer than the others can easily cause a wrinkled or fractured part. When problems are encountered, and the pressure setting is found to be correct, the pins should be carefully measured with a micrometer or vernier caliper. This step will determine if they are of the same length.

If the pins are the same length, they can be re-inserted into the bolster pin holes and checked with a dial indicator as shown in *Figure 5-17*. If a variation in length is found, it is either caused by the pins with worn-uneven depressions in the top of the piston wear plate or the cushion is damaged. The wear-plate can be repaired by regrinding.

The bolster pin holes will become larger with use. If this occurs, hardened

61

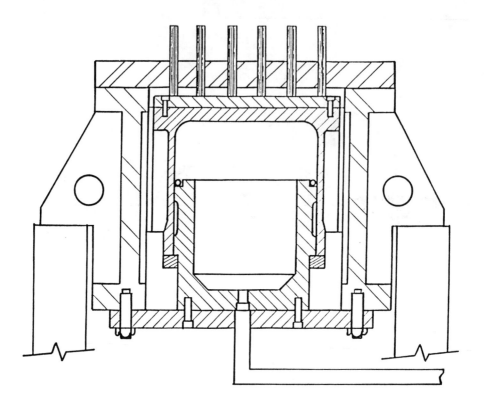

Figure 5-16. *Sectional view through a press bed and bolster illustrating a pneumatic die cushion.*

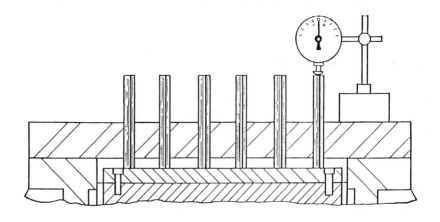

Figure 5-17. *Troubleshooting a die cushion system with a dial indicator.*

bushings can be fabricated and used to repair the worn holes. Generally, this is a permanent solution.

The die can also be a source of difficulty. With extended use, the pins can wear uneven depressions in the underside of draw-rings, pads, and subplates.

SETTING DRAW DIES

Bottoming the Die

If a die cushion is used, the pressure should be set to the correct value before bottoming with a blank in the die. It is important to maintain a database of correct values for each job and the presses in which it runs. Once the die is bottomed, some fine adjustment may be required to compensate for variations in material properties.

When bottoming double-action press dies, the blankholder should be adjusted first. If the press has a tonnage meter, the blankholder is adjusted to a historically correct tonnage value. It is important that the outer slide be adjusted before the draw punch is bottomed. In the event that the blankholder is too loose, folded metal may be drawn into the die and cause a slug mark on the draw punch or a reverse.

For large dies that draw irregular shapes, some diesetters make a close adjustment of the inner slide by placing clay on a reverse in the lower die cavity and adjusting the inner slide downward while cycling the press on the inch mode. Very serious press and die damage has occurred in this manner. If this practice is permitted, it is absolutely essential that the diesetter make certain that the reverse does not correspond with a milled-out area or eye bolt hole in the draw punch.

Safety When Bolting the Inner Slide

To guarantee that someone will not inadvertently open the press with a die partly fastened in, it is recommended to follow power-lockout procedure with the press on bottom whenever setting and removing a die. This is especially important when reaching through the access holes in the outer slide to manually bolt the inner slide to the punch plate.

Floating Draw Punch

Figure 5-18 illustrates self-contained nitrogen gas cylinders used to float a draw-die punch in a double action press. For large automotive body panel-dies with punches weighing up to 8 tons (7.87 metric tons), six 3-ton (27 kN) cylinders are used. Four cylinders would be sufficient. The two extra cylinders permit the production run to continue should any one cylinder fail. Cylinders generally last in excess of 500,000 strokes between seal replacements in this application.

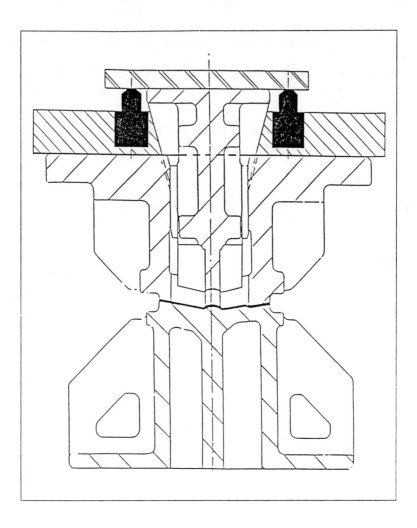

Figure 5-18. *Self-contained nitrogen gas cylinders used to float a draw-die punch. (Dadco Inc.)*

Cylinders without mounts are often used. They are placed in holes bored in the blankholder adaptor-plate or bull-ring. The punch adaptor plate should be inlaid with an air-hardening weld where the cylinder rod makes contact. The use of hardened steel contact blocks is not advised because they are apt to loosen and enter the die.

In addition to the obvious advantage of eliminating a diesetter task when setting the die, the floating punch draw-die is not affected by lateral movement of the press slides caused by worn or mis-adjusted presses. The chance of a punch or blank-holder wear-plate loosening and then falling into the die cavity is practically eliminated.

ADJUSTING KNOCK-OUT BARS

The purpose of knock-out bars in the ram is to strip or *knockout* the part at the top of the press stroke. The part is then removed from the press by such means as an air blast or shuttle unloader. Usually the knock-out bar(s) have captive pins that extend through the upper platten of the press. The bars are usually supported by springs so the dead weight of the bars and attached pins does not result in the part being ejected prematurely.

The knock-out pins in the press engage a knock plate that is recessed into the upper die shoe. In the case of small die sets with shanks, a single knock-out pin can be fitted in the center of the shank.

Actuating the Knock-out Bars. Adjustable-length rods attached to the press frame or crown that contact the knock-out bars at the top of the press stroke is the usual method of actuating the knock-out bars. The stationary rods are adjustable in length by means of a threaded extension which is locked in place with a jam-nut. Correctly adjusted, the system provides for positive knock-out action.

Errors to Avoid. If the adjustable-length rods do not sufficiently engage the knock-out bars, the parts may not be dependably ejected from the upper die. This can result in multiple hits and serious die damage.

Should the adjustable-length rods be set too long, the rods, knock-out bars and die may be damaged. It is very important that the diesetter make sure that the jam-nuts on the fixed rods be tightened properly. Otherwise, the adjusting screws may creep downward resulting in excessive knock-out forces.

Should the ram adjustment be raised for any reason, it is critical to first shorten the adjustable-length rods to avoid damage.

REFERENCES

1. David A. Smith, *Die Design Handbook*, Section 3, Die Engineering— Planning and Design, Society of Manufacturing Engineers, Dearborn, Michigan, 1990.

6

RELATIONSHIP OF QUICK DIE CHANGE TO EOQ AND JIT*

Pitfalls of Excessive Run-Ahead

Simple logic says it would be wise to run enough parts to satisfy production or shipping requirements for a long time in the future once good parts are produced. This plan would be true particularly when an extremely difficult setup followed by trial and error adjustments is involved. There are, however, many good reasons why this is not wise.

A better plan is to reduce the difficulty of the setup by adopting quick die change techniques and hardware. This will also greatly reduce the trial-and-error adjustments. Setup repeatability problems that are not corrected by quick die change (such as stock variation) should also be addressed.

Planning Amount and Frequency of Production

Many factors influence the exact amount of production. For example, there is a cost associated with rebanding partial coils of stock and returning them to inventory. For this reason, the savings realized by running integral numbers of coils should be factored into the decision making process on the amount of production to run. Economics of coil sizes is also a factor. Large coils are often less costly on a per pound basis and produce more parts per coil change.

Customer relationships have a very big influence on the frequency of production. Some customers insist on a certain number of days inventory being on hand at the vendor's shop as a safety stock. For example: the Michigan deer hunting season has serious implications for car part production. The number of hunters in the field may exceed the number of soldiers that make up the United States' standing army. There are only two solutions: Either run production ahead a week starting in October or shut down for the first week of deer hunting season.

WORKING TOWARD AN ECONOMIC ORDER QUANTITY OF ONE

Much has been written about JIT in the past few years. The purpose of JIT is to deliver parts to a production line *just in time* and to keep the line running

* Based upon a paper presented by Phillip Gibson, Regional Manager, Atlas Technologies, Atlanta, Georgia. The paper and spreadsheet information were presented at The SME Die and Pressroom Tooling clinic held in Chicago, August 29-30, 1989.

without a bank of parts as a ''safety stock.'' Without some other considerations, a crisis is built in at the end of every batch. The production line needs the necessary parts to keep running. If there were any glitches in the delivery of the parts to the line, it may be necessary to either shut the line down, or spend an inordinate amount of money to get the parts to the line.

What is Economic Order Quantity

Economic Order Quantity (EOQ) is the quantity of parts, either purchased or manufactured, that results in the lowest part cost while considering:
- For a purchased part:
  1. The purchase price,
  2. The cost for issuing and processing a purchase order,
  3. The cost for holding the part in stock, if all of the order is not used immediately.
- For a manufactured part, the considerations are:
  1. The cost to manufacture the part,
  2. The cost for setup of the equipment,
  3. The cost for holding the part in stock, if all of the parts are not used immediately.

Factors That Influence Economic Order Quantity

To determine the Economic Order Quantity (EOQ), it is required to know not only the part cost and setup cost, but also the manufacturing rate, annual demand for the part, and the cost for holding the part in stock on an annual basis.

Manufactured part cost consists of the material cost, labor per part, rent or amortization of the space used to manufacture the part, equipment and tool amortization, scrap from damage while storing or while in storage, scrap from obsolescence, loss of parts while in storage, fixed burden, variable burden, and freight costs involved. If one part is produced and used immediately, (and not considered the cost for changeover), the cost is that of the part. But if any quantity of parts requires keeping some of them in stock for any time, there is an associated cost of keeping the part. The cost for keeping the part is not just interest paid on the money tied up in the parts stored. It includes warehouse rent or amortization, damage for handling the parts to storage and out, loss of parts while in storage from lack of an information system, obsolescence, warehouse equipment such as fork trucks, racks, and bins, the cost of labor to put the parts in storage and to remove them, labor to maintain the inventory of the parts in stock, and insurance on the parts while in storage. The American Production and Inventory Control Society has determined that the average cost for keeping parts in stock is 38% per year.

To the cost of the part, add the cost for equipment changeover, or the cost for issuing and processing a purchase order. If there is only one part involved, the cost of that part is the total of the part cost plus the cost for changeover. If more than one part is made on a setup, the cost of that setup can be amortized over the quantity of parts made. The total cost of the part then depends on the total of the part cost, the amortized cost of the setup, and the amount put in the part for storage until its use.

The Economic Order Quantity. EOQ model identifies the order size that will minimize the sum of the annual costs of holding inventory and the annual costs of ordering inventory.

This model assumes that:

1. There is one product involved.
2. Annual usage (demand) requirements are known.
3. Usage is spread evenly throughout the year so that the usage rate is reasonably constant.
4. Lead time does not vary.
5. Each order is received in a single delivery.
6. There are no quantity discounts.

Determining Economic Order Quantity

Figure 6-1 illustrates how the costs of carrying parts in inventory are linearly related to order size. The formula is:

$$\text{Annual Carrying Cost} = \frac{Q}{2} H$$

Where Q = Order quantity in units.

$\quad H$ = Carrying cost in dollars per unit per year.

Example:

Let Q = 4500 units.

$\quad H$ = $.27 per unit per year carrying cost.

$$\frac{Q}{2} H \text{ or } \frac{4500}{2} \times \$.27 = 2250 \times \$.27 = \$607.50$$

Carrying costs are therefore a linear function of Q, and increase or decrease in direct proportion to the order quantity Q, as illustrated in *Figure 6-1*.

Figure 6-2 illustrates how ordering costs are both inversely and non-linearly related to order size. The slope of the curve becomes flatter as the order size increases because the fixed setup cost is spread over an ever greater number of units. The slope of the curve is described by:

$$\text{Annual Setup Cost} = \frac{D}{Q} S$$

$\quad S$ = Setup cost.

$\quad Q$ = Order quantity in units.

$\quad D$ = Demand in units per year.

Example:

Let D = 87,000 demand in units per year.

$\quad Q$ = 4500 order quantity units.

$\quad S$ = $275 in setup costs.

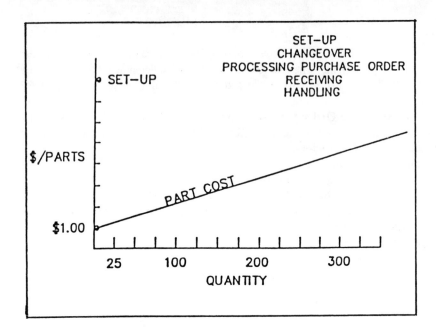

Figure 6-1. *Linear relationship of the cost of carrying parts in inventory to order size.*

$\dfrac{D}{Q}$ S or $\dfrac{87000}{4500} \times 275 = 19.3 \times 275 = \$5307.5$ for annual setup cost.

The total annual cost of carrying a part in inventory is given by

Total annual carrying cost for one part $= \dfrac{Q}{2} H + \dfrac{D}{Q} S$

Q = Order quantity in units.
H = Carrying costs in dollars per unit per year.
S = Setup cost.

Note: The total annual carrying cost for one part is equal to the annual carrying cost plus the annual ordering cost.

Figure 6-3 illustrates the U-shaped curve that describes how the total cost of setup and storage varies as a function of the number of pieces produced. The U-shaped curve reaches its minimum value at the quantity where the setup and carrying costs are equal.

An expression for the optimal order quantity Q_o can be obtained through the use of calculus. The result is the formula:

Optimum Order Quantity $= Q_o =$ the square root of $\dfrac{2DS}{H}$ or $\sqrt{\dfrac{2DS}{H}}$

D = Demand in units per year
S = Setup cost
H = Carrying costs in dollars per unit per year.

70

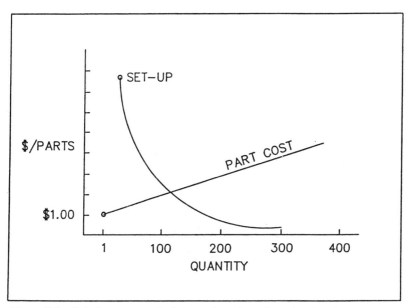

Figure 6-2. *Ordering costs are both inversely and non-linearly related to order size.*

Example:

Let $D = 87000$ demand units per year.

$S = \$275$ in setup costs.

$H = \$.27$ per unit per year carrying cost.

$$\sqrt{\frac{2DS}{H}} = \sqrt{\frac{2\,(87000 \times 275)}{\$.27}} = \sqrt{\frac{4.785 \times 10^7}{.27}}$$

$$= \sqrt{1.7722 \times 10^8} = 13312.0 \text{ units is the optimum order quantity.}$$

The low point of the total part cost line is the Economic Order Quantity, the quantity that results in the lowest part cost. If the company buys or builds more or less than the Economic Order Quantity, then more will be paid for each of the parts.

Reducing the EOQ

There are only two ways to reduce the EOQ. Either the cost of storage or the cost of setup must be reduced.

There are not many opportunities for reducing the costs associated with holding parts in inventory. Little can be done to reduce the cost of building space, money, or the likelihood of part obsolescence. Fortunately, from the formula, if either the cost of holding parts in inventory or the cost of setup equals zero, the EOQ becomes one. Spectacular setup cost reductions are possible.

Figure 6-4 illustrates how the EOQ curve changes as setup costs are reduced. If all setup costs are eliminated, the economic order quantity becomes one.

71

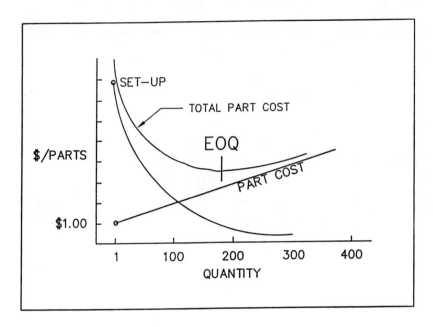

Figure 6-3. *The U-shaped curve that describes how the total cost of setup and storage varies as a function of the number of pieces produced.*

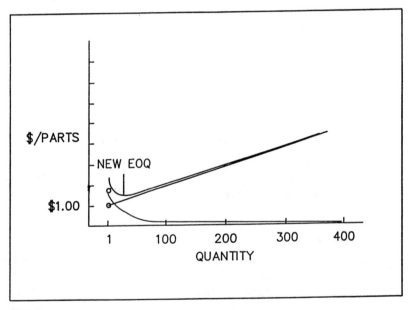

Figure 6-4. *The EOQ curve changes as setup costs are reduced.*

THE IMPACT ON JIT

Before JIT, a safety stock was kept for insurance against running out at the end of every batch. It was expensive insurance, and led to a certain amount of complacency in our manufacturing operations. As problems surfaced, a tendency arose to increase the safety stock, rather than cure the delivery problem.

This, of course, increased our average inventory, increased the risk of damage, loss, obsolescence, and the other means of increased cost caused by high inventories.

Figure 6-5 is a plot of inventory quantity on hand versus time. It indicates that there are 660 parts on hand today.

As time progresses, those parts were used at a rate indicated by the slope of the line in *Figure 6-6* the "Never-Lie" inventory control system projects that the safety stock level will be reached at the end of day six. Everyone has a "Never-Lie" inventory control system, of course.

When the order point is reached as shown in *Figure 6-7*, "Never-Lie" will trigger an order for either the manufacture of the parts in the shop, or the delivery of parts from a vendor. This assumes that EOQ is checked on a periodic basis, and the Reorder Point and safety stock is modified if necessary.

Under normal conditions, a new lot is manufactured. Normal conditions are having the raw material, the tools in operating condition, and the personnel available to make the parts. Remember, this is before JIT.

If reordering isn't done on time, or if there are any of the factors (raw material, tools, personnel, etc.) that are not available, there is safety stock to

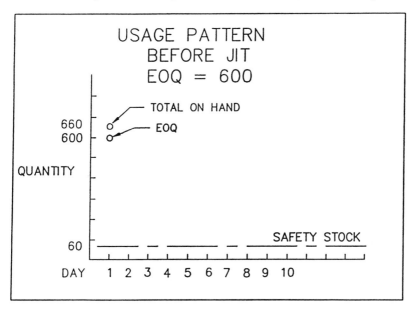

Figure 6-5. *A plot of inventory quantity on hand versus time showing that 660 parts are on hand.*

73

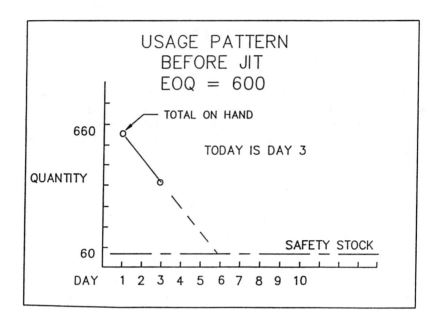

Figure 6-6. *As parts are used, the inventory decreases at a rate indicated by the slope of the line.*

protect against catastrophe on the production line. Production would receive the parts later, having maintained operations with the safety stock, and rebuild the safety stock when the next order arrives on time. The same usage pattern is true with a manufactured part.

The average inventory of a purchased part before JIT was the safety stock plus half of the Economic Order Quantity. Keep in mind, however, that enough warehouse space is needed to keep all parts in their Economic Order Quantity, or some fraction higher than half, because not all parts are used at the same rate.

Elimination of Safety Stock. JIT eliminated the safety stock, and in many cases did not consider that parts must be procured in their Economic Order Quantity. Only the average inventory by the amount of the safety stock was reduced. In many cases, this was very significant since safety stocks had become quite large.

With JIT, usage pattern remained the same, except that average inventory was reduced. The same is true of the manufactured parts—the average inventory was lower. Keep in mind that without doing something to reduce the EOQ, if the parts were made in less than the Economic Order Quantity to further reduce the work in process inventory, the amount paid for the parts was increased.

To reduce EOQ, the primary job is to reduce the cost of setup, or order cost (the cost to issue and process a purchase order), rather than the cost of the part. In fact, reducing the part cost increases the EOQ, resulting in more parts, not necessarily more dollars, with work-in-process. Without reducing the setup, reduction in part cost does not result in much of a reduction of the total part cost.

74

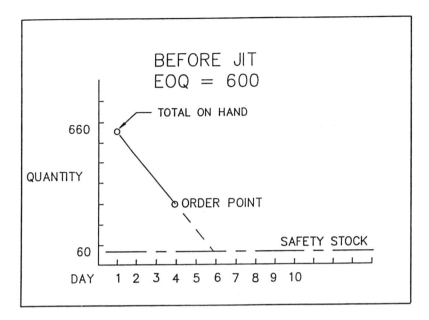

Figure 6-7. *The "Never Lie" inventory control system automatically generates an order for parts when the order point is reached.*

The total part cost is relatively flat at the point of the EOQ, so reducing the part cost by even 50% would result in a real reduction of the part cost by as little as 10%.

Most of us have heard of setups that take eight hours or more. It is possible to reduce an eight-hour setup to 30 minutes or less.

• Several points to decrease changeover cost should be kept in mind.

1. Be ready for a die change.
2. Semi-Automatic die change.
3. Automatic die change.

• We can reduce die change time to almost zero through the use of:

1. Point of use manufacturing
2. Transfer presses with gaggable tooling.
3. Design for automation.

The necessity for the considerations for manufacturing during the product design phase cannot be emphasized too strongly. It is absolutely mandatory that manufacturing engineers be involved in the product design at the outset of a new program. They are the ones who can help with the design so that the part can be manufactured with little or no die change.

An EOQ of one can be attained, and that can make JIT work without the hassle now associated with it.

ECONOMIC ORDER QUANTITY ANALYSIS

An easy, but often overlooked, way to bring objectivity into managing a pressroom is by doing a cost analysis. Cost analysis software is available, but common general-purpose spreadsheet software can also be used by plugging the variables and formulas into the spreadsheet cells.

Figure 6-8 illustrates the use of the popular Quattro program which does an EOQ engineering study. This spreadsheet provides an annual savings or loss based on changing any one of the variables entered into a cell. For example, if the annual savings to be realized by changing material specifications is desired, it can be determined by simply entering the new material size or cost per unit weight.

Data to Enter into Quattro

The spreadsheet shown in *Figure 6-8* can be set up in Quattro software by entering the following formulas and headings.

To save space, the colons used in columns one space wide used to provide an easy to use printout have been omitted. The equals sign row is also omitted.

Other spreadsheet programs can be used, although slight changes in the format of the cell formula entries may be required. The function of each calculation is described later in this chapter.

A2: **W12** 'ECONOMIC ORDER QUANTITY CALCULATIONS FOR
A3: **W12** 'ENGINEERING STUDY
A5: **W12** 'ENTER YOUR COMPANY NAME
A6: (D1) **W12** @TODAY
G6: (D6) **W12** @NOW
O6: 'MTL
Q6: 'MTL
S6: 'PRESS
U6: 'LABOR
Y6: 'TOTAL
AA6: 'TOTAL
AE6: 'LABOR
AG6: 'MTL & LBR
AK6: 'ANNUAL
AM6: 'KEEPING
AO6: 'TIME
AQ6: **W5** 'MEN
K7: **W3** 'PCS
M7: **W8** 'WT
O7: 'COST
Q7: 'COST
S7: 'COST
U7: 'COST
Y7: 'LABOR

```
ECONOMIC ORDER QUANTITY CALCULATIONS FOR
ENGINEERING STUDY
PRINT YOUR COMPANY NAME HERE
   Ø4-Jun-9Ø                    Ø8:52:25 AM
:              :       :       :          :         :
: PART NUMBER :OPTION:COIL   :  COIL      :         :
:              :      :WIDTH :  THICK     : PITCH   :
:=============:======:======:==========: ========:
:SAMPLE       :    1 : 18.5 :    Ø.192 :   27.75 :
:SAMPLE       :    2 : 18.5 :    Ø.192 :   27.75 :


              MTL       MTL       PRESS     LABOR
:PCS: WT   :  COST   :  COST   :  COST   : COST   :
:PER: PER  :  PER    :  PER    :  PER    : PER    :
:HIT: PIECE:  POUND  :  PART   :  HOUR   : HOUR   :
:===:======:=========:=========:=========:========:
: 2 :13.972 :$Ø.462Ø  : $6.4551 : $127.65 : $35.92 :
: 2 :13.972 :$Ø.462Ø  : $6.4551 : $127.65 : $35.92 :


           TOTAL     TOTAL              LABOR    MTL & LBR
:     :    LABOR :   COST   :PIECES:   COST   :  TOTAL   :
:OPR :    PER   :   PER    :PER   :   PER    :  PART    :
:REQD:    HOUR  :   HOUR   :HOUR  :   PIECE  :  COST    :
:====:=========:=========:======:=========:=========:
: 2  :  $71.84 :$199.49  :  47Ø :$Ø.4244  :$6.8795   :
: 2  :  $71.84 :$199.49  :  47Ø :$Ø.4244  :$6.8795   :


           ANNUAL    KEEPING   TIME      MEN
:         :   COST  :   COST  :  TO     : REQD :
:  ANNUAL :   OF    :   PER   :  SET-UP : TO   :
:  VOLUME :  KEEPING:   PART  :  MINUTES: SET  :
:=========:=========:=========:=========:======:
: 97,ØØØ  : 38.ØØØØ% : $2.6142 :    5Ø   :   2  :
: 97,ØØØ  : 38.ØØØØ% : $2.6142 :    2Ø   :   2  :


: TOTAL   :          :  SET-UPS: ANNUAL  : TOTAL   :
: SET-UP  :          :  PER    : SET-UP  : PART    :
: COST    :  EOQ     :  YEAR   : COST    : COST    :
:=========:=========:=========:=========:=========:
:$166.24  : 3512.37 : 27.62   : $4,591.Ø5: $6.9268 :
: $66.5Ø  : 2221.42 : 43.67   : $2,9Ø3.63: $6.9Ø95 :


: ANNUAL   : ANNUAL     : AVERAGE    : PER CENT  :
: SAVINGS  : COST       : INVENTORY  : INVENTORY :
:          :            : DOLLARS    : REDUCTION :
:==========:============:============:===========:
:          : $671,9Ø4.22: $12,164.82 :           :
: $1,687.41: $67Ø,216.81:  $7,674.39 :   36.91%  :
```

Figure 6-8. *Printout of the economic order quantity spreadsheet.*

AA7: 'COST
AC7: **W6** 'PIECES
AE7: 'COST
AG7: 'TOTAL
AK7: 'COST
AM7: 'COST
AO7: 'TO
AQ7: **W5** 'REQD
AS7: 'TOTAL
AW7: 'SETUPS
AY7: **W12** 'ANNUAL
BA7: 'TOTAL
BC7: **W12** 'ANNUAL
BE7: **W12** 'ANNUAL
BG7: **W12** 'AVERAGE
BI7: 'PER CENT
A8: **W12** 'PART NUMBER
C8: **W6** 'OPTION
E8: **W6** 'COIL
G8: **W12** 'COIL
K8: **W3** 'PER
M8: **W8** 'PER O8: 'PER
Q8: 'PER
S8: 'PER
U8: 'PER
W8: **W4** 'OPR
Y8: 'PER
AA8: 'PER
AC8: **W6** 'PER
AE8: 'PER
AF8: **W1** ':
AG8: 'PART
AI8: 'ANNUAL
AK8: 'OF
AM8: 'PER
AO8: 'SETUP
AQ8: **W5** 'TO
AS8: 'SETUP
AW8: 'PER
AY8: **W12 'SETUP**
BA8: ' PART
BC8: W12 'SAVINGS
BE8: **W12** 'COST
BG8: **W12** 'INVENTORY
BI8: 'INVENTORY

E9: **W6** 'WIDTH
G9: **W12** 'THICK
I9: 'PITCH
K9: **W3** 'HIT
M9: **W8** 'PIECE
O9: 'POUND
Q9: 'PART
S9: 'HOUR
U9: 'HOUR
W9: **W4** 'REQD
Y9: 'HOUR
AA9: 'HOUR
AC9: **W6** 'HOUR
AE9: 'PIECE
AG9: 'COST
AI9: 'VOLUME
AK9: 'KEEPING
AM9: 'PART
AO9: 'MINUTES
AQ9: **W5** 'SET
AS9: 'COST
AU9: 'EOQ
AW9: 'YEAR
AY9: **W12** 'COST
BA9: 'COST
BG9: **W12** 'DOLLARS
BI9: 'REDUCTION
A11: **W12** 'SAMPLE
C11: **W6** 1
E11: **W6** ENTER COIL WIDTH IN INCHES
G11: **W12** ENTER COIL THICKNESS IN INCHES
I11: ENTER PART LENGTH OR FEED PITCH
K11: **W3** ENTER NUMBER OF PIECES PER HIT
M11: (F3) **W8** @SUM(E11*G11*I11*0.2835)/(K11)
O11: (C4) ENTER MATERIAL COST IN DOLLARS PER POUND
Q11: (C4) @SUM(M11*O11)
S11: (C2) ENTER PRESS COST IN DOLLARS PER HOUR
U11: (C2) ENTER THE LABOR COST IN DOLLARS PER HOUR
W11: **W4** ENTER THE NUMBER OF OPERATORS REQUIRED
Y11: (C2) @SUM(U11*W11)
AA11: (C2) @SUM(S11+Y11)
AC11: **W6** ENTER THE NUMBER OF PIECES PRODUCED PER HOUR
AE11: (C4) @SUM(AA11/AC11)
AG11: (C4) @SUM(Q11+AE11)
AI11: (,0) ENTER THE ANNUAL VOLUME OF PIECES

AK11: (P4) 0.38
AM11: (C4) @SUM(AG11*AK11)
AO11: ENTER FIRST SETUP TIME IN MINUTES
AQ11: **W5** ENTER NUMBER OF DIESETTERS REQUIRED
AS11: (C2) @SUM(AO11/60)*(S11 + U11*AQ11)
AU11: (F2) @SUM((2*AS11*AI11)/(AM11))^0.5
AW11: (F2) @SUM(AI11/AU11)
AY11: (C2) **W12** @SUM(AS11*AW11)
BA11: (C4) @SUM(AY11/AI11) + AG11
BE11: (C2) **W12** @SUM(AI11*BA11)
BG11: (C2) **W12** @SUM(AU11/2)*BA11
A12: **W12** 'SAMPLE
C12: **W6** 2
E12: **W6** ENTER PART WIDTH IN INCHES
G12: **W12** ENTER PART THICKNESS IN INCHES
I12: ENTER PART LENGTH OR FEED PITCH
K12: **W3** ENTER NUMBER OF PIECES PER HIT
M12: (F3) **W8** @SUM(E12*G12*I12*0.2835)/(K12)
O12: (C4) ENTER MATERIAL COST IN DOLLARS PER POUND
Q12: (C4) @SUM(M12*O12)
S12: (C2) ENTER PRESS COST IN DOLLARS PER HOUR
U12: (C2) ENTER THE LABOR COST IN DOLLARS PER HOUR
W12: **W4** ENTER THE NUMBER OF OPERATORS REQUIRED
Y12: (C2) @SUM(U12*W12)
AA12: (C2) @SUM(S12 + Y12)
AC12: **W6** ENTER THE NUMBER OF PIECES PRODUCED PER HOUR
AE12: (C4) @SUM(AA12/AC12)
AG12: (C4) @SUM(Q12 + AE12)
AI12: (,0) ENTER THE ANNUAL VOLUME OF PIECES
AK12: (P4) 0.38
AM12: (C4) @SUM(AG12*AK12)
AO12: ENTER SECOND SETUP TIME IN MINUTES
AQ12: **W5** ENTER THE NUMBER OF DIESETTERS REQUIRED
AS12: (C2) @SUM(AO12/60)*(S12 + U12*AQ12)
AU12: (F2) @SUM((2*AS12*AI12)/(AM12))^0.5
AW12: (F2) @SUM(AI12/AU12)
AY12: (C2) **W12** @SUM(AS12*AW12)
BA12: (C4) @SUM(AY12/AI12) + AG12
BC12: (C2) **W12** @SUM(BA11-BA12)*AI11
BE12: (C2) **W12** @SUM(AI12*BA12)
BG12: (C2) **W12** @SUM(AU12/2)*BA12
BI12: (P2) @SUM(BG11-BG12)/BG11

Notes on the Formulas Used

Other spreadsheet programs can be used, although slight changes in the format of the cell formula entries may be required. The function of each calculation is described later in this chapter.

M11 Here the width, length (or pitch), and thickness in inches of the steel blank (or coil stock) is multiplied together to obtain the *volume of steel* in cubic inches used per press stroke. The result is then multiplied by 0.2835, the weight of a cubic inch of steel to obtain the *weight of steel* used per press stroke. Cell K11 the number of parts produced per press stroke is divided into the result to obtain the *weight of material* needed to make each individual part. Metric users must enter a different coefficient in place of 0.2835. The coefficient entered will be determined by the users preference for working with grams or kilograms and the length unit chosen.

Q11 The result of the calculation entered at M11 (above) is the material weight required to make each individual part. To obtain the *material cost per part* that figure is multiplied by the cost of steel used in dollars per pound entered at O11. Users of other than dollar monetary systems will want to modify this and other column headers to reflect the system used.

Y11 The *total labor cost per hour* is the product of the individual operator cost per hour entered in cell U11 multiplied by the number of operators entered at W11.

AA11 This cell calculates and displays the *total cost per hour other than material cost*. The press cost in dollars per hour entered at S11 is added to the total labor cost calculated at Y11.

AE11 Here the number of pieces produced per hour entered at AC11 is divided into the total cost per hour calculated at AA11 to give the *labor cost per individual piece*.

AG11 The *total part cost* is calculated by adding the total material cost per part (Q11) and the total labor cost calculated at AE11.

AK11 As was discussed earlier in this chapter, the *average costs of keeping a part in inventory for one year* as determined by The American Production and Inventory Control Society ranges from 19% to 38% per year. Keeping costs for metal stampings tend to be high because of rust and obsolescence. The 38% figure is entered at AK11. The powerful computational capabilities of a spreadsheet can calculate a more exact figure if desired. Additional columns can be inserted and such data as the cost of storage baskets, size of baskets, number of parts per basket, risk factor for obsolescence, annual cost per cubic foot of warehouse space, and the cost of money. It is feasible to generate a very precise figure for each individual part with very little effort.

AM11 In this cell, the *annual keeping cost per part* is determined by multiplying the total part cost from cell AG11 by 0.38 which was entered in cell AK11.

AS11 Setup times are entered into cell AO11 in minutes. Since minutes is the normal unit of time measurement for setup times and hours determine costs, the

81

contents of cell AO11 is divided by 60 to give setup times in hours. Labor cost per hour (cell U11) is multiplied by the number of diesetters required (cell AQ11) to give the hourly setup cost. This figure is added to press cost per hour (cell S11) and the total is multiplied by the setup time in hours figured in the first part of the formula to yield the *total cost per setup*.

AU11 The formula in this cell is the heart of the spreadsheet. This classic formula can be found in most textbooks on inventory management.

AW11 The number of *setups required per year* is determined by dividing the economic order quantity which is displayed in cell AU11 into the annual volume entered into cell AI11.

AW11 Calculation of the *annual setup cost* which includes both press time and labor, is done by multiplying the total setup cost (AS11) by the number of setups per year (AW11).

BA11 In this cell, the total part cost including the cost of setup is calculated. To do so, the annual setup cost from cell AY11 is divided by the annual volume (AI11). The result is the setup cost per part. The total press, material and labor cost from cell AG11 is added to this to yield the *total part cost*.

BE11 The annual *cost to produce and store the part* is calculated by multiplying the annual volume (AI11) by the total part cost (BA11).

BG11 Here, the economic order quantity (AU11) is divided by two to yield the average number of pieces in inventory. The result is then multiplied by the total part cost (BA11) to calculate and display the *average inventory in dollars*. It is assumed that no safety stock is maintained and that the parts are used at a linear rate.

Cells A12 Through BG12 except BC12 The cells having formulas are the same as those in row 11. The second row is needed to do *A to B comparisons*. An easy way to use this spreadsheet is to enter all data into the first row and then copy those cells to the second row. This must not be done with columns BC and BI however, because they are blank in the first row and have formulas in the second row.

BC12 Here, the *annual savings* is calculated by subtracting the second total part cost in cell BA12 from the first part cost in cell BA11. The result is then multiplied by the annual volume from cell AI11.

BI12 To calculate the *percentage of inventory reduction*, the second average inventory in dollars (BG12) is subtracted from the first average (BG11). The first average inventory in dollars is then divided into the result to yield the percentage of inventory reduction.

Using and Improving the Spreadsheet. As presented here, the program will run in an IBM PC-XT® or compatible system using several popular spreadsheet programs. The faster MS-DOS® machines are desirable if it is expanded to do a great many more calculations. The author regularly uses it in clients' shops with a laptop computer equipped with two 3.5 inch 720K flexible diskette drives.

Users of other systems including mainframe computers that may not be compatible with this method of calculation can enter appropriate formulas to accomplish the calculations stated earlier.

An easy way to keep data secure and avoid long recalculation times is to copy the spreadsheet under a file specification that corresponds to a part or job number. A separate file is then maintained for each part A to B comparison. As described and shown in *Figure 6-8*, only 8.4K of storage capacity is required.

What can be done to improve the usefulness and accuracy of this spreadsheet is limited only by the imagination. Both the originator, Phillip Gibson, and the author would appreciate any improvements made to this spread sheet.

Another spreadsheet cost study application is covered in chapter 9.

Determining Economic Order Quantity. Textbooks on inventory management often cite several basic equations that are used to determine the economic order quantity. *Production Operations Management* by William J. Stevenson is a good source of information on the subject.[1]

REFERENCES

1. William J. Stevenson, *Production Operations Management*, Richard D. Irwin, Inc. Homewood, Ill., 1990.

7

A STRATEGY TO INSTITUTE QUICK DIE CHANGE

IMPORTANCE OF QUICK DIE CHANGE

The use of quick die change methods and equipment can increase the stamping shop capacity without increasing the size of the facility and purchasing more presses. By increasing press up-time from 50% to 90%, shop capacity goes up 80%. Quick die change can also improve quality and reduce inventory. Just-in-Time manufacturing can be an elusive goal without quick die change.

Increased Capacity

The time expended while setting up a stamping press is essentially idle press time. Setup time reduction is the most cost-effective means to increase the capacity of a stamping plant. The required capital expenditure is low compared to the cost of increased floor space and additional presses.

Improved Quality

Quick die change techniques require the exact duplication of a standardized setup. Examples of this are positive die location and common shut heights. The elimination of trial-and-error techniques practically guarantees repeatability.

Scrap Reduction

The goal of quick die change is to quickly change from one standardized setup to another and produce top-quality parts when production resumes. The setup repeatability that quick die change requires insures that the first hit produces a good part. Trial-and-error adjustments usually produce unavoidable scrap. Eliminating these adjustments will eliminate the scrap.

Job Security

Metal stamping is a very competitive business. Staying in business depends upon making a profit. *World class* means the ability to meet the challenge of any shop in the world in terms of deliverable quality, actual productivity, and real profitability. Backing away from the challenge simply means that ultimate defeat and insolvency has been accepted.

Safety

Conversion to quick die change provides an opportunity to improve die clamping methods. For example, if strap clamps are currently being used in conjunction with poorly made setup blocks, the quick die change conversion is an opportunity to adopt more secure clamping methods.

Die and Press Maintenance Costs

A very large percentage of total die and press damage occurs when diesetting. Shut-height errors are a common source of difficulty. These will no longer be a problem if a common shut-height is established. Quick die change requires secure die handling methods. Such improvements will insure that dies are not accidentally dropped.

Reduced Inventory

The increased press up-time and productivity made possible by quick die change can cause the warehouse to overflow rather quickly. The reduced setup cost and increased setup confidence make possible low economic order quantities (EOQ) and short production runs. As was illustrated in Chapter 6, JIT is a realistic goal.

LIFE IN A VERY TRADITIONAL SHOP

The following example is from an old, well established automotive supplier's stamping plant. This supplier is well respected in the industry and has established a relationship with several automakers as a preferred source for quality stampings. At the outset of an in-plant training program, management had a limited goal of reducing some sources of variability in the process, but not to the extent that complete quick die change requires.

Their objections to adopting quick die change were:
1. It was too expensive–special die trucks, hydraulic clamps, and bolster rollers were required.
2. Quick die change was impractical because the dies needed to be adapted to many different presses.
3. Restricting a die to be used only in a single press or small group of presses would limit the "manufacturing flexibility" that had been developed over the years.

Not all of the objections were valid. In simple terms, the root cause in any process variation is all of the variables in the process. Arguments two and three, as stated earlier, *are* the sources of some of the process variation that they wished to reduce.

Background

A typical stamping shop that makes the small intricate stampings for cars is a good example. The presses used are a mixture of press types and sizes. These presses were purchased in order to expand the shop capacity.

The straightside presses usually range from 200 to 500 tons (1.780 to 4.448 MN) and have a variety of bed sizes, shut heights, and load or pass heights. These presses are normally used to run progressive dies.

The remainder of the presses are usually gap-frame or open-back inclinable (OBI) presses. These presses are used for single operation and small progressive dies.

Flexibility of Scheduling Requirements

When production was scheduled, a die set request was issued. But it did not specify which press the required die(s) should be used in. This decision was left up to the production foreman on the shift in which the dieset was to take place.

The actual choice was usually decided by press availability. This is often thought of as true manufacturing flexibility. The diesetters somehow always manage to accomplish the setup by scrounging parallels, setup blocks, straps and coupling nuts from storage areas around the shop.

In reality, this practice reflected a nearly total lack of planning. Field expediency was the rule of the shop. Once these factors were recognized by the CEO of the company, a change in the way that the press room was managed became a top priority.

Employee Training Was a Supported Activity

Achieving and retaining the preferred supplier status requires that a number of programs be in place at the plant. Increasingly, the automaker's audit teams require that the supplier budget funds for training in many areas including setup reduction.

Quick die change cannot be achieved by simply sending the diesetters to a quick die change clinic or by arranging an in-plant seminar on quick die change methods. Likewise, the purchase of quick die change hardware such as fast mechanical clamps, hydraulic clamps, a specialized die transporter, bolster rollers, and die locators, will not necessarily increase press up-time. The whole organization of a stamping facility must gear up to support a quick die change program. *Figure 13-1* illustrates the activities in a stamping plant that must support the quick die change teams that set the dies.

DEVELOPING A PLAN

A strategy is needed to get an increase in press availability and up-time. This is done through the careful planning of quick die change techniques and hardware in an existing plant. Each plant activity has a responsibility to fulfill in order to convert an existing plant to a quick die change system.

A good way to start is to evaluate the primary requirements of the quick die change conversion program.

The Action Plan Primary Requirements

In a combat situation, the first rule of battle is never to cut your own supply line. Any modifications to existing equipment, or installation of new equipment, must not be permitted to:
- Disrupt production schedules.
- Compromise quality.
- Reduce process repeatability.
- Reduce productivity.
- Compromise safety.
- Require large capital outlays.
- Fail to be cost-effective.
- In addition, due to the limited production life of a given automotive stamping die due to obsolescence, the payback time generally was required to be under 18 months.

SPC Data Added Perspective

The involvement of the quality assurance manager in planning the quick die change conversion process at an early stage of the project was critical to success. SPC (Statistical Process Control) data clearly illustrates that designating a primary or home press for each job resulted in stability of the SPC data. Jobs that ran constantly well within control limits in one press would result in serious out-of-control problems in a different press. Many of the root causal factors of this process variation phenomena are discussed in Chapters 8, 15 and the case studies.

At the urging of the quality control manager, top management decided to go ahead and evaluate the value of a conservative quick die change conversion program.

Types of Die Adaptations Proposed

Through attendance at a quick die change clinic and tours of other contract shops, the key management personnel decided to reduce the time to set a progressive die in a straightside press. The goal was to reduce the average of two hours to twenty minues.

The old system made use of loose parallels and a nearly infinite variety of threaded rods, tee-nuts, washers, straps, and setup blocks. Back strain was a problem due the number and weight of parallel bars that required manual placement for each dieset. Setup repeatability as shown by SPC data was not good.

The following goals were agreed upon:
- Maintain the ability to set dies with fork trucks.
- Permanently attach parallels to the die shoes where a payback of under 18 months could be realized.
- Devise a means to insure setup repeatability through setup duplication in a primary or home press where possible.

Safety Considerations When Using Fork-Lift Trucks

As in many stamping shops world-wide, fork-lift trucks were used to set the dies. One advantage in maintaining the ability to quickly and safely set dies with fork trucks is that the same driver can load and unload semi-trucks when not setting dies. A dedicated battery-powered die truck is apt to cost twice as much and move half as fast as a fork-lift truck of similar lifting capacity, and die trucks are ill-suited for material handling activities when not setting dies.

Die trucks do offer a safety advantage as compared to fork trucks; there is little danger of dropping the die from the die truck platform, while there is a substantial liability of doing so in the case of a fork truck. This can easily occur if the die shifts sideways. Lifting a pallet or part basket is safe because each has a structure that completely surrounds the forks and prevents lateral movement.

A good way to increase the handling security of dies set with fork trucks is to permanently attach parallels to the lower die shoe. A subplate attached under the parallels further increases handling security. If scrap chutes are used, all except the two where the forks are inserted can be permanently installed in the die. These two chutes can either be pulled out and replaced to permit die handling, or stored on top of the die.

A most important consideration is not to exceed the lifting capacity of the truck. This can be avoided by actually weighing the die including any attached parallels and subplates. If the additional parallels and subplates are planned, and the actual die weight is known, simple engineering formulas can be used to calculate the total weight after the adaptation is completed. Chapter 9 illustrates how to do this with a simple spreadsheet program.

Engineering Cost Studies

Determining a reasonable payback period is often necessary in order to cost justify a quick die change conversion project. This was a primary requirement of both the CEO and the accountant. The spreadsheet illustrated in chapter 9 was developed to satisfy this requirement.

Process Variability Reduction

This was perhaps the most important consideration. This goal was achieved by adoption of the primary press concept. The main obstacle was not how to determine the best home press; that is explained in the next chapter. Scheduling was taken out of the hands of the shop foreman and assigned to a scheduler who was assisted by a database, using production management software on the plant's mainframe computer.

Using this conservative approach, a gradual quick die change program that satisfied management's goals was put into place and achieved over a period of one year.

8

GROUPING PRESSES AND DIES FOR QUICK DIE CHANGE

Evaluating Presses and Dies for Grouping

Several good arguments can be made for designating a home or primary press for each die. In fact, many stampers do so on the part-process sheets. Always using a die in the same press improves process repeatability from one run to another.

The amount that a press deflects per ton varies from press to press. It is especially true when comparing presses made by different manufacturers. This can be a critical factor when maintaining dies at a common shut height. Chapter 11 has information on the strategy for maintaining a common shut height for dies and presses.

There are a great many other factors that limit which two or more presses that are co-primary for a die. For example, a straight side press in good condition remains level if symmetrically loaded. A gap-frame press has an unavoidable angular deflection of approximately 0.0015 in. (0.038 mm) per 1.0 in. (25.4 mm) of front to back bed distance at full load.

A large cutting die with close clearances may run satisfactorily in the straightside press and be damaged each time an attempt is made to run it in a gap-frame press, even though the gap press had plenty of tonnage and bed size.

Some attempts have been made to reduce the angular deflection inherent in gap frame machines by fitting the open side of the machine with tie rods or keyed tie bars. But this will reduce the angular deflection by only a small percentage. The combined cross-sectional area of the rods or bars is small compared to that of the frame on the opposite side of the die space. In addition, the rods or bars will not permit access to the full press opening for the large workpieces.

Manufacturing Flexibility

Manufacturing flexibility is the main reason for wishing to set the same die in more than one press. An example of where this works rather well can be found in the current generation of integrated automotive stamping and assembly plants. There are usually several large tandem lines with identical presses and two or more similar transfer press lines.

For flexibility, especially in the event that a press line should be unavailable, the presses and dies are maintained at an identical shut height. Even the automation fingers and air moving press bolsters must be interchangeable from one line to another.

There are many pitfalls when considering such interchangeability. Chapter 11 provides detailed information on many factors that must be considered when interchanging dies among presses operated at a common shut height setting.

DEALING WITH A MIX OF EQUIPMENT

A Typical Contract Stamper's Dilemma

Many contract stampers started business years ago by running service parts and other low-volume jobs. These were jobs that large automotive stamping plants as well as high volume contract shops couldn't afford to run on automated presses. It simply was not profitable to use high-volume automated transfer presses and tandem lines for short-run hand-loaded work.

Mix of Work

The mix of work tends to be diverse. To be successful, contract stampers must establish a ''can do'' reputation. No work within the shop's specialty is turned down, provided there is sufficient plant capacity and a profit can be made on the job.

In most cases, the customer retains ownership of the tooling and does not enter into a long-term agreement with the stamper. A minimum commitment on the part of the customer means that the stamper is reluctant to invest in such items as permanently mounted parallels and subplates which are needed for quick die change adaptation.

Types of Presses Used

The type of press chosen by a small contract stamper is often determined by what is available at an affordable price when additional stamping capacity is needed. Often, used machinery is purchased for this reason. This sometimes results in presses with a great diversity of tonnage capacities, shut heights and bolster sizes.

Used Presses Are Often a Problem

Every new press is built with a specific category of work in mind. When buying a used press, the selection criteria often does not go beyond the following considerations:

1. Is the tonnage capacity sufficient for the job?
2. Is the bed size large enough?
3. What repairs are required?
4. How much does the press cost?

Presses Have Personalities

Presses deflect differently under load. If dies are operated at a common shut height, this is an important factor when grouping presses.

A good blanking press should be of very robust construction to resist deflection and hence limit the severity of snap-thru energy release. A blanking press should have a short stroke to keep the actual metal shearing velocity to reasonable speeds.

Presses designed for deep drawing often have much longer stroke lengths than a blanker of comparable size. The greater stroke length permits deep drawing to be performed and still have a large enough opening to permit easy part removal. Drawing presses, as compared to blanking presses,can usually tolerate greater deflections per unit of loading without adversely affecting the process.

In addition, feeding equipment may vary from press to press, alignment is not the same on all presses, and speeds may vary.[1]

EVERY SHOP NEEDS A PLAN

Determining which press to use should be based on a predetermined plan. It should not be a decision largely determined by which presses are available at that moment.

Grouping Presses

Once a decision is made to group presses for flexible scheduling, a plan is needed. Usually the large straightside presses are a logical place to begin the evaluation. There are several reasons why this makes sense:
1. These presses often run high-volume jobs.
2. These presses are the most expensive.
3. These presses have the best feeders and auxiliary equipment.
4. These presses offer the greatest opportunity for a quick payback.

Build a Press Database

Most shops maintain records of all of their presses. This information is needed to perform preventive maintenance and order spare parts. Press specifications are also needed by process engineers in order to determine process feasibility. In the event that accurate information is not available, a database should be developed.

Data Storage

The best place to store the information is in a computerized database. There are a number of database software packages that make doing this quite easy. While a mainframe system can be used for this purpose, the newer desktop personal computers are powerful enough to easily store all of the information for the equipment in a large pressroom.

Gathering the Data

Figure 8-1 illustrates a form developed for surveying presses on the shop floor when starting such a database. The information concerns only the parameters required for grouping presses for quick die change and manufacturing flexibility.

PRESS DATA WORKSHEET

PRESS NUMBER	DATE
TYPE	

MAXIMUM PASS HEIGHT
MAXIMUM SHUT HEIGHT
WIDTH OF BOLSTER (L–R)
DEPTH OF BOLSTER (F–B)
SCRAP REMOVAL METHOD
TONNAGE
STROKE
STROKES PER MINUTE MAX   MIN
TYPE OF FEEDER
TYPE OF DECOILER
TYPE OF STRAIGHTENER
TYPE OF LUBRICATOR
MAXIMUM THICKNESS
MAXIMUM WIDTH
MAXIMUM PITCH

Figure 8-1. *Worksheet for gathering data for a press grouping feasibility study.*

If press maintenance information is being gathered, data on motor horse-power, frame size, motor speed, type and number of drive belts etc. will be needed.

Chapter 16 has information on selecting maintenance database software. A common database program may also be configured to do the job.

COMMON PRESS FACTORS

Maximum Pass Height

Unless the press bolster has an opening to discharge scrap, any scrap generated will have to be removed by either gravity or mechanically assisted means. Where feasible, gravity chutes are often the easiest and simplest means for discharging both scrap and finished parts.

If dies are operated on permanently attached parallels,it is usually possible to avoid adjusting the stock feeder, a factor that can easily save five or more minutes per dieset.

Available Shut Height

Another important factor to consider is the amount of shut height and range of adjustment of each press. Not only does this determine the upper die buildup requirements, it is required for common shut height decisions.

Ram Risers

It may be found that the shut height adjustment at one press will not permit interchanging dies between presses without the need for parallels on top of the dies. Perhaps that press was designed for a deep drawing application and is now being used exclusively for progressive die operation. Not only does the placement of heavy parallels on top of the die delay diesetting, it can result in back strain.

A permanently attached ram riser can be attached to the upper slide, if there is a rare need for shut height capability. This riser can even incorporate built-in hydraulic die clamps if desired.

Ram risers are either fabricated from steel plate or cast from grey iron. The major cost in either case is for the required machine work. Usually, it is desirable to have standard JIC T-slots in the riser. Cutting T-slots costs approximately $3.00 an inch (25.4 mm).

For the shop wishing to improve operations within a limited budget, adapting a ram riser from a used equipment dealer may be a good way to save money. Generally, one can expect to pay about one half of the cost of the new material for such equipment.

An allowance for re-machining should be included when estimating cost. Used risers are normally badly rusted and have a lot of "battle scars" that should be cleaned up.

Always check to be sure that there is enough press counterbalance capacity to support the extra weight of the riser and the heaviest upper die to be used. Used bolster plates can be used for ram risers. If weight is a problem, investigate milling lightening slots. *Figure 8-2* illustrates a ram riser made from a press bolster by machining lightening slots.

A simple cost study will reveal where the best payback is to be obtained. The payback can be achieved either by avoiding the cost of permanently installing parallels on the dies, or in the setup time reduction. This will avoid the need to place parallels on top of the die in the press.

A hidden savings is that the riser will provide better support for the upper die shoe than parallels. This can improve quality and reduce die maintenance in some operations.

Bolster Size

When matching dies to available presses, bolster size is a very important factor. Not only does it determine the maximum die size, it can also determine scrap shedding feasibility.

Chapter 9 illustrates the use of a spreadsheet to evaluate press adaptations for operation on parallels. This includes a means to calculate scrap chute angles based on bolster width.

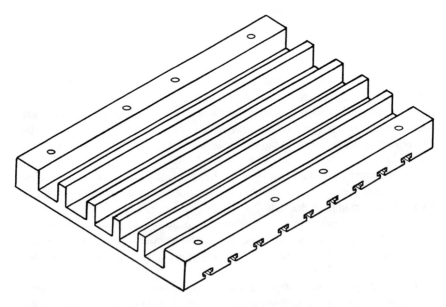

Figure 8-2. *A surplus press bolster converted into a ram riser for reducing excess press shutheight by milling lightening slots.*

Tonnage

Available tonnage is certainly an important factor. Not only must the press not be overloaded at any time, the load must be centered and the die shoes must properly cover the bolster.

There must also be enough flywheel energy to do the desired work throughout the press stroke. Even though the press may not be overloaded from a peak tonnage standpoint, the flywheel may slow excessively, particularly when deep drawing.[1]

Press Speed

The actual *metalworking speed* is a very important factor in stamping. The actual speed is a product of several factors including stroke length, strokes-per-minute (SPM), distance from the bottom of stroke, and press motion curve.

Just as the speed of a machine tool such as a lathe is a major factor in determining tool bit life and surface finish, the actual forming and cutting speed is a press personality factor that must be considered along with stamping flexibility concerns.

Deflection

Deflection in any machine is unavoidable. Knowing when press deflection will be a problem is an important success factor in pressworking management. Deflection is also a factor that affects the success of the stamping process in straightside machines.

If dies are interchanged between presses that deflect differently for a given amount of tonnage, the ability to operate dies at a common shut height will be limited (Chapter 11).

A further consideration is the effect of deflection on snap-thru energy in blanking operations. A cutting die that can be used successfully in a very stiff machine may shake the building when operated in a press fabricated from lightweight steel plate. Chapter 29 has detailed information about the effect of press deflection on snap-thru energy.

Press Condition

Problems such as a slight twist in a crankshaft can result in irregular motion of the press slide. In the case of a straightside having two or more slide connections, both sides of the slide may not reach bottom dead center simultaneously. Dies having close clearances may wear rapidly in such a press.

Jobs such as flattening small heavy details and setting non-critical emboss-ments can often be run satisfactorily provided full press tonnage is not required. The size of the workpiece in relationship to press size is a factor in such a case. Chapter 15 has detailed information on how to diagnose such problems.

USING EXISTING RECORDS

Existing records can form a basis for determining the best press to assign a given job to. Records should include:
- production efficiency.
- die maintenance costs.
- press maintenance costs.
- labor cost per part.
- scrap rates.
- labor costs.
- quality issues.
- Determining the best presses for a given job will depend to a large extent upon how extensive and accessible the data is. For example, if all of the data listed above is accessible from a common computerized source by press, job, part, and die number, it probably can be sorted in a number of useful ways and reports easily generated. This will permit decision making based upon good factual data.
- If, on the other hand, the data is in the form of hand written time cards and repair part invoices, the job will be very difficult. This is not much better for making a management decision than oral history and educated guesses.

Important Factors That Should Weigh a Decision

The main consideration in assigning a job to a primary or home press will tend to be where the job ran the best. This is based on the maximum number of pieces per hour produced. This has a pitfall. Nearly all jobs will be loaded in the best presses which can have a drastic effect on plant capacity.

There are other factors to consider such as:
- In which press or press line was the job consistently achieving the highest percentage of theoretical machine capacity?
- Operation in which the machine or line resulted in low die maintenance costs.
- What operation (as determined by SPC data) verifies the most consistent quality.

CRITICAL FACTORS IN RUNNING JOBS IN THE HOME PRESS

The proven benefits of the primary or home press concept in improving and stabilizing quality are beyond dispute. It is a difficult goal to achieve in many stamping shops. Some critical factors are:
- Advanced planning of production.
- Better teamwork in many shops.
- An effective preventive maintenance must be in place to avoid scheduling problems due to breakdowns.
- The capacity to do work must be accurately known.

Success Factors

To be successful in obtaining improved quality and machine utilization while meeting delivery requirements, there should be:
- A backup plan in case of press downtime.
- A backup plan in the event of die problems.
- The ability to cope with normal stock variation such as the normal range of stock camber.
- Engineering cost studies done on a routine basis to insure that the most cost effective solution to any problem is followed.
- Utilization of those quick die change methods that offer a reasonable payback.
- An ongoing emphasis on maximization of human resources.

REFERENCES

1. Donald F. Wilhelm, *Understanding Presses and Press Operations*, Society of Manufacturing Engineers, Dearborn, Michigan 1981.

9

USING A SPREADSHEET TO MAKE ENGINEERING COST STUDIES

Chapter 6 illustrated the use of spreadsheet programs to determine the economic order quantity (EOQ) of stampings to run. Spreadsheets are a powerful tool for doing complex calculations. The effect of a change in any of the data entered into a cell results in a rapid recalculation of the data displayed in the other cells. In essence, a proposed change in material cost, wage rates, manpower requirements, or how overhead affects "the bottom line" can be seen quickly.

AVOID COSTLY FAILURES

Inventory Control Failures

Examples of good ideas that were failures abound in the metal stamping business. Some contract shops have been known to attempt just in time (JIT) manufacturing based upon the application of inventory control software without making any quick die change improvements. It is possible to bankrupt the company in the process. Such plans typically seem to work fine with a few growing pains for about 40 days while the inventory is depleted. At that point, the warehouse is nearly empty and the plant is making emergency diesets around the clock seven days a week.

The usual problem is that the true cost of setting dies is not accurately known. The economic order quantity spreadsheet (Chapter 6) required the setup time and other known factors to be entered for computing the actual setup cost.

Quick Die Change Adaptation Failures

Chapters 7 and 8 explained that adapting existing dies for quick die change involves a number of considerations such as available shut height and bolster sizes, as well as quality and productivity issues. Do not assume. It is not uncommon for the toolroom to adapt a die with fixed parallels and a subplate only to find that it is too heavy to handle with existing equipment. The scrap chute angle may also be insufficient. As will be pointed out in case studies, especially in Chapters 20, 22 and 24, it is important to have a success story to build upon early in the program. An early failure tends to reinforce trust in the status quo.

Example of a Failure

Figure 9-1 illustrates a section through a press bed and lower die shoe. The press bolster (*1*) is 50 in. (1.27 m) wide. The die shoe width (*2*) is 40 in. (1.016 m).

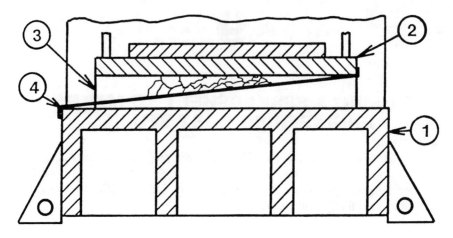

Figure 9-1. *Section through press bed and lower die: (1) 50 in. (1.27 m) wide press bed; (2) section through 40 in. (1.016 m) wide lower die shoe; (3) 10 in. (254 mm) high parallel due to limited press shut height; (4) scrap chute having an inadequate 12.53 degree fall angle which causes the scrap to jam up.*

Due to press pass-height limitations, the highest parallel (*3*) that could be permanently installed on the die shoe was 10 in. (254 mm).

This pass or feed height limitation resulted in a scrap chute (*4*) angle of 12.53 degrees which was insufficient. As a result, scrap builds up on the chute and frequent manual removal is required to avoid die damage.

Example of the Same Die Successfully Set in Another Press

Figure 9-2 illustrates a section through a press bed and lower die shoe. The press bolster (*1*) is 55 in. (1.379 m) wide. The die shoe width (*2*) is 40 in. (1.016 m). This press has 10 in. (254 mm) greater pass height than the previous example, permitting the use of 20 in.-(508 mm-) high parallels (*3*). This provides a scrap chute (*4*) fall angle of 22.84 degrees, which is sufficient in this case to insure positive scrap discharge.

Analysis of Success Factors in the Second Press

Permanently attached parallels in the second press worked well because the greater pass-height permitted enough scrap-chute fall-angle. This insured the positive discharge of scrap. The extra 10 in. (254 mm) of pass-height made up for the slightly wider bolster size.

Other changes in the five groups of steel parallels and plate used for adaptation included:

Group 1. The three 3 in.-(76.2 mm-) wide by 40 in.- (1.016 m-) long

102

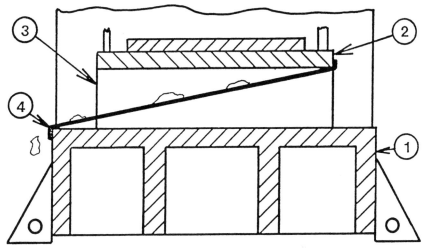

Figure 9-2. *Section through press bed and lower die: (1) 55 in. (1.379 m) wide press bed; (2) section through 40 in. (1.016 m) wide lower die shoe; (3) 20 in. (508 mm) high parallel permitted by adequate press shut height; (4) scrap chute having an adequate 22.84 degree fall angle.*

parallels were doubled in height to 20 in. (50.8 mm). These parallels have steps and slots milled into each end to permit insertion of the fastening bolts for securing the lower die to the bolster.

Group 2. The six 1.5 in.-(38.1-mm) wide parallels, that provide additional compressive support for the lower die shoe, were increased in thickness by 2 in. (50.8 mm) to provide additional stiffness. The other dimensional changes were the same as group 1.

Group 3. The size and cost of the lower subplate was the same for setting the die in either press.

Group 4. The low pass-height of the first press also resulted in excessive shut-height at the minimum slide adjustment setting. This required the use of parallels on the upper die shoe. A number of nitrogen cylinders installed in the upper die shoe were intended to be installed against the upper slide for support.

When upper parallels were used, an additional steel plate was required to back up the cylinders to prevent breakage of the attaching screws during normal cycling. This plate was not needed in the second press.

Group 5. As was stated in group 4 above, the upper parallels were eliminated.

As the following spreadsheet indicates, the second conversion was less expensive than the first one, and achieved the desired result in a predictable manner.

THE SPREADSHEET USED

The spreadsheet illustrated in *Figure 9-3* is designed to perform feasibility calculations including the following:
1. Bolster width.
2. Size of die shoes.
3. Estimated volume of tool steel.
4. Size and number of five groups of parallels (or plates).
5. Cost per pound of each of the five groups of plates and parallel stocks.
6. Labor cost estimate per parallel or plate.
7. Miscellaneous material costs.
8. Miscellaneous adaptation labor costs.
9. Press cost per hour.
10. Setup employee labor cost per hour.
11. Size of setup team before a change.
12. Size of setup team after a change.
13. Setup time before a change.
14. Setup time after a change.

```
: CONVERSION COST                                      :
: ENGINEERING STUDY                                    :
: DIE IDENTIFICATION :          TYPE  OF  DIE          :
:====================:=================================:
:   JOB 3743         :  PROGRESSIVE                    :
:   JOB 3743         :  PROGRESSIVE                    :


: PRIMARY  BOLSTER   LOWER SHOE SIZES     WEIGHT:
: PRESS :  WIDTH :  X = DIE STEEL EST   LOWER  :
:       :  INCHES:  L:   W:   H:   X:   SHOE   :
:=======:========:====:====:====:====:========:
:      19:       5Ø:  96:  4Ø:   5: 1.5: 7Ø76.16:
:      27:       55:  96:  4Ø:   5: 1.5: 7Ø76.16:


: UPPER    :  WEIGHT  :  WEIGHT    :              :
:Y = PUNCH STEEL EST:  UPPER       :   DIE W/O   :
:   L:   W:   H :  Y :  SHOE        :   RISERS    :
:====:====:====:====:=============:=============:
:  96:  4Ø:   4:   1:  5443.2      :   12519.36  :
:  96:  4Ø:   4:   1:  5443.2      :   12519.36  :
```

Figure 9-3. *Spreadsheet printout for performing engineering cost and feasibility studies of quick die change adaptations to existing dies and presses.*

```
:           BOTTOM           :   :    :    :
:          PARALLELS         : T : H :  L :
:===============================:====:====:====:
: BOILERPLATE W/BOLT SLOT     : 3 : 10 : 40 :
: BOILERPLATE W/BOLT SLOT     : 3 : 20 : 40 :


: LABOR    :MATERIAL :         :        :       :
: EA       :PER      : WEIGHT :        :       :
: EST      :POUND    :   EA   : COST EA :NUMBER:
:=========:=========:========:========:======:
:$100.00  : $0.55   :340.20  : $287.11 :   3  :
:$110.00  : $0.55   :680.40  : $484.22 :   3  :

:   WEIGHT :    COST    :  SCRAP :  CHUTE    :
:   FIRST  :    FIRST   :  CHUTE :  LENGTH   :
:   GROUP  :    GROUP   :  ANGLE :  INCHES   :
:=================================================
:  1020.60 :    $861.33 : 12.53 :   46.10   :
:  2041.20 :  $1,452.66 : 22.84 :   51.54   :

:           TYPE          :      :      :      :
: .          OF           :  T   :  H   :  L   :
:         MATERIAL        :      :      :      :
:=================================================
:    LOWER PARALLEL  : 1.5 :  10  :  40  :
:    LOWER PARALLEL  :  2  :  20  :  40  :


: LABOR :  MATERIAL:        :        :       :
: EA    :  PER     : WEIGHT :        :       :
: EST   :  POUND   : EA     : COST EA: NUMBER:
=================================================
: $25.00 :  $0.62  :  170.1 : $130.46:   6  :
: $27.00 :  $0.62  :  453.6 : $308.23:   6  :

: WEIGHT :    COST    :       TYPE        :
: SECOND :    SECOND  :        OF         :
: GROUP  :    GROUP   :     PARALLEL      :
=================================================
:  1020.6 :   $782.77  :  LOWER SUB-PLATE :
:  2721.6 : $1,849.39  :  LOWER SUB-PLATE :


:   :   : :LABOR   :MATERIAL:          :        :
: T :H :L : EA     :  PER    : WEIGHT : COST EA :
:   :   : :EST     : POUND   :  EA    :         :
:=================================================
:1.5:40:96:$400.00:  $0.71  : 1632.96:$1,559.40:
:1.5:40:96:$400.00:  $0.71  : 1632.96:$1,559.40:
```

Figure 9-3. *(Continued)*

105

:	NUMBER :	WEIGHT THIRD GROUP :	COST THIRD GROUP :
:	1 :	1632.96 :	$1,559.40 :
:	1 :	1632.96 :	$1,559.40 :

:	TYPE OF PARALLEL	:	T :	H :	L :
: PLATE TO BACK UP NITRO CYL:			1 :	40 :	96 :
: NOT NEEDED			:	:	:

: LABOR EA EST :	MATERIAL PER POUND :	WEIGHT EA :	COST EA :	NUMBER:
: $400.00:	$0.74 :	1088.64:	$1,205.59:	1 :
: :	:	0 :	$0.00:	:

: WEIGHT FOURTH GROUP :	COST FOURTH GROUP :	TYPE OF PARALLEL :
: 1088.64 :	$1,205.59:	UPPER WITH BOLT SLOT :
: 0 :	$0.00:	NOT NEEDED :

: T :	H :	L :	LABOR EA EST :	MATERIAL PER POUND :	WEIGHT EA :	COST EA :
: 3 :	10:	40:	$100.00:	$0.55 :	340.2:	$287.11 :
: :	:	:	:	:	0 :	$0.00 :

:NUMBER:	WEIGHT FIFTH GROUP :	COST FIFTH GROUP :	TOTAL PARALLEL WEIGHT :	TOTAL PARALLEL COST :
: 6 :	2041.2 :	$1,722.66:	6804.0 :	$6,131.76:
: :	0 :	$0.00:	6395.8 :	$4,861.45:

Figure 9-3. *(Continued)*

MISC COST SOURCE	:	AMOUNT	:
GRADE 8 BOLTS	:	$275.00	:
GRADE 8 BOLTS	:	$142.00	:

MISC LABOR COST	:	HOURLY RATE	:	HOURS	:
ASSEMBLE	:	$37.00	:	2	:
ASSEMBLE	:	$37.00	:	1.7	:

AMOUNT	:	TOTAL CONVERSION COST	:	TOTAL DIE WEIGHT	:	SETUP PER YEAR	:	PRESS COST/ HOUR	:
$74.00	:	$6,480.76	:	19323.4	:	27	:	$197.00	:
$62.90	:	$5,066.35	:	18915.1	:	27	:	$223.00	:

ACTUAL SETUP TIME MIN	:	SIZE SETUP TEAM	:	COST LABOR HOUR	:	OLD LABOR COST	:	OLD TOTAL COST PER SETUP	:
80	:	2	:	$35.00	:	$93.33	:	$356.00	:
80	:	2	:	$35.00	:	$93.33	:	$390.67	:

NEW SETUP TIME	:	SIZE SETUP TEAM	:	NEW LABOR COST	:	NEW TOTAL COST PER SETUP	:	SAVINGS PER SETUP	:
32	:	3	:	$56.00	:	$161.07	:	$194.93	:
32	:	3	:	$56.00	:	$174.93	:	$215.73	:

ANNUAL SAVINGS	:	PAYBACK TIME MONTHS	:
$5,263.20	:	14.78	:
$5,824.80	:	10.44	:

Figure 9-3. *(Continued)*

MAXIMIZING COST EFFECTIVENESS

Look for the Unexpected Savings in Cost Studies

Engineering cost studies should be used as a tool to take advantage of the many opportunities that exist in every company to improve manufacturing operations. When looking for a payback, be as creative as possible.

For example, if the goal is to set dies in the shortest possible time, the size of the dieset team may be increased, and more hardware purchased. There are a number of good reasons for permitting such expenditures. These include achieving such desirable objectives as:

- Developing enthusiasm in the workforce for productivity improvements.
- Entering a diesetting competition.
- Providing a "bragging point" for the sales department.
- Increasing the capacity to produce stampings when enlargement of facilities is not possible.
- Avoiding the cost of press purchases and building enlargements that would result in excessive capacity.

NOTES ON HOW THE SPREADSHEET WORKS

Data to Enter into Quattro.

The spreadsheet shown in *Figure 9-3* can be set up in Quattro software by entering the formulas and headings shown in *Figure 9-4*.

To save space, blank cells as well as the colons and equal signs used to separate the cells have been omitted.

Other spreadsheet programs can be used, although slight changes in the format of the cell formula entries may be required. The function of each calculation is described later in this chapter.

Description of Formulas

At *I5*, the length (*E5*), width (*F5*) and thickness (*G5*) (in inches) of the lower die shoe are multiplied together to obtain the *volume of steel* in cubic inches. An allowance is made for the weight of the die sections by estimating how thick they would be if spread out evenly over the entire area of the die shoe. (Students are taught to imagine the steel in a molten or plastic state.) This estimate, entered at *H5*, is added to the thickness dimension (*G5*) prior to multiplication. The result is then multiplied by 0.2835, the weight of a cubic inch of steel, to obtain the *weight of the lower shoe*.

By following the methods outlined in this chapter, students have been able to calculate total die weights including existing subplates and parallels consistently to within 2% of actual weight. The error tends to be on the low side because holes are not factored in the calculations. Weighing the die is advised to meet government requirements. In the case of iron shoes and parallels, a slight error will result because iron is less dense than steel.

```
A1:  [W2Ø] 'CONVERSION COST
C1:  'PRIMARY
D1:  'BOLSTER
E1:  [W5] 'LOWER SHOE SIZES
I1:  'WEIGHT
J1:  [W5] 'UPPR
N1:  'WEIGHT
O1:  'WEIGHT
P1:  [W3Ø] '
T1:  [W9] 'LABOR
U1:  'MATERIAL
Y1:  'WEIGHT
Z1:  [W12] 'COST
AA1: 'SCRAP
AB1: 'CHUTE
AC1: [W3Ø] 'TYPE
AG1: 'LABOR
AH1: 'MATERIAL
AL1: 'WEIGHT
AM1: [W12] 'COST
AN1: [W3Ø] 'TYPE
AR1: ' LABOR
AS1: ' MATERIAL
AW1: ' WEIGHT
AX1: [W1Ø] 'COST
AY1: [W3Ø] 'TYPE
BC1: ' LABOR
BD1: ' MATERIAL
BH1: ' WEIGHT
BI1: [W12] 'COST
BJ1: [W3Ø] 'TYPE
BN1: ' LABOR
BO1: ' MATERIAL
BS1: ' WEIGHT
BT1: [W1Ø] 'COST
BU1: ' TOTAL
BV1: [W12] 'TOTAL
BW1: [W31] 'MISC
BY1: [W31] 'MISC
CC1: [W1Ø] 'TOTAL
CD1: ' TOTAL
CE1: [W7] 'SETUP
CF1: ' PRESS
CG1: [W1Ø] 'ACTUAL
CH1: [W7] 'SIZE
CI1: ' COST
CJ1: [W12] 'OLD
CK1: [W12] 'OLD TOTAL
```

Figure 9-4. *Listing of spreadsheet cell entries used to make a setup improvement engineering cost study using a popular spreadsheet program.*

```
CL1: [W7] 'NEW
CM1: [W7] 'SIZE
CN1: [W12] 'NEW
CO1: [W12] 'NEW TOTAL
CP1: [W12] 'SAVINGS
CQ1: [W12] 'ANNUAL
CR1: ' PAYBACK
A2: [W20] 'ENGINEERING STUDY
C2: ' PRESS
D2: ' WIDTH
E2: [W5] 'X = DIE STEEL EST
I2: ' LOWER
J2: [W5] 'Y = PUNCH STEEL EST
N2: ' UPPER
O2: ' DIE W/O
P2: [W30] 'BOTTOM
T2: [W9] 'EA
U2: ' PER
V2: ' WEIGHT
Y2: ' FIRST
Z2: [W12] 'FIRST
AA2: '  CHUTE
AB2: '  LENGTH
AC2: [W30] 'OF
AG2: ' EA
AH2: ' PER
AI2: ' WEIGHT
AL2: ' SECOND
AM2: [W12] 'SECOND
AN2: [W30] 'OF
AR2: ' EA
AS2: ' PER
AT2: ' WEIGHT
AW2: ' THIRD
AX2: [W10] 'THIRD
AY2: [W30] 'OF
BC2: ' EA
BD2: ' PER
BE2: ' WEIGHT
BH2: ' FOURTH
BI2: [W12] 'FOURTH
BJ2: [W30] 'OF
BN2: ' EA
BO2: ' PER
BP2: ' WEIGHT
BS2: ' FIFTH
BT2: [W10] '   FIFTH
BU2: ' PARALLEL
BV2: [W12] 'PARALLEL
BW2: [W31] 'COST
BY2: [W31] 'LABOR
BZ2: ' HOURLY
CC2: [W10] 'CONVERSION
CD2: ' DIE
CE2: [W7] ' PER
CF2: ' COST/
CG2: [W10] ' SETUP
```

Figure 9-4. *(Continued)*

110

```
CH2: [W7] ' SETUP
CI2: ' LABOR
CJ2: [W12] 'LABOR
CK2: [W12] 'COST PER
CL2: [W7] 'SETUP
CM2: [W7] 'SETUP
CN2: [W12] 'LABOR
CO2: [W12] 'COST PER
CP2: [W12] 'PER
CQ2: [W12] 'SAVINGS
CR2: ' TIME
A3: [W2Ø] 'DIE IDENTIFICATION
B3: [W35] 'TYPE  OF  DIE
D3: ' INCHES
E3: [W5] '  L
F3: [W5] '  W
G3: [W5] '  H
H3: [W5] '  X
I3: ' SHOE
J3: [W5] '  L
K3: [W5] '  W
L3: [W5] '  H
M3: [W5] '  Y
N3: ' SHOE
O3: ' RISERS
P3: [W3Ø] 'PARALLEL
Q3: [W5] '  T
R3: [W5] '  H
S3: [W5] '  L
T3: [W9] ' EST
U3: ' POUND
V3: ' EA
W3: ' COST EA
X3: [W8] ' NUMBER
Y3: ' GROUP
Z3: [W12] ' GROUP
AA3: 'ANGLE
AB3: 'INCHES
AC3: [W3Ø] 'PARALLEL
AD3: [W5] 'T
AE3: [W5] 'H
AF3: [W5] 'L
AG3: ' EST
AH3: ' POUND
AI3: ' EA
AJ3: ' COST EA
AK3: [W8] ' NUMBER
AL3: ' GROUP
AM3: [W12] 'GROUP
AN3: [W3Ø] 'PARALLEL
AO3: [W5] '  T
AP3: [W5] '  H
AQ3: [W5] '  L
AR3: ' EST
AS3: ' POUND
AT3: ' EA
AU3: [W1Ø] 'COST EA
```

Figure 9-4. (*Continued*)

111

```
AV3:  [W8]  'NUMBER
AW3:  '  GROUP
AX3:  [W1Ø]  'GROUP
AY3:  [W3Ø]  'PARALLEL
AZ3:  [W5]  '   T
BA3:  [W5]  '   H
BB3:  [W5]  '   L
BC3:  '  EST
BD3:  '  POUND
BE3:  '  EA
BF3:  [W1Ø]  'COST EA
BG3:  [W8]  'NUMBER
BH3:  '  GROUP
BI3:  [W12]  'GROUP
BJ3:  [W3Ø]  'PARALLEL
BK3:  [W5]  '   T
BL3:  [W5]  '   H
BM3:  [W5]  '   L
BN3:  '  EST
BO3:  '  POUND
BP3:  '  EA
BQ3:  '  COST EA
BR3:  [W8]  '  NUMBER
BS3:  '  GROUP
BT3:  [W1Ø]  'GROUP
BU3:  '  WEIGHT
BV3:  [W12]  'COST
BW3:  [W31]  'SOURCE
BX3:  [W12]  'AMOUNT
BY3:  [W31]  'COST
BZ3:  '   RATE
CA3:  '   HOURS
CB3:  [W12]  'AMOUNT
CC3:  [W1Ø]  'COST
CD3:  '  WEIGHT
CE3:  [W7]  'YEAR
CF3:  '  HOUR
CG3:  [W1Ø]  'TIME MIN
CH3:  [W7]  'TEAM
CI3:  '  HOUR
CJ3:  [W12]  'COST
CK3:  [W12]  'SETUP
CL3:  [W7]  'TIME
CM3:  [W7]  'TEAM
CN3:  [W12]  'COST
CO3:  [W12]  'SETUP
CP3:  [W12]  'SETUP
CR3:  '  MONTHS
A5:  [W2Ø]  'JOB 3743
B5:  [W35]  'PROGRESSIVE
C5:  19
D5:  5Ø
E5:  [W5]  96
F5:  [W5]  4Ø
G5:  [W5]  5
H5:  [W5]  1.5
I5:  @SUM((E5*F5*(G5+H5)*Ø.2835))
```

Figure 9-4. (*Continued*)

```
J5:  [W5] 96
K5:  [W5] 40
L5:  [W5] 4
M5:  [W5] 1
N5:  @SUM((J5*K5*(L5+M5)*0.2835))
O5:  @SUM(I5+N5)
P5:  [W30] 'BOILERPLATE W/BOLT SLOT
Q5:  [W5] 3
R5:  [W5] 10
S5:  [W5] 40
T5:  (C2) [W9] 100
U5:  (C2) 0.55
V5:  (F2) @SUM(Q5*R5*S5*0.2835)
W5:  @SUM(V5*U5)+T5
X5:  [W8] 3
Y5:  (F2) @SUM(V5*X5)
Z5:  (C2) [W12] @SUM(W5*X5)
AA5: (F2) @ATAN((R5)/((D5-F5)/2+(F5)))*57.3
AB5: (F2) @SQRT((R5*R5)+((D5-F5)/2+F5)*((D5-F5)/2+F5))
AC5: [W30] 'LOWER PARALLEL
AD5: [W5] 1.5
AE5: [W5] 10
AF5: [W5] 40
AG5: (C2) 25
AH5: (C2) 0.62
AI5: @SUM(AD5*AE5*AF5*0.2835)
AJ5: (C2) @SUM(AI5*AH5)+AG5
AK5: [W8] 6
AL5: @SUM(AI5*AK5)
AM5: (C2) [W12] @SUM(AJ5*AK5)
AN5: [W30] 'LOWER SUB-PLATE
AO5: [W5] 1.5
AP5: [W5] 40
AQ5: [W5] 96
AR5: (C2) 400
AS5: (C2) 0.71
AT5: @SUM(AO5*AP5*AQ5*0.2835)
AU5: (C2) [W10] @SUM(AT5*AS5)+AR5
AV5: [W8] 1
AW5: @SUM(AT5*AV5)
AX5: (C2) [W10] @SUM(AU5*AV5)
AY5: [W30] 'PLATE TO BACK UP NITRO CYL
AZ5: [W5] 1
BA5: [W5] 40
BB5: [W5] 96
BC5: (C2) 400
BD5: (C2) 0.74
BE5: @SUM(AZ5*BA5*BB5*0.2835)
BF5: (C2) [W10] @SUM(BE5*BD5)+BC5
BG5: [W8] 1
BH5: @SUM(BE5*BG5)
BI5: (C2) [W12] @SUM(BF5*BG5)
BJ5: [W30] 'UPPER WITH BOLT SLOT
BK5: [W5] 3
BL5: [W5] 10
BM5: [W5] 40
BN5: (C2) 100
```

Figure 9-4. *(Continued)*

113

```
BO5: (C2) Ø.55
BP5: @SUM(BK5*BL5*BM5*Ø.2835)
BQ5: @SUM(BP5*BO5)+BN5
BR5: [W8] 6
BS5: @SUM(BP5*BR5)
BT5: (C2) [W1Ø] @SUM(BQ5*BR5)
BU5: (F1) @SUM(Y5+AL5+AW5+BH5+BS5)
BV5: (C2) [W12] @SUM(Z5+AM5+AX5+BI5+BT5)
BW5: [W31] 'GRADE 8 BOLTS
BX5: (C2) [W12] 275
BY5: [W31] 'ASSEMBLE
BZ5: (C2) 37
CA5: 2
CB5: (C2) [W12] @SUM(BZ5*CA5)
CC5: (C2) [W1Ø] @SUM(BV5+BX5+CB5)
CD5: (F1) @SUM(O5+BU5)
CE5: [W7] 27
CF5: (C2) 197
CG5: [W1Ø] 8Ø
CH5: [W7] 2
CI5: (C2) 35
CJ5: (C2) [W12] @SUM(CG5/6Ø)*(CH5*CI5)
CK5: (C2) [W12] @SUM(CG5/6Ø)*(CF5)+CJ5
CL5: [W7] 32
CM5: [W7] 3
CN5: (C2) [W12] @SUM(CL5/6Ø)*(CI5*CM5)
CO5: (C2) [W12] @SUM((CL5/6Ø)*(CF5))+CN5
CP5: (C2) [W12] @SUM(CK5-CO5)
CQ5: (C2) [W12] @SUM(CP5*CE5)
CR5: (F2) @SUM(CC5/CQ5)*12
A6: [W2Ø] '   JOB 3743
B6: [W35] 'PROGRESSIVE
C6: 27
D6: 55
E6: [W5] 96
F6: [W5] 4Ø
G6: [W5] 5
H6: [W5] 1.5
I6: @SUM((E6*F6*(G6+H6)*Ø.2835))
J6: [W5] 96
K6: [W5] 4Ø
L6: [W5] 4
M6: [W5] 1
N6: @SUM((J6*K6*(L6+M6)*Ø.2835))
O6: @SUM(I6+N6)
P6: [W3Ø] 'BOILERPLATE W/BOLT SLOT
Q6: [W5] 3
R6: [W5] 2Ø
S6: [W5] 4Ø
T6: (C2) [W9] 11Ø
U6: (C2) Ø.55
V6: (F2) @SUM(Q6*R6*S6*Ø.2835)
W6: @SUM(V6*U6)+T6
X6: [W8] 3
Y6: (F2) @SUM(V6*X6)
Z6: (C2) [W12] @SUM(W6*X6)
AA6: (F2) @ATAN((R6)/((D6-F6)/2+(F6)))*57.3
```

Figure 9-4. *(Continued)*

114

```
AB6:  (F2) @SQRT((R6*R6)+((D6-F6)/2+F6)*((D6-F6)/2+F6))
AC6:  [W30] 'LOWER PARALLEL
AD6:  [W5] 2
AE6:  [W5] 20
AF6:  [W5] 40
AG6:  (C2) 27
AH6:  (C2) 0.62
AI6:  @SUM(AD6*AE6*AF6*0.2835)
AJ6:  (C2) @SUM(AI6*AH6)+AG6
AK6:  [W8] 6
AL6:  @SUM(AI6*AK6)
AM6:  (C2) [W12] @SUM(AJ6*AK6)
AN6:  [W30] 'LOWER SUB-PLATE
AO6:  [W5] 1.5
AP6:  [W5] 40
AQ6:  [W5] 96
AR6:  (C2) 400
AS6:  (C2) 0.71
AT6:  @SUM(AO6*AP6*AQ6*0.2835)
AU6:  (C2) [W10] @SUM(AT6*AS6)+AR6
AV6:  [W8] 1
AW6:  @SUM(AT6*AV6)
AX6:  (C2) [W10] @SUM(AU6*AV6)
AY6:  [W30] 'NOT NEEDED
BE6:  @SUM(AZ6*BA6*BB6*0.2835)
BF6:  (C2) [W10] @SUM(BE6*BD6)+BC6
BH6:  @SUM(BE6*BG6)
BI6:  (C2) [W12] @SUM(BF6*BG6)
BJ6:  [W30] 'NOT NEEDED
BP6:  @SUM(BK6*BL6*BM6*0.2835)
BQ6:  @SUM(BP6*BO6)+BN6
BS6:  @SUM(BP6*BR6)
BT6:  (C2) [W10] @SUM(BQ6*BR6)
BU6:  (F1) @SUM(Y6+AL6+AW6+BH6+BS6)
BV6:  (C2) [W12] @SUM(Z6+AM6+AX6+BI6+BT6)
BW6:  [W31] 'GRADE 8 BOLTS
BX6:  (C2) [W12] 142
BY6:  [W31] 'ASSEMBLE
BZ6:  (C2) 37
CA6:  1.7
CB6:  (C2) [W12] @SUM(BZ6*CA6)
CC6:  (C2) [W10] @SUM(BV6+BX6+CB6)
CD6:  (F1) @SUM(O6+BU6)
CE6:  [W7] 27
CF6:  (C2) 223
CG6:  [W10] 80
CH6:  [W7] 2
CI6:  (C2) 35
CJ6:  (C2) [W12] @SUM(CG6/60)*(CH6*CI6)
CK6:  (C2) [W12] @SUM(CG6/60)*(CF6)+CJ6
CL6:  [W7] 32
CM6:  [W7] 3
CN6:  (C2) [W12] @SUM(CL6/60)*(CI6*CM6)
CO6:  (C2) [W12] @SUM((CL6/60)*(CF6))+CN6
CP6:  (C2) [W12] @SUM(CK6-CO6)
CQ6:  (C2) [W12] @SUM(CP6*CE6)
CR6:  (F2) @SUM(CC6/CQ6)*12
```

Figure 9-4. *(Continued)*

115

Metric users must enter a different coefficient in place of 0.2835. The coefficient entered will be determined by the user's preference for working with grams or kilograms and the length unit chosen.

In cell *N5,* the same calculations as cell *I5* determine the *weight of the upper die shoe* including the tool steel.

I5 The lower shoe weight and *N5,* the upper shoe weight are added together to give the *total die weight* in cell *O5* without subplates, risers and parallels.

At *V5,* the thickness, height and length dimensions of the first group of parallels used on the lower shoe are multiplied and the *weight* determined by multiplying the result by 0.2835.

In cell *W5,* to find the *cost of each bottom parallel*, the weight determined in *V5* is multiplied by the material cost-per-pound (*U5*), and the labor cost (*T5*) added to the result. Users of other monetary systems will want to modify the column headers to reflect the system used.

At *Y5* the *weight of the first group* is calculated by multiplying the individual weight (*V5*) times the number of parallels(*X5*).

Other descriptions include:

Z5: To determine the *cost of the first group of parallels*, the individual cost (*W5*) is multiplied by the number of parallels (*X5*).

AA5: This is one of the most interesting cells in the spreadsheet. In here, the lower die shoe width (*F5*) is subtracted from the bolster width (*D5*) and the result divided by two to determine the horizontal distance of the edge of the die shoe from the edge of the bolster. It is assumed that the die is centered in the press. The width of the die shoe is then added to the result to obtain the horizontal distance of the back edge of the die shoe from the edge of the bolster. The result is divided into the height of the lower parallels (*R5*) to yield the arctangent of the *scrap chute angle*. The arctangent is converted into degrees by multiplying by 57.3, the number of degrees in a radian. While this may sound a bit complicated, the spreadsheet will automatically do the calculations provided that the cell formulas are entered correctly.

AB5: The pythagorean theorem is used to determine the *length of the scrap chute*. The square of the lower parallel height (*R5*) is added to the square of the horizontal distance of the back edge of the lower die shoe to the edge of the bolster. The latter distance is calculated in the same manner as that done in cell *AA5*. The answer is obtained by extracting the square root of the sum.

AI5 through *AM5* formulas are entered exactly the same way as cells *V5* through *Z5*. In this case, *weight and cost factors for a second thinner set of lower die parallels* are calculated.

AT5 through *AX5* formulas are entered exactly the same way as cells *V5* through *Z5*. In this case, *weight and cost factors for a single lower subplate* are calculated.

BE5 through *BI5* formulas are entered exactly the same way as cells *V5* through *Z5*. In this case, *weight and cost factors for a single plate* needed to provide support for nitrogen cylinders on the upper die shoe are calculated.

BP5 through *BT5* formulas are entered exactly the same way as cells *V5*

116

through *Z5*. In this case, *weight and cost factors for the upper die parallels* are calculated.

At *BU5,* to obtain the *total parallel weight*, the group total weight cells *Y5*, *AL5*, *AW5*, *BH5* and *BS5* are added together.

Others of note:

BV5: In a similar fashion to cell *BU5*, the cost of the individual parallel groups *Z5*, *AM5*, *AX5*, *BI5* and *BT5* are added together to obtain the *total parallel cost*.

CB5: Here, the hourly labor cost (*BZ5*) is multiplied by the number of hours of miscellaneous labor (*CA5*) to obtain the *total miscellaneous labor cost*.

CC5: To obtain the *total conversion cost*, the total parallel cost (*BV5*) is added together with the miscellaneous cost (*BX5*) and the miscellaneous labor cost (*CB5*).

CD5: The *total weight* is calculated by adding the total die weight (*O5*) to the total weight of added plate and parallels. (*BU5*).

CJ5: To determine the labor cost for performing a setup before conversion, the setup time in minutes (*CG5*) is divided by 60 to obtain the time in hours. The result is multiplied by the number of persons on the setup team (*CH5*) and the labor cost per hour (*CI5*) to obtain the *old labor cost*.

CK5: The *total setup cost before conversion* is calculated by dividing the setup time in minutes (*CG5*) by 60 to obtain the time in hours. The result is multiplied by the cost of press time (*CF5*). Cell *CJ5,* the total labor cost for setup, is added to the result to display the total setup cost before conversion.

CN5: To determine the *labor cost to perform a setup after conversion*, the setup time in minutes (*CL5*) is divided by 60 to obtain the time in hours. The result is multiplied by the number of persons on the setup team (*CM5*) and the labor cost per hour (*CI5*), to obtain the labor cost.

CO5: The *total cost of a setup after conversion* is calculated by dividing the setup time in minutes (*CL5*) by 60 to obtain the time in hours. The result is multiplied by the cost of press time (*CF5*). Cell *CN5,* the total labor cost for setup, is added to the result to display the total setup cost after conversion.

CP5: The *savings per setup* is calculated by subtracting the new setup cost (*CO5*) from the old setup cost (*CK5*).

CQ5: The *annual savings* is found by multiplying the number of setups per year (*CP5*) by the savings per setup (*CE5*).

CR5: This is what the plant comptroller and CEO want to see, the *payback time in months*. It is calculated by dividing the total conversion cost (*CC5*) by the annual savings *(CQ5)* and dividing the result by 12 to convert years into months.

Comparing the Cost Factors of Another Method

The second row of the spreadsheet 6 showing formulas is a mirror image of the formulas in the row above 5. The size and cost factors are entered into the cells in exactly the same way in order to make a direct A to B comparison of the effect of any change.

Modifying the Spreadsheet

The engineering cost and feasibility studies that can be made with a spreadsheet of this type are limited chiefly by human imagination. The author would be pleased to hear from persons who use this and similar spreadsheets for pressworking calculations, especially regarding new applications and improvements.

DEDICATED COMMERCIAL SOFTWARE

The popular spreadsheet programs that work very well for tasks such as illustrated in Chapter 6 and this chapter, can be adapted to a variety of tasks such as maintenance planning and project management. In spite of their versatility, they may not be a good choice for complex tasks such as maintenance project management.

Simple to use, menu-driven software that requires little training is available for such large dedicated tasks. The user is prompted to make the correct entries, and explicit graphic displays and printouts show the results. Database queries are available at the touch of a function key.

Commercial Project Management Software

The term "project management software" can be misleading. The software package does not manage the project; a skilled project manager, as well as a team of engineers and technicians, is needed to insure success when installing an automated press line, complete stamping facility or other major project.

Critical Path Analysis

Such software is generally based on the principle of *critical path analysis*, a concept that originated years ago in determining the most efficient use of long-distance telephone call routing circuits. The critical path involves all tasks that must wait upon the completion of another task in order to be commenced.

A Simple Application: Building a Die

For example, building a die typically depends upon simple tasks such as ordering or building the die shoes, obtaining tool steel, ordering perishable details, laying out details, heat treating. routing machine work, etc. Many, but not all, of the tasks can be done simultaneously.

Experience would dictate that receiving and commencing all possible work to the die shoes should be done first. This may not be the best choice from a time saving standpoint. The limiting factor may be found to be the amount of wire burn and conventional EDM work required on critical die sections. A machine backlog may further extend the minimum completion date.

An experienced diemaker would know that the EDM work would either need to be scheduled for completion on overtime or jobbed out to another shop in order to advance the completion date. The software will offer this as an option also.

Types of Data to be Entered

Each individual task and the time required for completion must be entered. The sequence of events that cannot be varied, such as hardening the tool steel prior to EDM work and drilling holes prior to heat-treat, are also entered. Cost factors including overtime and outside contracting are other inputs, to name a few of the required entries.

Forms of Data Output

Depending upon the sophistication of the program, a number of reports can be generated. These include the cost of shortest possible completion time as well as the length and cost of the most economical completion time. Factors such as the cost of money are factored in automatically.

To visualize how a complex interdependent project must proceed toward completion, most software packages have extensive graphics displays using lines and boxes depicting the interdependency of the tasks. Generally, the *critical path* is described as the longest sequence of tasks while awaiting the completion of a previous path before the next path is started.

Saving Time and Money

Reducing the task interdependency in this path can save both time and money. Spending money on overtime or expensive contracted help on a critical project phase can save money in the long run. For example, getting a hot new product to market quickly can have a critical advantage in a competitive marketplace. Money spent on building tooling as a crash program may well be recouped many times within several months.

Using Critical Path Analysis as an Educational Tool

Using examples of real projects can provide a graphic example as to how critical path analysis actually works while demonstrating an important lesson in economics. An excellent object lesson is to analyze why a job with large cost overruns went sour.

The actual sequence of events, time used to perform operations, and money expended on a job is analyzed systematically with project management software.

MAINTENANCE MANAGEMENT SOFTWARE

Chapter 16 compares a commercially available maintenance management software package, used by The Ford Motor Company in their body and trim stamping operations, with a manual paperwork tracking system used by Mazda Motor Manufacturing (USA) Corporation in Flat Rock, Michigan.

Comparing Computerized and Manual Systems

Both systems are used to schedule and track tool and die repair activities. The Ford system requires a mainframe system and a number of user terminals throughout the die repair areas. The Mazda system makes use of corkboards, workorder holders attached to the dies and filing cabinets. Both systems require frequent planning meetings.

Selecting a Computerized Maintenance Management System

There are over 200 suppliers of maintenance management software packages. Chapter 27 explains a simple step-by-step method of choosing the software supplier that is best suited to serve the present and future needs of your maintenance operation.

10

EQUIPPING PRESSES FOR QUICK DIE CHANGE

PRESS EQUIPMENT DESIGNED FOR RAPID EXCHANGING OF DIES

One of the central features of modern tandem and transfer press die exchanging systems is the moving press bolster system. This arrangement permits a second moving bolster outside of the press to be prestaged for the next dieset.

An Ideal Arrangement

As stated in Chapter One, Danly Machine was a pioneer in developing presses equipped for quick die change. The most rapid exchanging of dies will occur if both bolsters can move simultaneously in one side of the press and out the other. Danly QDC™ tandem lines, that are over 20-years-old, routinely change over and produce a different part in under nine minutes. Danly sold this system to many manufacturers around the world including the Japanese automaker Toyota in 1959.

CUSTOM-BUILT QUICK DIE CHANGE SYSTEMS*

Although a wide variety of methods are used for die change systems, several basic concepts are normally utilized.

Tee-slot Lifters

First, instead of dragging or skidding the dies out of the press like a caveman pulling his load, modern die change systems have reapplied the same caveman's invention: the wheel with these die change systems, the die move on rollers out of the press rather than skidding. This reduces frictional forces so that the die is moved smoothly and efficiently. To accomplish this rolling feature, most modern systems use hydraulic or pneumatic tee-slot lifters. Other types of lifters are

*Based on a paper (MF87-603) by Dan Leighton, Atlas Automation, Inc., Division of Automated Manufacturing Systems, Fenton, Michigan. Presented at: "Quick Die Change" May 2-3, 1989, Detroit, Michigan, sponsored by the Society of Manufacturing Engineers.

available requiring bolster modifications. *Figure 10-1* illustrates a Tee-slot lifter installation.

These lifters raise the die or die subplate from the press bolster and place it on wheels. This reduces the force required to move the die to approximately 1% of its total weight. When equipment is designed for this concept, a safety factor should be applied, and total thrust should be 10% of the weight to be moved. In contrast, when the skidding technique is used, the equipment must be designed for 70% of the weight. These higher loads mean that the equipment is seven times heavier, with higher initial and potential maintenance costs.

Subplates

Secondly, many systems use subplates. A subplate is normally the same size as the press bed and approximately 2 in. to 3 in. (50.8 mm to 76.2 mm). Most subplates have tapped hole patterns to mount a number of different dies, location holes to locate the various dies accurately on the plate and hold-down slots or holes to attach the plate to the bolster. *Figure 19-3* illustrates a subplate with two dies attached.

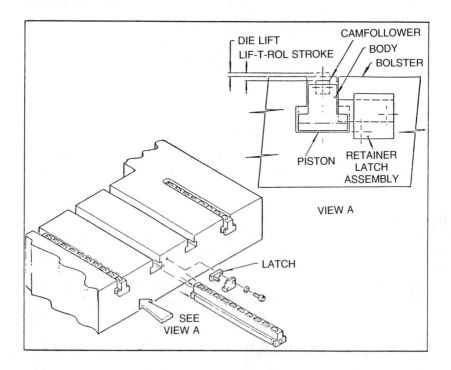

Figure 10-1. *Tee-slot lifters retrofitted into existing Tee-slots to permit ease of die movement. (Atlas Automation, Inc.)*

In certain cases involving only a small quantity of dies, the dies are permanently attached to the subplates. Some thicker plates have Tee-slots and keyways. The exception to this is when the dies on a particular job are designed and built with outside dimensions identical to the press and the die press mechanism. The subplate is important to the die change system for the following reasons:

- *Smooth Surface* provides a smooth surface for the hydraulic Tee-slot lifters to roll against rather than the various holes and cut-outs normally found on the bottom surface of dies.
- *Tool Holder* allows mounting of any size die in the press similar to a toolholder in a machining center.
- *Pre-staging* provides the opportunity to prestage the die on the subplate during production, thereby keeping the die change time and work stoppage on the press to a minimum.
- *Location* provides consistent location of the die in the press through the use of a keyway or side guides. This assists in realigning automation and attachment to the press and ram. No prying or jacking the die into position is required.
- *Ease of Attachment* with the consistent location in the press, bolt-down slots are provided which are in the same location on each die change and allow the same-length bolt to be used time after time.
- *Cleanliness* keeps the bolster and hydraulic Tee-slot lifters clean since the only time the press is exposed is during a die change.

TYPES OF DIE CHANGE SYSTEMS

Systems to change dies range from simple hydraulic Tee-slot lifters and bolster extensions on a single press, to automatic die cart systems for large multi-press stamping lines or rolling bolsters. The most efficient system for a plant should be designed around the specific requirements at the location in question. The list in *Figure 10-2* shows the types of systems that could be used.

A. BOLSTER EXTENSIONS
  1. Removable Bolster Extensions,
  2. Swing Away Bolster Extensions,
  3. Fixed Bolster Extensions, or
  4. Mobile Bolster Extensions.
B. DIE TABLES
  1. Fixed Height Table.
  2. Adjustable Height Table.

Figure 10-2. *Types of die change systems.*

Options:

    a. Portable,

    b. Tilting,

    c. Disappearing,

    d. Lift Die, or

    e. Rotary Type.

3. Skid Type–Fixed Height.

4. Skid Type–Adjustable Height.

5. Tee Table.

    a. Powered Push/Pull Type.

    b. Unpowered.

6. Self-propelled Mobile Die Tables.

C. DIE CARTS

  1. Transfer Carts,

  2. Single Station Carts, or

  3. Dual Station Carts.

Options:

    a. Unpowered,

    b. Air Powered,

    c. Electric Powered,

    d. Air-Hydraulic Powered,

    e. Electric/Hydraulic Powered,

    f. Die Storage or Prestaging Racks,

    g. Height Variation,

    h. Long Reach Type,

    i. Rotary Type,

    j. Load Rails or Rollers,

    k. Drop Deck Design,

    l. Vertically Actuated Grippers,

    m. Light Duty,

    n. Medium Duty, or

    o. Heavy Duty.

D. ROLLING BOLSTERS

  1. Single Axis, or

  2. Dual Axis.

Figure 10-2. *(Continued)*

DESCRIPTION OF VARIOUS TYPES OF DIE CHANGE SYSTEMS

The simplest system uses bolster extensions, (fixed, pivoted, mobile, or removable), mounted to the front and/or back of the press as illustrated in *Figure 10-3*. *Figure 22-3* also illustrates an application for these devices. These

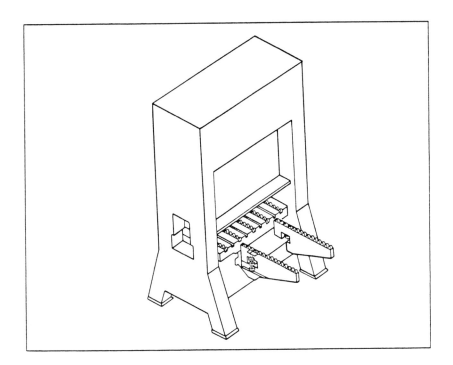

Figure 10-3. *Bolster extensions mounted to the front and/or back of the press to support dies being installed or removed from the press. (Atlas Automation, Inc.)*

extensions support a new die ready to install, or an old die when it is removed from the press. Hydraulic Tee-slot lifters are installed in the bolster Tee-slots to reduce the force required to move the die into and out of the press. The dies are rolled manually if they weigh less than 5,000 pounds (2,275 kg). To accurately locate the die in the press, side guides or keyways are used on the press and bolster extensions.

The advantages of this type of system are low cost and ease of installation. The disadvantages are that dies cannot be prestaged without interfering with either the front or rear of the press. In other words, the die change cannot start until the press area is clear of the operator and production has stopped.

Die Change Tables

The next step in die change equipment is a die table. As noted in the previous summary of die change systems, there are a number of types of die tables that can be used. The simplest is a fixed-height table that remains in place on one side or on the end of the press. This type is illustrated in *Figure 10-4*. Automation can be built around or over this table as required. Hydraulic Tee-slot lifters reduce the forces required and assist in accurate placement of the subplate/die in the press.

125

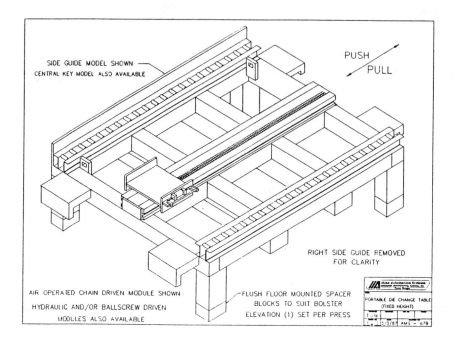

Figure 10-4. *An example of a simple die change table having a fixed-height table that remains in place on one side or end of the press. (Atlas Automation, Inc.)*

An adjustable-height die table such as in *Figure 10-5* could be used for an installation servicing two adjacent presses of different heights or as a portable table servicing several different presses with varying heights. The portable table would normally be transported from place to place by forklift or crane.

There are two advantages to die tables. The first is low cost. Secondly, they provide a way to accomplish die change when the bolster-to-floor height is below 12 in. (305 mm) or when there is not enough room to move carts out into the aisle area. The disadvantage of a die table is that prestaging cannot be accomplished prior to shut-down of production.

Tee Tables

Another approach to die change is the "Tee Table." This concept uses hydraulic Tee-slot lifters in the press bolster plus side guides or a keyway to control left-to-right location. As in the previous systems, dies are mounted to subplates so that all sizes of dies appear to be the same size in the die change system. A three-station powered roller conveyor *(Figure 10-6)* is mounted

126

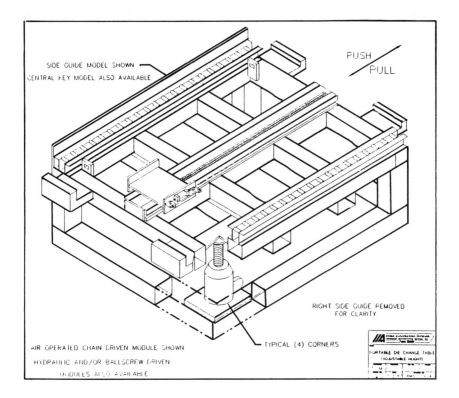

SIDE GUIDE MODEL SHOWN
CENTRAL KEY MODEL ALSO AVAILABLE

PUSH
PULL

RIGHT SIDE GUIDE REMOVED
FOR CLARITY

AIR OPERATED CHAIN DRIVEN MODULE SHOWN

HYDRAULIC AND/OR BALLSCREW DRIVEN

MODULES ALSO AVAILABLE

TYPICAL (4) CORNERS

PORTABLE DIE CHANGE TABLE
(ADJUSTABLE HEIGHT)

Figure 10-5. *An adjustable-height die table can also be used for an installation servicing two adjacent presses of different heights. (Atlas Automation, Inc.)*

behind, and parallel to the bed of the press. Pivoted or fixed bolster extensions equipped with rollers are mounted to this table and pin to the bed of the press when the die is ready to be moved. The pivoting feature permits ease of access to the press. The cam-follower rollers on the extensions provide support and side guiding for the die and subplate as it is being removed from the press. The hydraulic Tee-slot lifters are raised after the die is unclamped from the bolster.

Heavier dies are rolled out using a powered push-pull module. A new die is located on one end of the three-station powered conveyor. After the die is removed from the press, it is lowered onto the powered conveyor, and both the old die and the new die are moved simultaneously to place the new die in the center of the conveyor and in line with the press. The new die is then rolled into the press to a fixed stop. The hydraulic Tee-slot lifters are lowered and the die is bolted or hydraulically clamped to the bolster.

For lightweight die installations, a manual system uses a two-station linear actuator. In this type of system, the die is pulled out of the press onto one linear actuator carriage equipped with nonpowered rollers. This carriage is pushed to one side and the second carriage, with the new die, is pushed into the center position. The new die is pushed into the press and clamped in final position.

The only disadvantage of the Tee-table system is that it takes up a fixed area behind the press. The important advantages of the system are low cost and quick

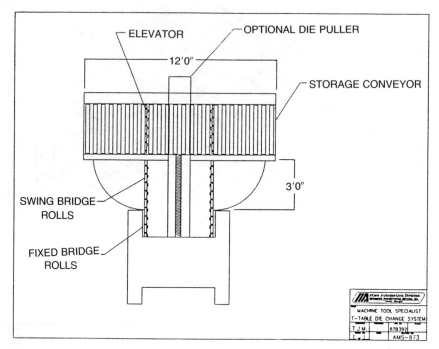

Figure 10-6. *A three-station powered roller conveyor called a Tee Table is mounted behind, and parallel, to the bed of the press to aid quick die change. (Atlas Automation, Inc.)*

changes without the use of forklift trucks or cranes. In addition, this system does not effect either side or the front of the press, and can be used for two presses back to back with the addition of another set of bolster extensions on the other side of the table.

Self-propelled Die Tables

In certain cases, a mobile self-propelled die table may be required where space is at a premium or the press-room layout precludes any other options. This system utilizes a storage battery-powered walk-behind device with a die table attached to the top of the power unit. The portable unit illustrated in *Figure 10-7* allows removal or insertion of the subplate and die from presses or high-density die storage racks in the range of 20 in. (0.5 m) to 80 in. (2.0 m) from floor level. A maximum of 12,000 pounds (5,455 kg) can be handled with this unit. The front corners of the platform attach to the press bolster or the die rack and are leveled with the power unit for easy removal or insertion. Additional units are available for heavier dies but they do not have the lift-stroke capacity to store dies in multilevel storage racks.

Because of the various press sizes that may be considered, a center key is used for alignment, which in turn requires a thicker subplate. A minimum of two

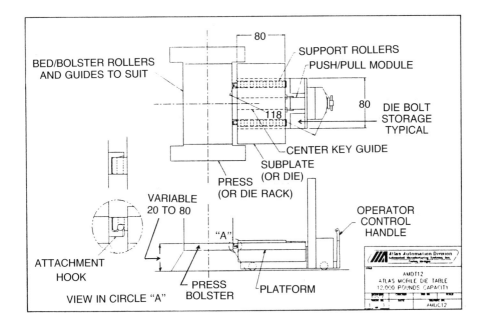

Figure 10-7. *A mobile self-propelled die table utilizes a storage battery-powered walk-behind device with a die table attached to the top of the power unit. (Atlas Automation, Inc.)*

subplates are required for each press to be serviced by this system.

The main advantage of this system is versatility. A number of presses, regardless of their relationship to one another, can be serviced by the same unit. The main disadvantage is the increased time needed for the die change due to the various steps required. Also there is a greater dependency on operator skills to transfer the new die to the press correctly, level, and make the change in a smooth and efficient manner, and then unhook and transfer the old die to a transfer station.

Die Carts

Another approach to quick die change is the use of die carts. These devices come in a number of designs and configurations depending upon the situations at the plant location. These systems also utilize subplates.

One possibility is a double-station die cart system illustrated in *Figure 10-8*. This is a good approach when the front or back of the press is congested with automation or other equipment. Flush floor tracks are installed on one side of the press. In this case, the new subplate and die are prestaged on one side of the cart while production is being run in the press.

129

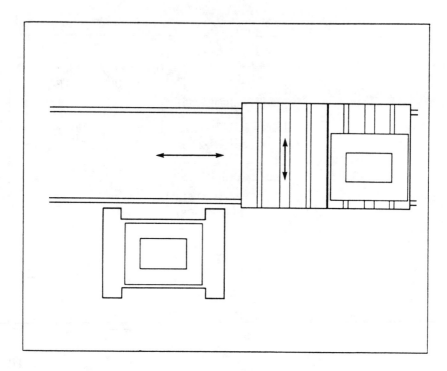

Figure 10-8. *A double-station die-cart system is a good approach when the front or back of the press is congested with automation or other equipment. (Atlas Automation, Inc.)*

When production is complete, the die cart is moved into position and the old subplate and die are rolled onto the empty station. The cart is then moved so that the station with the new subplate and die is in line with the press. The subplate and die are then rolled into the press, and the die cart is moved to its storage area away from the press. At this point, the automation can be rolled back into position and production can restart in a manner of minutes.

Using Die Carts With Storage Racks

Another possibility is to use a single cart with storage racks. This system allows dies to be stored adjacent to the press at bolster heights and utilizes a smaller single-station cart for making the die change *(Figure 10-9)*. Flush floor rails are installed on one side of the press. In this case, the new subplate and die would be on the racks and at least one rack must be empty. When production is complete, the die cart is moved into position in front of the press, and the subplate and die are rolled onto the cart. The die cart is then moved to the storage rack to store the old die and get the new one to place in the press. Finally, the die cart is stored out of the press area.

This system is less expensive than the double-station cart and only increases

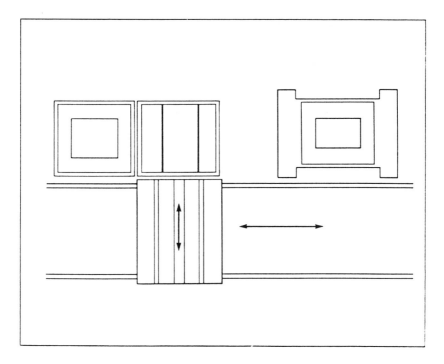

Figure 10-9. *A single cart used with storage racks allows dies to be stored adjacent to the press at bolster heights. (Atlas Automation, Inc.)*

the die change time by a few minutes. Flexibility is an important advantage of this system because additional storage racks can be added at any time as space permits. This system does not need the use of forklift trucks and cranes once the dies are placed on the racks.

Two-die Cart System

Another option is a two-die cart system such as the one illustrated in *Figure 10-10*. One cart is on the front of the press while the other is located at the back. Flush floor tracks are installed on both sides of the press. A new die is prestaged on a subplate on one cart while both carts are in the storage position and production is running. When production is completed, the automation is moved out of the way and the carts are moved into position. The old subplate and die are rolled onto the empty cart and the new subplate and die are rolled into the press from the second cart. When the die change is finished, the carts are moved back to the storage position.

The main advantage of this type of system is that it can handle very large dies and it allows the fastest possible die change. The one disadvantage is higher cost due to the two carts and a double track.

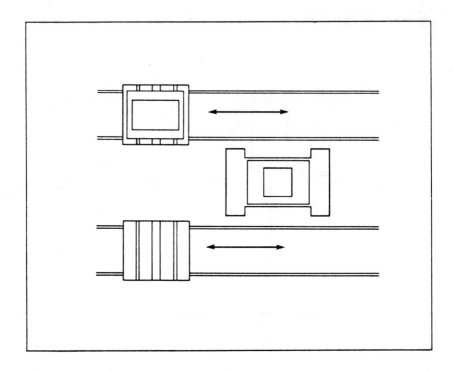

Figure 10-10. *A two-die cart system: one cart is on the front of the press while the other is located at the back. (Atlas Automation, Inc.)*

Proper Applications for These Systems

Any of the previous examples could be used for press access, if the press considered has windows. This is often required if the front and back of the press are tied-up with equipment. An example of this sort of situation would be a blanking press with coil handling equipment and stacking systems that are located on the front and back of the press.

Multiple press lines can easily utilize die carts. *Figure 10-11* illustrates a press line with three presses. Four carts are used for the die change. During production, die carts are prestaged with the new dies on subplates. When production is complete, the automation is moved out of the way, and the die carts are moved into position in line with the presses. The top cart, which is empty, pulls the old die out of press number one. The next cart pulls the old die out of press number two while pushing the new die into press number one. The third and fourth carts do the same routine as the first two carts, completely changing the balance of dies. The carts are moved out of the way and the automation is reinstalled, often utilizing the same flush floor tracks. Production resumes in a matter of minutes since automation is easily setup with the accurate die location obtained with the carts.

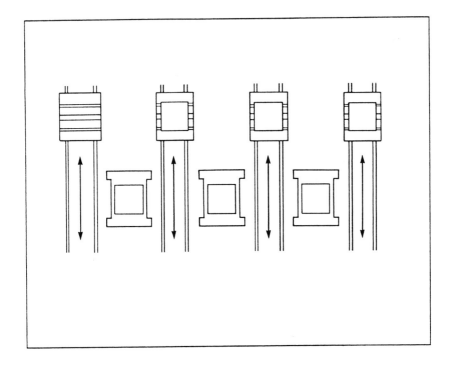

Figure 10-11. *A three-press line using four carts for the die change. (Atlas Automation, Inc.)*

The advantage of this system is that all dies for the next run can be stored or prestaged on the carts. No storage racks are necessary, unless storage for the third run is desired. This is the quickest die change possible for a complete line since two dies are removed or installed at the same time. The main disadvantage is cost, since one more cart than the number of presses is required. Another disadvantage is space, since the carts must go into the aisle for storage and prestaging.

With the proper layout of equipment, this die cart system can be utilized for a second or third line of presses. This, of course, reduces the cost of the die change system on a per press basis and allows a better return on investment.

In some press rooms, the spacing from one press to another and/or building restrictions require that an additional cart be installed. Large variations in bolster height can require the use of an additional cart. Minor variations in bolster height of one to three inches can be handled with an optional cart design.

Ideally, the press location should be designed to best utilize a die cart system. However, this is usually impractical on existing facilities. Most die cart systems must be tailored to the conditions that exist at the customer's plant.

Factors that must be considered when a system is designed for an application are:
1. Size of press bed.
2. Bolster height from floor.
3. Weight of dies to be moved.
4. Size of dies to be moved.
5. Frequency of change.
6. Availability of floor space.
7. Automation used.
8. Availability of crane or fork lift.
9. Is there enough shut height adjustment to allow a two inch subplate under dies?
10. Location of die storage.
11. Number of dies to be changed.
12. Use of cushion pins.
13. Tee-slots in bolster? Size?

SIMPLE LIGHT-DUTY DIE CART*

Figure 10-12 illustrates a simple locally fabricated die cart made of common structural and hardware components. The wheels are made of phenolic and have a groove in the center to permit them to be guided by a track made of strap-iron affixed to the floor. The table rotates on eight small wheels attached to the framework. The exploded view shows only one of the rollers supported by the angle-irons welded to the table top. A means (not shown) is provided to prevent the die from falling off the cart while in transit. A typical application would be transporting dies from a storage or a prestaging area to and from the press(es).

*Based on a paper by Ron Wilson, Production Superintendent, Calsonic Yorozu Corp., Morrison, Tennessee; presented at: "Quick Die Change" June 20-21, 1990 Toronto, Ontario, sponsored by the Society of Manufacturing Engineers.

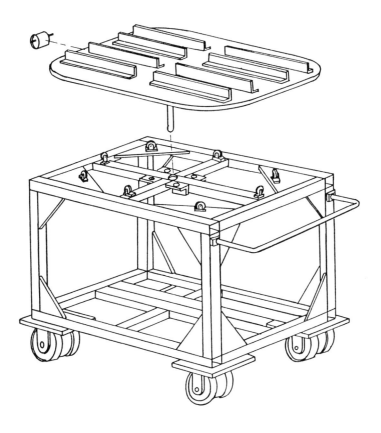

Figure 10-12. *An exploded view of a simple light-duty die cart. (Calsonic Yorozu Corp.)*

11

OPERATING DIES AT A COMMON SHUT HEIGHT*

INTRODUCTION

An important way to improve stamping flexibility is to maintain all dies at a common shut height or standard increments of shut heights. This avoids the need to make shut height adjustments when exchanging dies.

A well-thought-out common shut height program can speed diesetting and help avoid die and press damage.[1,2]

This procedure was developed based on an engineering study done by the author at the Ford Motor Company Woodhaven, Michigan, Stamping Plant during 1986.

AVOIDING DAMAGE DURING SETUP

There are classic stories of severe die and/or press damage that had been caused by insufficient shut height during setup before closing the press (*Figure 2-1*). In all cases, the damage could have been greatly reduced or avoided altogether if the press had been inched slowly and the crankshaft degree indicator checked consistently.

Sources of Shut Height Readout Error

Having a shut height indicator is not a cure-all for avoiding such damage. Some types of shut height indicators can lose their memory should power to the press be shut off or an internal back-up battery fail. This could result in an incorrect figure being displayed. *Caution during inching must always be the rule.*

Also, there is no guarantee that any one shut height indicator will agree with another of the same type. Some indicators use a rotary resolver to measure the number of revolutions of the slide adjustment mechanism jackshaft. Division by the ''N'' function of the readout device is used to convert turns into inches or metric units.

Uneven screw wear and inaccurate calibration when the unit was installed are other sources of error. Take extra care when setting a die in a press that is different from the one in which the die shut height was calibrated.

*Based on experimental stress analysis work done by the author at the Ford Motor Company Woodhaven Stamping Plant from 1986 to 1988.[1]

Diesetter Error

Some presses are equipped with a means to automatically adjust the shut height to a preset value based on a computerized library of correct settings for each job. In such cases, obtaining the correct setting usually depends upon the diesetter entering the correct die or job number. A simple miscommunication or a transposed figure can quickly add up to thousands of dollars lost due to wrecked tooling and press damage.

A Dangerous Assumption

Many writers and speakers on the subject of setup reduction define die shut height standardization as making all die shut heights the same as the press shut height. This is basically correct as far as the concept is concerned. However, in cases where tonnage requirements at the bottom of the stroke differ greatly from job to job, serious difficulties can result from such a simple assumption. This is because corrections for die and press deflection are required if optimal results are to be achieved.

It is possible to make a slide adjustment on a press when changing dies even when widely differing tonnage requirements are involved. To achieve this desirable goal, an understanding of how mechanical presses actually develop tonnage is helpful.

HOW A PRESS DEVELOPS TONNAGE

It is obvious that shut height adjustments do make a big difference in tonnage. Damaged presses and broken dies are often the result of too little shut height. When this occurs, tonnages far in excess of press capacity may be developed.

When the shut height is adjusted so the die halves just touch, zero tonnage is developed. To develop tonnage, the shut height must be reduced further. When this is done, the die is actually compressed slightly and, at the same time, parts of the press such as columns, links, pitmans, ram, bed, tie rods, etc. are either compressed or stretched. This occurs because the press and die must obey the same physical laws that describe the behavior of a coiled steel spring.

The Coiled Spring Analogy

A coiled spring produces no force in its relaxed position. It must be either compressed or stretched to produce a force. Just as a coil spring deflects an amount that is proportional to applied pressure within its working limits, a press and die deflect an amount that is directly in proportion to developed tonnage within the maximum ratings of the press.

Figure 11-1 illustrates three coiled springs supported by a beam. The undeflected length of spring (*Figure 11-1A*) is 5 in. (127 mm). Placing a 10-pound (4.55-kg) weight (*Figure 11-1B*) on the free end stretches or deflects the spring an additional inch (25.4 mm).

138

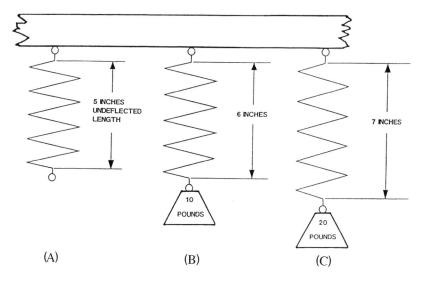

Figure 11-1. *The linear relationship of spring loading to spring deflection which demonstrates* Hooke's Law: (A) *5 in. (127 mm) undeflected length;* (B) *a 10-pound (4.55-kg) weight stretches the spring 1 in. (25.4 mm) to a length of 6 in. (152.4 mm);* (C) *a 20-pound (9.09-kg) weight stretches the spring 2 in. (50.8 mm) beyond its undeflected length to 7 in. (177.8 mm).*

Doubling the weight doubles the deflection. A 20-lb. (9.09-kg) weight stretches the spring two inches (50.8 mm) as illustrated in *Figure 11-1C.*

This behavior of springs has excellent repeatability provided that the spring is not overloaded and permanently stretched. *Hooke's Law* states that a body will deform in proportion to the applied force provided the proportional limit is not exceeded. This fundamental physical law is the basis upon which mechanical devices ranging from the simple spring weighing scale to the mechanical stamping press operate.

Behavior of Solid Steel Under Load

Spring-like behavior is also found in solids other than coiled springs. Every solid substance has a property known as *elasticity*; that is, they will stretch or compress slightly under load.

A steel cube 1 in. (25.4 mm) on a side will compress 0.001 in. (0.0254 mm) when subjected to a force of 29,000 pounds (129 kN). This is illustrated in *Figure 11-2.* This number is correct within ±3% for all common mild and tool steels even if the latter are hardened. The amount of change is linear provided that the applied forces do exceed the proportional limit of the steel. Hardening the steel only serves to extend the linear range by increasing the proportional limit.

The amount that a solid will change dimensions under a given load is termed its *modulus of elasticity* or *Young's Modulus.*

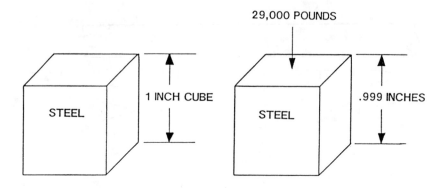

29,000 POUNDS

1 INCH CUBE

STEEL

.999 INCHES

STEEL

YOUNG'S MODULUS, OR MODULUS OF ELASTICITY

Figure 11-2. *A pressure of 29,000 psi (199 kPa) will compress a 1 in. (25.4 mm) steel cube 0.001 in. (0.0254 mm); this is an operational example of* Young's Modulus.

Other metals behave differently. For example, cast iron will compress more than steel for a given load due to its porous structure. The result is that the modulus of elasticity for cast iron is also substantially lower and much less certain than that of steel.

APPLYING THE LAW OF THE SPRING TO PRESSES

Press deflection relates directly to the amount of tonnage that the press is developing. When the press is adjusted so that the dies just make contact, no tonnage is developed. To develop tonnage, the slide must be adjusted below the setting where die contact first occurs.

When tonnage is developed, the press members are distorted or deflected slightly. Just as a coil spring must change shape in order to develop pressure, press members are deflected when a press develops tonnage. *Figure 2-7* is an exaggerated illustration of how a press deflects when tonnage is developed.

Normal Press Deflection Under Load

An approximate figure for the amount of stretch that occurs in a straight-side mechanical press between zero and maximum tonnage is on the order of 0.001 in. (0.025 mm) per corner for each ton (8.9 kN) available on that corner. The amount of deflection in large press is greater than many people expect. For example, a 1000-ton (8.9-MN) press has 250 tons (2.2 MN) available on each corner, and deflects or stretches about 0.250 in. (6.36 mm) when adjusted to produce full tonnage.

Example of Slide Adjustment Increasing Tonnage

If 650 tons (5.8 MN) are required to form a part at the bottom of the press stroke and only 450 tons (4.0 MN) are being developed, adjusting the slide downward 0.050 in. (1.27 mm) will result in an additional 200 tons (1.8 MN) being developed. This is based on a 0.001 in. (0.025 mm) adjustment resulting in one additional ton (8.897 kN) being developed on each corner, or four tons (35.6 kN) total. Thus, an 0.050 in. (1.27 mm) adjustment results in the 200-ton (1.8-MN) change.

This amount, which varies from press to press, can provide a basis for estimating the effect of slide adjustments on actual tonnages. A proven method of making an exact measurement using load cells is covered in detail later in this chapter.

Cutting Dies Are an Exception

Figure 11-3 is an actual press tonnage waveform signature of a cutting operation made by a high-speed chart recorder that was connected to the analog output of a press tonnage meter. Cutting dies that perform blanking, piercing, and trimming operations usually do all of their work before the bottom of the press stroke is reached. The figure illustrates this fact from actual pressworking operations involving the blanking and piercing of heavy metal.

The same is normally true of flanging dies unless the flange radius is "spanked" at the bottom of the stroke to correct for springback.[3,4]

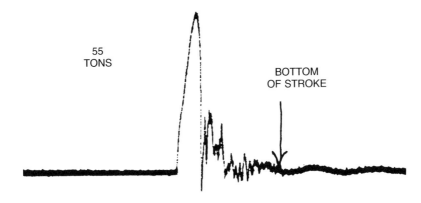

Figure 11-3. *A press tonnage* waveform signature *of a cutting operation which shows that all of the work is actually done on the downstroke of the press before bottom dead center (180 deg) is reached.*

WHY DIE SHUT HEIGHT MAY VARY ACCORDING TO TONNAGE REQUIREMENTS

As stated earlier, the assumption that making all die shut heights equal and adjusting the press shut height to the same value can sometimes have undesirable consequences. This is especially true if some dies require high tonnages at the bottom of a stroke and others do not. Compensation for press deflection may be needed and this factor may require a fine adjustment of the actual die shut height if slide adjustments are not to be made.

The amount of press deflection for an equal amount of developed tonnage varies from press to press. Presses that are of very robust construction deflect less than lightly built machines. To determine if the dies operate at a common shut height and can be interchanged between presses of different types, the actual amount of deflection for a given unit of loading should be measured with load cells.

Measuring Actual Press Deflection With Load Cells

The load cells are placed in the die space on strong supports (*Figure 11-4*). Generally four load cells are used, to measure any out-of-parallel condition. The use of at least one load cell per slide connection is recommended.

A 0.030 in. (0.76-mm) thick shim is placed under each load cell. The press is adjusted to produce full rated press tonnage when striking the load cells (*Figure 11-5*). Additional shims are added as needed to obtain equal tonnage on all load cells. The 0.030 in. (0.76-mm) shims are removed and the total drop in tonnage noted. For tests in presses under 200 tons (1.8 mN) thinner test shims will be needed.

The total drop in tonnage is divided into the thickness of the test shim material. The result in thousandths of an inch is the amount of press deflection that occurs for each ton of increased pressure.

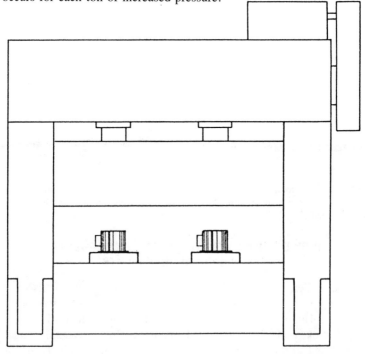

Figure 11-4. *Load cells placed in the press die space to measure press deflection.*[6]

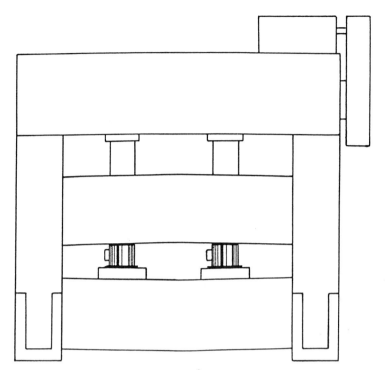

Figure 11-5. *Striking load cells at full tonnage.*[6]

It is often useful to think of deflection in terms of tons per end or corner of the slide, depending on the number of slide connections. To obtain incremental deflection factor in these terms, simply multiply the incremental deflection factor by two or four respectively. This figure is useful when analyzing the effect of slide out-of-level or offset loading conditions.[5,6]

INCREMENTAL DEFLECTION FACTOR

By definition, an *incremental deflection factor* is the amount of press shut height decrease, or die shut height increase that will result in a press tonnage increase of four tons (35.6 kN) total or one ton (8.9 kN) per corner. The best way to make an exact determination is by using calibration load cells, although an accurate tonnage meter can also provide the data. Chapter 15 explains how this concept is used to analyze process variation problems traceable to poor press alignment and offset loading.[7]

An Approximate Figure

The results of many tests made with load cells in straight-side presses show a tight grouping of incremental deflection factors for presses of similar construction. Expressed as deflection per ton per corner they range from

0.0008 in. (0.02 mm) for presses with cast steel members to 0.0015 in. (0.038 mm) for light-weight welded construction. An approximate figure is 0.001 in. (0.025 mm) per ton per corner.

AN EXAMPLE OF WHY DIE SHUT HEIGHT MAY NEED COMPENSATION

The concept of compensating die shut height for the amount of tonnage required at the bottom of the press stroke is best explained by an example:

A 1,000-ton (8.896-MN) press is the second press in a four-press tandem line. Depending on the job being run, this press either trims a stamping requiring 55 tons (489 kn), or embosses a large heavy stamping requiring the full press capacity of 1,000 tons (8.896 kN).

Retrofitting

In order to accomplish quick die change, the line has been retrofitted with automatic die changing carts and hydraulic clamps. To further enhance the ability to change dies quickly, all presses and dies are to be operated at a common shut height of 26 in. (660 mm).

In attempting to achieve the goal of common shut height, all presses were carefully adjusted to the 26 in. (660 mm) setting while empty. Likewise, all dies were carefully adjusted to the common shut height by milling shimming or adding subplates and/or parallels (*Figure 11-6*).

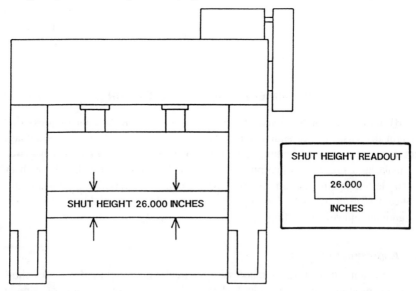

Figure 11-6. *A example of a straightside press with an accurate* shut height indicator *adjusted for a common shut height of 26 in. (660 mm).*

Measurement and Testing

When a trim die was operated in this press no difficulty was encountered. *Figure 11-7* illustrates a normal tonnage meter reading for such an operation. All of the work is done before the die closes fully, as illustrated by the tonnage meter waveform of *Figure 11-3*. Cutting dies, flanging dies and drawing dies that do not require work at the bottom of the press stroke probably can all be operated in these presses without much further consideration of slide adjustments. All that will be required is to maintain the correct static press and die dimensions.

When the die used to emboss the heavy stamping was set in the press at the 26 in. (660-mm) shut height setting, no tonnage was developed. This is

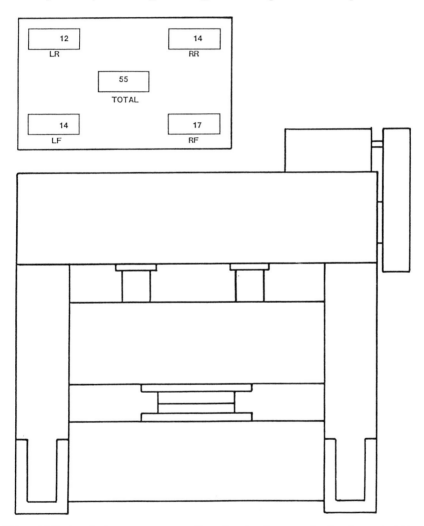

Figure 11-7. *A typical tonnage meter reading of a trimming operation in a large straight side press.*

145

illustrated in *Figure 11-8*, which depicts the press on bottom dead center with no tonnage indicated on the tonnage meter. Some tonnage would be developed when stock was inserted into the die. The exact amount would be governed by stock thickness and the size of the blank.

From the previous press deflection tests done with load cells, the slide must be adjusted downward approximately 0.250 in. (6.35 mm) in order to develop the 1,000 tons (8.896 kN) required to emboss the heavy stamping (*Figure 11-9*). An exaggerated view is shown in *Figure 11-10* of the press deflection needed to develop the high tonnage required. (For purposes of illustration, a small die is shown. As a general rule, the die shoe must cover at least 70% of the press bed

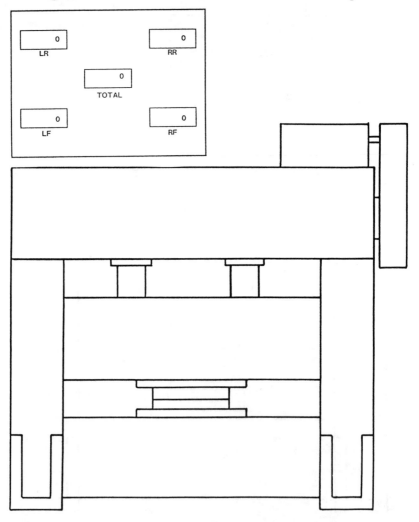

Figure 11-8. *When the press and die are both adjusted to exactly the same common shut height setting, no tonnage is developed upon die closure.*

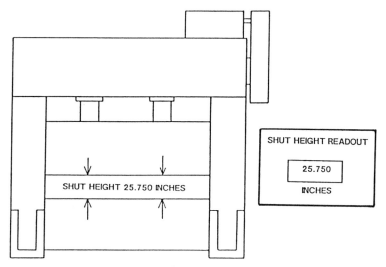

Figure 11-9. *Adjusting the slide downward .0250 in. (6.35 mm) will develop the 1,000 tons (8.896 kN) required to emboss a heavy stamping.*

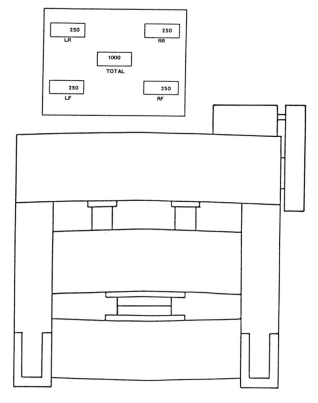

Figure 11-10. *An exaggerated view of the press deflection needed to develop the 1,000 tons (8.896 kN) required to emboss a heavy stamping.*

when full press tonnage is to be developed.)

In an actual press shop situation, the diesetter almost certainly will proceed to adjust the slide downward when it is apparent that a good embossed stamping was not produced. What was actually needed was a 0.250 in. (6.35 mm) shim to be placed on the die to produce the required tonnage.

Figure 11-11 illustrates a typical waveform signature taken from the tonnage meter of a press doing heavy embossing or coining. Note that the peak tonnage is developed at bottom dead center.

When changing dies from the heavy embossing operation to the trimming operation, severe die damage will result if the slide is not raised back to the 26 in. (660 mm) common shut height setting shown in *Figure 11-6*. The amount of downward adjustment required after metal-to-metal die contact first occurred, in the case of the heavy embossing operation, will result in a severe shut height error for the trimming die.

Figure 11-12 illustrates the die damage and associated tonnage meter reading that can be expected in the event that the press slide adjustment is not restored to the "common shut height" value. In reality, the desired goal of operating the dies at a common shut height has not been met because:
- Slide adjustments are still needed, which cause potential errors.
- Assuming that adjustments are not needed, causes errors.
- Die and press damage avoidance is not realized.

Careful analysis is required in order to develop a good action plan, so that no slide adjustments are required when setting dies. This should include the effect of press deflection on common shut height.

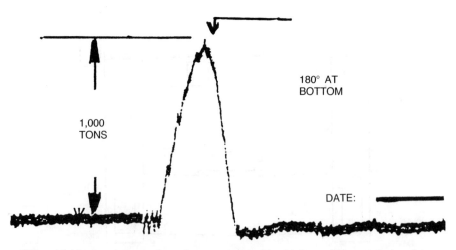

1,000 TONS

180° AT BOTTOM

DATE:

Figure 11-11. *A typical waveform signature made with a high-speed chart recorder of data taken from the tonnage meter analog output of a press doing heavy embossing or coining; the peak tonnage is developed at bottom dead center.*

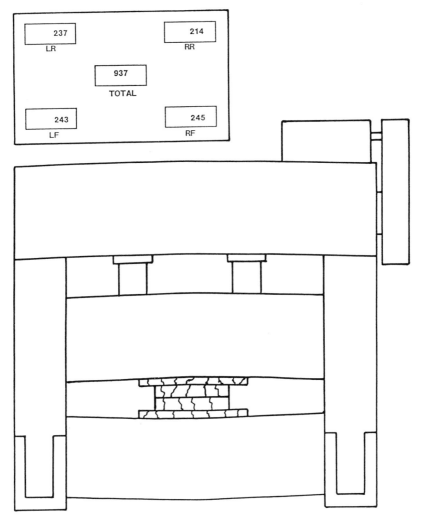

Figure 11-12. *When changing dies from the heavy embossing operation to the trimming operation, severe die damage will result if the slide is not raised back to the 26-in. (660-mm) common shut height setting shown in* Figure 11-6.

COMMON PRESS SHUT HEIGHT ADJUSTMENT PROCEDURE

Decide What the Shut Height Will Be

The first step is to decide upon the common shut height to be used, and to adjust the press to this figure with the slide exactly on bottom dead center. An accurate inside micrometer or calibrated end measuring rod used with a toolmaker's adjustable parallel is a good way to make this measurement.

Provide a Method to Measure the Press Opening

Figure 11-13 illustrates the use of a special end measuring rod that can be easily fabricated in most shops. The baseplate (1) can be made of mild steel, although tool-steel that has been both hardened and ground will provide better long-term service.

The rod (2) can be made of solid shafting for short to medium lengths. The weight and transportability of the standard for large press openings will be less of a problem if steel tubing is used for the center sections. The end plugs can be secured with welds or solder prior to machining. The rod (2) is secured to the baseplate (1) with a socket head capscrew (not shown).

The exact length of the rod must be accurately measured. One way to do this is to use the numerical readout data from the machine tool that was used to cut it to length. Using a coordinate measuring machine is another good way to make an accurate measurement.

Making an Accurate Press Shut Height Measurement

To take the measurement, a toolmaker's adjustable parallel or planer/shaper gage (3) is used to measure the space between the rod and the press slide as shown in *Figure 11-13*. The thickness of the adjustable parallel is simply measured with a micrometer and added to the length of the rod and the thickness of the baseplate to obtain the total reading.

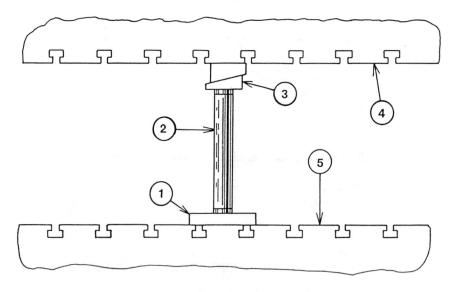

Figure 11-13. *A simple means to determine actual press shut height accurately through the use of a simple, easy to fabricate measuring standard: (1) baseplate made of hardened tool steel; (2) end measuring rod calibrated in a coordinate measuring machine or machine tool having an accurate digital readout; (3) toolmaker's adjustable parallel or planer/shaper gage used to measure exact height above measuring rod to slide; (4) press slide; (5) press bolster.*

Sources of Error

To obtain uniform measurements at different locations in the press opening, the press must be in good condition and the slide parallel with the bed. In fact, the measurement method illustrated in *Figure 11-13* can also be used as a press inspection procedure.

To insure that all excess play has been drawn up in the bearings, the counterbalance air pressure should be raised to a higher setting than that required to balance the weight of the slide alone. Chapter 17 provides information on the operation of the counterbalance system.

The press must be exactly at 180 crankshaft degrees or exactly at bottom dead center. This should be verified with a dial indicator.

The parallelism of the slide to the bed or bolster should be checked with a dial indicator attached to a test rod. Check all four corners and the middle as well. If the slide has a low place in the center due to overloading damage, this fact should be known. Keep a record of the readings for future reference. Parallelism errors should be corrected before establishing the common press shut height figure.

Accuracy of Adjustment

Settings as close as 0.002 in. (0.0508 mm) can be maintained provided that the press is in good condition. The size of the machine is a factor. Slight differences in readings taken at the four corners should be averaged out. A record of the exact locations of the measurements should be maintained to assure repeatability when it is necessary to re-establish the setting.

Setting Shut Height Readout Devices

The use of the calibrated end measuring rod illustrated in *Figure 11-13* is an excellent way to set and verify the accuracy of shut height readout devices. Portable measuring equipment using the principle of laser interferometry can also be used, but the end measuring rod is rugged and low in cost, and its principle of operation is obvious to any mechanic.

There are classic horror stories of needless die damage because someone thought setting a shut height indicator with a tape measure would provide sufficient accuracy. The use of simple procedures like the home-made end measuring rod together with employee training can help avoid such problems.

COMMON DIE SHUT HEIGHT ADJUSTMENT PROCEDURE

Once a common press shut height is established, all dies are then designed and built to this common shut height dimension. As was just discussed, the dies will need fine tuning of the actual measured shut heights if the die requires substantial tonnage when fully closed. The best procedure is to increase the die shut height from the nominal common value enough to obtain the required tonnage. If the

151

required tonnage and the incremental deflection factor of the the press are known, the amount of compensation can be calculated.

Often, it is cost effective to modify existing dies to a common shut height dimension by shimming or machining. If the die is equipped with a subplate or parallels, any needed shims can be placed between these details and the die shoe.

Making Fine Adjustments

There are several ways to determine the amount of fine adjustment to shut height needed to achieve correct tonnage values. In all cases, the method should depend on accurate measurement of both physical dimensions and operating forces.

A Tonnage Meter is Helpful

Set the die and bottom carefully to the common shut height while observing the tonnage readings to avoid overload damage. Note the tonnage required to produce a part at the common shut height setting. Compare this tonnage reading with that which is known to be correct for the process. Low readings are corrected by adding shims and high readings corrected by removing shims or re-machining.[1,2]

Use the Shut Height Indicator

Provided that it is properly calibrated and provides accurate information at all settings, a shut height indicator such as that shown in *Figure 11-6 and Figure 11-9* can provide the basis for quickly fine-tuning shut heights. Any deviation from the nominal target value can then be corrected by milling or shimming.

The amount of adjustment required to achieve the correct tonnage is exactly equal to the amount of die shut height change needed.

MAINTAINING A COMMON SHUT HEIGHT

Once common shut heights are achieved for a group of dies, factors such as die wear and die rework can cause a drift or abrupt change from the established nominal value.

The Effect of Die Wear

Die wear may result in the shut height becoming less than the normal value. For example, as the draw beads on a draw die blankholder wear, the increased pressure that is required to properly hold the blank is obtained by adjusting the slide for more tonnage, which decreases shut height. This is also true of restriking and embossing dies. As the working surfaces wear away, increased pressure is needed to produce an acceptable part. This may be achieved by using added shims or using thicker shims. Quality considerations and available tonnage constraints place a limit on how far this practice should be permitted before die rework is required.

Shim Adjustment May be Required After Rework

After dies are reworked, adjustment of the shims and buildup or milling of the die shoe(s) may again be necessary. Check the die in a tryout press with an exact way to measure shut height and tonnage prior to returning the die to production. This can help to avoid delays. The use of the measuring rod shown in *Figure 11-13* is an excellent means to make a precise measurement in the press.

Reworked dies must be bottomed carefully since it must be assumed that a substantial change in shut height may have resulted.

PROCEDURE FOR TRANSFER PRESSES

Transfer presses that have a number of separate dies under a common slide require special consideration when adjusting the dies to a common shut height. The reason is that the bed of the transfer press, like other presses, deflects downward much like an archer's bow when stressed. The ram does much the same to a lesser extent depending upon where the loading is in relationship to the pitmans or plungers.

Figure 11-14 illustrates a transfer press (feed rails not shown) having four dies that are just touching. *Figure 11-15* is an exaggerated view of the result of a

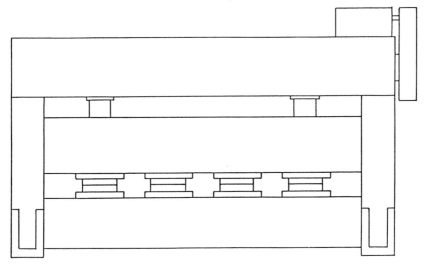

Figure 11-14. *A transfer press with four dies.*

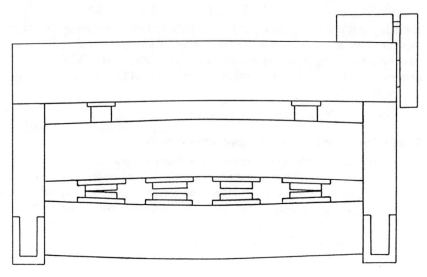

Figure 11-15. *An exaggerated view of the unavoidable bed and slide deflection in a large transfer press that requires compensation.*

normal unavoidable bed and slide deflection.

As a result of this deflection under loading, additional tonnage may be required for the middle dies to close evenly. This excessive tonnage results in extreme compression of the other dies. Reduced part quality often results due to coining marks, off-angle flanges, burred trim edges and many other problems. Extra tonnage can be self-defeating because it results in even more press deflection. In extreme cases, dies can be broken, and sparks literally fly as illustrated in *Figure 11-16*.

Avoiding Problems Through Good Process Planning

One solution is to design the processes that require high tonnage operations at the bottom of the press stroke—operations such as forming, embossing, and coining—and move them to the end of the press bed. Dies that complete their work before full press closure, such as trim, pierce, and flange dies, are then located in the center of the press. The bed deflection condition is not a problem since the flanging and trimming operations are completed before the press is completely closed.

Shim the Center Dies

Another solution is to shim the dies in the middle of the press to compensate for press deflection.The tonnage for each die when operated alone in a conventional press at a common shut height should equal the total required to produce a good part in a transfer press. If the required tonnage is higher, energy is being wasted, excessive die wear may occur and quality may be compromised.

154

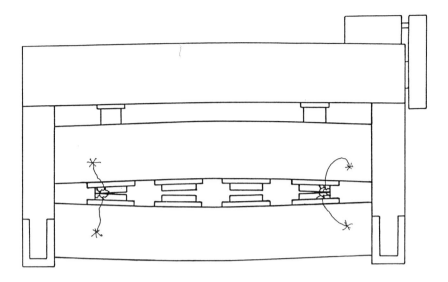

Figure 11-16. *In extreme cases, deflection under loading results in extreme* compression *of the outer dies, resulting in broken tooling.*

Once the dies can be operated in the transfer press at the proper total tonnage, individual die shut heights may be assumed to be correct.

Visual Troubleshooting Techniques

If die shut height fine-tuning is needed to achieve the correct total tonnage, it can be done by carefully examining the part(s) hit in each individual die for hard marks or other signs of over-bottoming. If equalizer blocks are used, check to see if they may be imprinting the striking surfaces. Such a visual examination can provide the basis for a cut and try approach to establishing correct individual shut heights.

If an individual die in the transfer press is suspected of having too much shut height, remove that die and hit the other dies with parts in them while noting how much the total tonnage drops. The amount by which the drop exceeds the measured process tonnage for that die is the excess that must be reduced by lowering that die's shut height.

How This Procedure Was Developed

The experimental data is based on an engineering capability study done with four dies used to produce an automotive door intrusion bar. The dies were set up in a 2,000-ton (17.79-MN) blanking press that had temporary strain transducers installed on each of the four columns. There were also strain transducers installed in the dies. All transducers were calibrated with load cells.

The process was successful. While there were differences in coincidence of tonnage peaks as measured on a high-speed chart recorder, it was determined that

155

this had no adverse effect on the process.

The results were virtually identical with both tonnage meter numerical values and waveform signature analysis results when the dies were run in the new transfer press.

In-Die Force Monitoring in Transfer Presses

Guesswork as to the fine tuning of transfer press shut heights can be greatly lessened if the compression of a die member is measured with a bolt-on strain transducer or removable bore hole probe while the die is being tested in a conventional press.

The bolt-on strain transducers designed for press tonnage meter applications are especially convenient because they can be installed easily while a die is in a storage area or in the press. These strain sensors are normally bolted to welded-on pads that can be accurately positioned by means of a low-cost welding fixture.

A good location is on the die parallels, or some other member that is compressed in a known way during normal die functioning. The object is to adjust shut heights of the individual dies to duplicate the strain measurements that were acceptable when the dies were operated in a tryout press. If the readings are given in terms of microstrain, the actual loading of the member can be estimated from the cross-sectional area and type of material by using simple engineering formulas.

The strain transducers, or *strain links* as they are sometimes called, are calibrated devices and can be removed from the dies and interchanged with repeatability of 2% or better. Transducer readout is accomplished with a portable battery-powered instrument that also provides an analog output for chart recorder or oscillographic analysis. All of this specialized stress analysis equipment including calibration load cells are generally available from the manufacturers of tonnage meters.

INTERCHANGING DIES BETWEEN PRESSES AT A COMMON SHUT HEIGHT

In order to provide for manufacturing flexibility and possible equipment breakdowns, it is important to be able to run dies in more than one press. This is generally feasible in the case of presses built to a common design by the same manufacturer.

As already stated, it is generally possible to operate cutting dies in a variety of presses with widely varying incremental deflection factors. All of the work is done before the bottom of the press stroke. It is theoretically possible to do the same with dies that require large forces at the bottom of the press stroke provided that the appropriate shimming adjustment is done prior to dieset. Because of the degree of care required, this is seldom done.

The Practice at Modern Automotive Stamping Operations

A common example of interchanging dies between presses at a common shut height is found in the pressrooms of integrated automotive stamping facilities. Chapter 21 is a case study of the Mazda Flat Rock, Michigan, facility.

Mazda has consistently done well in the Chilton's *Automotive Industries* magazine annual die change challenge competition. The correct die height adjustment data is contained in an ADC data file and the accuracy of automatic shut height adjustment is ±0.004 in. (0.1 mm). But to improve die change speed and to avoid errors, avoiding all adjustments where possible is the rule of the shop. The dies are carefully checked for common shut heights in a tryout press having an accurate shut height indicator.

An Important Stamping Flexibility Limiting Factor

The new pressroom at the Ford Motor Company (Wayne, Michigan) Integrated Stamping and Assembly Facility is closely patterned after the Mazda Flat Rock plant. Stamping Manager Robert Prucka and Facility Engineer Steve Cool report that maintaining dies that are interchanged between presses at a common shut height is not a problem. The small details in the stamping process that can cause precise shut height maintenance problems are analyzed and controlled with tonnage meter and waveform signature analysis data.

A major problem discovered during the start-up phase of the facility was transfer finger position errors between supposedly identical transfer press lines. In metal stamping, one must always assume that anything can be machined or adjusted incorrectly. As part of the plant's continuous improvement program everything from bolster shot pin hole locations to the actual motion curve of the presses is being examined and standardized to the greatest extent possible.

IMPORTANT POINTS TO REMEMBER

Maintaining dies at a common shut height, or groups of shut heights, will provide benefits that go beyond improvements in stamping flexibility and setup time reduction. Die change damage avoidance and part quality improvement are additional benefits to be realized from adopting this method. Adjusting dies to a common shut height may require more work than simply milling or shimming dies to a common figure. Even so, the procedure is simple. Never view the procedure as a black art requiring laborious die spotting and shimming in the press. Several important points are:

1. Always *standardize the press shut height* with the press empty and on bottom dead center.
2. As a general rule, flange, pierce, and trim dies can have the same shut height as the press.
3. Presses *must* deflect to develop tonnage.
4. Dies that require substantial tonnages at the bottom of the press stroke may require a slight increase in shut height to compensate for press deflection.
5. If both the press incremental deflection factor, and tonnage required at

bottom of the stroke are known, the exact die shut height can be calculated.
6. Multi-die transfer presses require special consideration, but the procedure is still straightforward.

REFERENCES

1. David A. Smith, "Adjusting Dies to a Common Shut Height," SME/FMA Technical Paper TE89-565, Society of Manufacturing Engineers, Dearborn, Michigan, 1989.
2. David A. Smith, "How to Improve Hit-to-hit Time With a Tonnage Monitor," SME Technical Paper TE88-780, Society of Manufacturing Engineers, Dearborn, Michigan, 1989.
3. David A. Smith, *Die Design Handbook*, Section 6, "Bending of Metals," Society of Manufacturing Engineers, Dearborn, Michigan, 1990.
4. Charles Wick, John Benedict, Raymond Veilleux, *Tool and Manufacturing Engineers Handbook,* Volume 2/Forming. Society of Manufacturing Engineers, Dearborn, Michigan, 1984.
5. David A. Smith, "Why Press Slide Out of Parallel Problems Affect Part Quality and Available Tonnage," SME Technical Paper TE88-442, Society of Manufacturing Engineers, Dearborn, Michigan, 1988.
6. Donald F. Wilhelm, "Measuring Loads on Mechanical Presses," SME Conference Proceeding, Society of Manufacturing Engineers, Dearborn, Michigan, 1988.
7. David A. Smith, *Die Design Handbook,* Section 27, "Press Data," Society of Manufacturing Engineers, Dearborn, Michigan, 1990.

12

EMPLOYEE TRAINING, ACCEPTANCE AND INVOLVEMENT

THE SURVIVAL INSTINCT

Diesetters, diemakers, maintenance employees, and operators all want to do a good job.

These persons equate skill upgrading with enhancement of job security and are willing to change their work habits. Training in basic metal stamping skills with an emphasis on setup repeatability and equipment damage avoidance is a proven means to improve quality while reducing costs.

Employee acceptance of improved diesetting methods is no longer the problem that it might have been a decade ago. Anyone who is presently employed in the metal stamping industry is almost certainly working in a shop that has adopted improved manufacturing methods such as statistical process control (SPC), effective preventative maintenance and inventory reduction.

Everyone probably knows someone else who has lost their job as a direct result of domestic or foreign competition. Survival is a powerful motivating factor.

Training in Proper Procedures is Needed

Nearly every stamping manager has identified poor diesetting practices as a major cause of equipment damage and quality problems in their plants. The cause of poor practices is usually a lack of proper procedures, equipment, and training. Proper diesetting practices are an absolute requirement if a reduction in setup time and improved setup repeatability is to be realized.

EFFECTIVE TRAINING

Employee involvement and interaction is a proven method to improve work methods and quality. The familiar employee involvement groups and quality improvement circles have been a boon to the manufacturers who have provided the required support and follow-up to get the group's ideas implemented. Chapter 13 covers the support that management must provide if a team approach to diesetting and process repeatability improvements are to be realized.

Diesetters, diemakers, maintenance employees, and operators should meet regularly in the plant for training and a discussion of methods to improve overall plant performance. The meeting can be a key to reaching continuous improvement goals.

Respected Experts Can be Valuable

A wise person once observed that to be considered an expert, one must be at least 50 miles from home. The use of instructors from outside the company together with active management participation is a good way to keep the group fluid and maintain the continuous improvement focus. Even though in-plant management has been trying for years to drive home the same message that the outside expert brings to the plant, management should participate to show that the information is important. Chapter 20—a case from General Motor's Lansing, Michigan BOC plant—points out that a visit by Japanese setup reduction expert Shigeo Shingo was a means to launch their successful setup reduction program.

SOURCES OF LECTURERS AND INSTRUCTORS

An effective instructor must do much more than keep the class awake while driving important points home through repetition. The instructor should be able to work with the group including management to solve actual in-plant problems. While a strong metal stamping background is very desirable, it is not absolutely necessary. A generalized setup reduction specialist can provide training in how to identify opportunities for diesetting improvement.

Local School Systems

The adult education departments in some local school systems can arrange for instructors from either the school system or community to conduct training. In most cases, the training can be conducted in-plant, although an off-site facility may have advantages such as freedom from job-related interruptions.

Leaders of setup teams in other area stamping plants often make good instructors. Even though the instructor does not have a teaching degree, a background of hands-on experience in how to get the job done is invaluable. Generally, the school's adult education department can assist by helping the instructor organize lesson plans and reproduce training materials.

Often the school system pays a fixed fee per hour to adult education instructors. The fee is the same for teaching basket weaving, ballroom dancing or setup reduction. It may be necessary to subsidize the instructor's fee to get the person that you want. This may or may not be permitted by the school system's rules.

Government Grants

Money may be available to pay all or part of the training costs through government grants. Adult education administrators can provide information on available grants and how to obtain them. A grant program usually imposes restrictions on the number of instruction hours and can require paperwork. It is usually more important to get the desired instructor for the hours that are actually needed than it is to get educational grant funds.

Community Colleges

The same types of instructors and programs are usually available through community colleges as is the case with public school adult education departments. Usually community colleges can draw on a larger base of available instructors and may be better able to administer in-plant training than is a public school system.

Colleges and Universities

Several colleges and universities sponsor one to three-day training seminars on the subject of setup reduction. In addition to their own staff, they also draw on instructors from management consulting groups as well as independent consultants and trainers. The number of speakers is usually between one and four.

This training is usually fairly generic, dealing with the overall topic of setup reduction on all types of machinery and processing equipment. The methodology that they teach can help spot the opportunities in your plant for setup time reduction and process repeatability improvements.

Professional Engineering Societies

Trade associations and professional engineering societies sponsor seminars on many topics including quick die changing. These seminars tend to be more practical than those sponsored by universities and management consulting groups.

Another advantage of these seminars is that the speaker's panel is much larger and each speaker addresses an area of specialty or individual expertise. The cost is often lower because the speakers are either independent consultants who wish to showcase their talents or manufacturing specialists supplied by their employers without charge. Some presentations are occasionally flawed by commercialism, but both the conference chairperson and parent association or society are careful to avoid this happening.

Increasingly, trade associations either directly supply or can recommend members who can provide turnkey in-plant training and consulting services.

Management Consulting Groups

An advantage of management consulting groups is that they usually have a full-time staff of skilled trainers with a strong business background. Whenever a hot new area requiring training (such as vendor certification, bar coding etc.) emerges, these firms can quickly have specialists gather information on the subject and get training materials and training on-line quickly.

Independent Consultants and Trainers

There are a handful of independent consultants who provide quick die change training. Often they work for one or more of the sources already listed. For long-term in-plant training and consulting work, they are usually the best bargain obtainable.

In some cases, their services include design and engineering work. For example, they just don't tell you that a locating pin hole needs to be drilled in a press bolster, they will show you where to drill the hole and the correct material specification for the pin that goes into the hole.

INSTRUCTOR QUALIFICATIONS

Bad training can be worse than no training at all. It does little good to get an expert in large automotive transfer presses to train diesetters in a small contract stamping shop on how to prestage transfer press air moving bolsters. Such instructors have been shocked to learn that such shops typically set dies with fork lift trucks. Make sure that the instructor is familiar with your class of work. Request samples of the training materials that the instructor intends to use. It is important that the instructor be totally familiar with the training materials. It is a bad idea to hire an instructor who intends to keep a paragraph ahead of the class in the textbook. Instructors in personal computer operation and MS-DOS have been known to get away with this. But it won't work with diesetters and chaos will occur.

Request and Check References

An investment in training is too important to leave the instructor's ability and qualifications to chance. The recommendation of a trusted associate who knows of the instructor's skills firsthand is more important than a resume.

MEETING ROOM REQUIREMENTS

A skilled instructor who is determined to get results can accomplish amazingly effective training in a small stamping shop lunch room over the din of the machinery just outside of a non-soundproofed door. This situation is far from ideal. Many instructors would refuse such assignments, especially if they had to lug a screen, flip chart easel and projector through the plant and up a steep stairway in order to conduct classes. When the cost of time off the job is considered together with the instructor's fee, training costs for a dozen diesetters attending a two-hour class can exceed a thousand dollars. Arguments for using lunchrooms range from not wanting shop grime tracked into the corporate conference room to paying for a conference room at a local hotel or just being a foolish extravagance. This doesn't make good economic and psychological sense when the other costs and benefits of good training are considered.

Good Ventilation is Important

This is seldom a problem in modern facilities unless smoking is permitted. A sizable percentage of workers in industry do smoke, and a rational decision should be made as to whether or not to permit smoking in the meeting room. Considerations are company rules, state and local laws, and the amount of ventilation available. Usually the Human Resources Director or Plant Manager is the appropriate person to decide the issue, if it becomes a problem.

Everyone Must be Able to Hear the Speaker

This is not as simple a problem as one might think. Hearing loss is a problem in the stamping industry. This is especially true in the case of older workers who may have the combined effects of noise induced hearing loss and the loss of hearing acuity attributable to aging. Employees with over 20 years' stamping experience may have worked in shops with high noise levels before hearing conservation programs were mandated by federal law.

Most persons with such hearing losses can hear satisfactorily if:
1. The level of background noise from air handling equipment, projector cooling blowers, etc., is not excessive.
2. The level of sound transmitted into the meeting room from outside sources is not excessive.
3. The ratio of direct to reflected sound reaching the listener is high.
4. Sound reinforcing equipment is adjusted to emphasize the frequency range from 1,800 to 4,000 HZ.

Most of these factors are predetermined by the design of the meeting room. Hearing loss is so widespread in industry that an acoustically suitable training room should be considered a must for effective training to take place.

A Comfortable Temperature is Necessary

This is a requirement if the training is not to be interrupted by the occassional snore of sleeping trainees. The temperature should not exceed 72°F (22°C). The instructor should have control over the temperature. A good idea is to reduce the temperature several degrees when breaking for lunch in the case of a day-long conference to help keep everyone awake. The temperature need not be restored until first afternoon break unless someone complains of being cold.

Room Layout for Good Vision

The layout of the room depends upon the type of meeting to be conducted and the number of attendees. A good room layout for 15 to 30 persons is a U shaped table layout. Such an arrangement encourages lively interaction by the participants because they can see and hear each other easily. The projector can be placed away from the tables to reduce the noise and resulting distraction to those seated near it.

Comfortable Seating

Metal or molded plastic chairs become quite uncomfortable rather quickly.

Good upholstered chairs with ample padding contribute greatly to both the comfort and the attention of those in attendance.

Audio Visual Equipment

High-quality equipment such as slide projectors, overhead transparency projectors, motion picture projectors and video equipment is a must. Nothing is more foolish than to interrupt a training class for want of a spare projector bulb when the manufacturer states that they can be expected to fail after a few hours of use. Audio visual equipment, like presses and dies, requires regular maintenance and spare parts. Video equipment is particularly important as many companies tape their die changes for later review. A large blackboard or flip chart easel with lots of blank pages and a supply of markers is necessary when fielding questions and recording points brought out during group discussions. An overhead transparency projector with blank transparencies also is suitable.

Freedom From Distractions

Nothing is more disturbing to an instructor who is conducting in-plant training than to have the meeting frequently interrupted by persons needing to ask questions of an individual participant. Depending upon the number of participants and the cost of the instructor, in-plant training can easily have a total cost of $500 to $2,000 an hour. Most presses are not figured at that high an hourly rate. Even if the question only takes a couple of minutes to answer, it completely distracts the group's attention from the business at hand. The cost to the company is hard to measure. Clearly, the training is not as effective as it might otherwise be. Often conducting the training away from the plant has advantages in improved effectiveness that outweigh the additional cost. Lawrence Munson's book, "How to Conduct Training Seminars,"[1] is a good source of general information on specialized technical training, including the pros and cons of meeting formats.

TRAINING MATERIALS AND INSTRUCTION

Very few training materials exist on the subject of diesetting. Companies usually have their own in-house standards that range from verbal instructions and crude sketches to formalized die construction standards including diesetting methods that encompass several volumes.

A standard source for many years in contract stamping shops has been Ernest Urbas' *Die Setters Training Manual*.[2] A substantial amount of diesetting information is contained in *Die Makers Text* by Jim Geary[3] and the *Die Design Handbook* edited by the author.[4] Generalized setup reduction information is contained in *A Revolution in Manufacturing: The SMED*

System by Shigeo Shingo [5] and *Setup Reduction* by Jerry Claunch and Philip Stang.[6]

One purpose intended for this work is to serve as a book of instruction in both conventional and quick die changing techniques.

DAMAGE AVOIDANCE INSTRUCTION

A proven way to avoid the costs associated with press and die damage is to show the pressroom employees why everyday bad practices damage equipment. Visual aids such as simple drawings, overhead transparencies or photographs can be used to illustrate a sequence of events. Chapter two has an example of a cartoon intended to illustrate a point. *Figure 2-1* illustrates a gross error in press shut height resulting from the diesetter failing to check the press opening with a tape measure before inserting the die. *Figure 2-2* through *Figure 2-5* are just a few examples of simple line drawings that were prepared for in-plant diesetter training. *Figure 2-11* has been found useful in explaining to both diesetters and press operators the sequence of events that can occur when stock is stamped improperly in a progressive die. The art work exaggerates the amount of movement to emphasize the message. To tell an employee not to let mis-hits occur is not enough. They need to understand exactly why the practice is forbidden.

Learning to Respect the Machine

If your shop is fortunate enough to have an unofficial resident cartoonist (the person who draws cartoons depicting outstanding boo-boos), you may wish to have this person prepare drawings for display in the shop that illustrate good versus bad practices. A little humor is good for morale. In the case of *Figure 2-1*, the artist, Alex McNeilly, is a diemaker who also is a skilled part-time commercial artist.

The Diemaker's Point-of-view Adds Insight

Having experienced diemakers in the class is very helpful. They are usually more than happy to share their point-of-view on the cause and effect relationships of poor pressroom practices and equipment damage.

Let Quality Control Add Perspective

All burrs, distorted trim edges, and off-angle flanges from dies that once produced top-quality parts have a root cause. Often this root cause is not normal die wear, but rather, improper stamping. Quality control managers and technicians are willing to share SPC and Pareto chart data that illustrates the problems associated with setting the die in a bad press or the effect of stamping damage.

Encourage Honesty in Reporting Damage

Whenever damage to equipment occurs through some careless act, there are usually several "versions" of the cause. If one were to accept and analyze all reports at face value, the conclusion would be that nearly all damage to presses and dies takes place on the night shift during normal production runs.

Improper Stampings Are All Too Common

One important way that management can reduce the incidence of press and die damage through careless acts is to encourage "no fault" reporting of all mis-hits. Off gage stampings and progression strips provide valuable information to the diemaker about possible die damage. Analysis of the root cause of an improper stamping should also determine the need for sensor protection. Incorrectly reported bad stampings that occurred during production can result in unwarranted suspicion of the sensor's value in pressworking metal.

STRATEGY FOR SCHEDULING TRAINING

When and how to schedule diesetter training must take into consideration their need to set dies and service the needs of production. In-plant diesetter training usually must be conducted on overtime, either before or after the normal shift. If the instructor is an employee or local person, it may be feasible to conduct an hour or two of training for the afternoon shift in the early afternoon prior to their normal starting time, followed by the same training for the day shift employees on overtime. If there are any midnight shift employees to be trained, it can either be done in the morning after their normal quitting time, or by having them attend one of the day or afternoon shift meetings. If an in-plant training seminar is planned, it may be feasible to schedule it during a vacation shutdown period or other scheduled non- production period. Increasingly, union contracts require employee training as an alternative to layoff. The most important consideration is that training be designated as a high priority. Management should attend team training meetings. Interruptions must not be permitted. If the meeting is interrupted to discuss production problems, or if members must leave the meeting to take care of production problems, the message will be that the meeting and setup reduction program is not important.

UNION INVOLVEMENT

In the author's experience, union shops are as easy to conduct training in as non-union shops. The union leadership has always been cooperative and enthusiastic about the results that they expected in terms of job security enhancement.

Communications and Involvement. The union officers in a plant are the chosen leadership in a democratic organization. It is important to communicate with the union leadership concerning any plans for employee training. Any union leader wants the facts before being questioned by the membership concerning any new program.

If they are not informed in advance, they will not be able to answer the union member's questions about the effect of new methods on existing work rules. This will result in unwarranted opposition that can easily set back the program.

Honesty is Vital

To be accepted, the goal of a setup reduction program should not be to reduce the head count of the workforce. Securing more work because of reduced costs is a concept that makes sense. If reassignments are envisioned, indicate this at the outset and work with the union leadership to provide a smooth transition. Workforce reduction through attrition may be an acceptable means to reduce the workforce. Layoffs that are a direct result of union acquiescence to a change in work methods are not politically acceptable.

PRODUCTION MANAGEMENT ACCEPTANCE

It is every bit as important to communicate with first line production management concerning the goals of training in setup reduction training as it is the union. In reality, the union has no vested interest in the status quo. Consciously or unconsciously, production management has a responsibility in continuing to manage a crisis. In some shops, nearly every dieset is handled as a crisis.

Managing a Crisis

The production supervisor is an expert at knowing what will and will not work in a crisis. Like the captain of a ship dodging icebergs, the supervisor is an expert at managing an incessant crisis-like event. Scheduling foul-ups are expected as the norm in the shop. Almost any scheduling mistake can be accommodated. (Many production supervisors think that they invented flexible manufacturing.) Supervisors may not see any reason to change. No captain wants to abandon his ship. Why should the diesetters want to change? Why do they need training? If they have any questions, it is his or her job to answer them.

The production supervisor knows that the diesetters are experts at scrounging. Somehow, they always get the job setup and running. They can set any die in just about any press—even if the die shoe hangs over the edge of the bolster by a foot. The supervisor has a solid reputation of always getting the job to run and the parts are delivered on time.

KILLING TWO BIRDS WITH ONE STONE

Since it is important to secure the acceptance in advance of both the union leadership and first line supervision, it may be wise to do so at the same time.

A simple solution may be in advanced training for both supervision and the union leadership. Everyone appreciates perks. Field trips are always lots of fun. Sending such a group of employees out of town to a setup reduction conference or seminar is a simple way to establish several important points:

1. We trust you out of our sight.
2. Your opinions and report are of value to us.
3. Setup improvements are important to our corporate goals.

Be sure to encourage the delegation to eat well and enjoy their leisure time. The informal atmosphere at a conference center is a good place to talk over concerns and goals. It is important for everyone to learn that the corporate goal of efficiency and profitability is not contrary to the legitimate concerns of the union and first line management.

HAVE STUDENTS DEVELOP THEIR OWN WORK RULES

The steps outlined in *Figure 12-1* are to set a progressive die. The steps were developed by the diesetters in a unionized first-tier automotive contract stamping shop. The union leadership was very supportive of the training conducted in this plant. The shop steward's enlightened view was simply that improved work methods would increase the capacity of the shop to secure more work. In addition to the obvious job security enhancement, improved employee safety was an issue prompting union support. The diesetting team was encouraged to list all of the problems that they encountered when setting a progressive die in a 500 ton (4.4 MN) straight side press. Then, as a group, they developed a sequence of action items together with the reasons for the actions.

Avoid Pity Parties

There was once a quick die change team who earned the nickname of ''The Crybabies,'' simply because their meetings to critique their own performance often broke down into a mutual pity party. The unfortunate effect of this self-pity was that they did not get the support that they desired from the other plant activities simply because it was believed that nothing could please them.

In that case, the cure was to provide training in effective problem solving and communications. There are many examples of how to accomplish this in the case studies. The fact remains that the quick die change teams may need help in effectively communicating their needs in a positive way.

The case studies provide information on how to secure employee acceptance, develop communication skills, and develop effective teams.

1. ACTION:	Get ready. Clean up bolster, feeder, and around press. Clean top and bottom of die.	
REASON:	A clean area is a safer area. Clean the area so no one slips on slugs and gets hurt. Make sure that there are no slugs on die or bolster to spoil parallelism.	
2. ACTION:	When removing a die, raise slide slightly before inching press on bottom.	
REASON:	To avoid sticking press on bottom.	
3. ACTION:	Inch press on bottom. Adjust for correct shut height plus a small safety factor. Place new die in correct location square with bolster and feeder. If parallels are used, make sure that they are correct for the job. Check the diesetting process instruction sheet. Tie down with secure approved bolts or clamps.	
REASON:	To insure a safe repeatable setup.	
4. ACTION:	If air pins are used, make sure that they are all the correct length. Make sure that press cushion is properly equalized. Follow the diesetting process instruction sheet.	
REASON:	Unequal or improper pins will cock the die pad or draw ring. The load height will not be correct. The press cushion will be damaged.	
5. ACTION:	Adjust feed height and lineup to die. Adjust feed pitch to specification stamped on the die.	
REASON:	To get the setup to run without trial and error.	
6. ACTION:	Place chutes, scrap hopper, and parts container in proper location.	
REASON:	To avoid running parts and scrap on the floor.	
7. ACTION:	Start coil and adjust stock straightener. Feed stock into die to correct location. Make the first stamping. Advance stock with feeder. Make sure location is correct. Follow the diesetting process instruction sheet.	
REASON:	To insure that setup is correct and to be sure not to damage die.	
8. ACTION:	Run stock through the die and recheck stop blocks. If available check tonnage meter against specifications stamped on the die and on diesetting process instruction sheet. If tonnage reading is not correct, find out why before running production.	
REASON:	The second adjustment is to compensate for press deflection under load. Correct tonnage means that the target setup was repeated.	
9. ACTION:	Get the gages and check first parts. Submit parts for quality control approval only if they are OK. If not, correct reason for parts not being OK.	
REASON:	It is a waste of time to submit off standard parts for quality control approval.	
10. ACTION:	Double check setup. Install the part blow-off if needed. Check for proper cushion and counterbalance pressure. Make sure everything runs properly. Follow the instructions on the diesetting process sheet.	
REASON:	To insure that setup is production ready.	

Figure 12-1. *Steps to set a progressive die developed by a diesetting team.*

SUGGESTION SYSTEMS

Employee suggestion systems provide a structured means to tap the latent creative genius of the workforce. The voluntary submission of suggestions is an important way for persons who want to contribute to improvements in the efficiency of the workplace to have their voice heard.

Employee suggestions can be a valuable source of ideas to reduce setup times. If a suggestion program is to be used, management must make a long-term commitment to support it.

Fairness is essential. Employees will not take part in a suggestion system unless they are assured of fair impartial evaluation of their ideas and fair compensation for the ideas that are adopted. Compensation is usually based upon a formula that awards the employee a percentage of the savings to the company.

It is extremely important to administer the program with a common set of rules company-wide. If the availability of the program depends upon the whim of an individual foreman or manager, an employee may have a friend submit their suggestion where the program is supported by management and split the award. Full control must be exercised by top management, or chaos will ensue. Careful evaluation is required. Time must be provided for administration of the suggestion system and for careful evaluation of all suggestions submitted. If the suggestion is adopted, the actual savings should be determined in the same manner that the payback on any proposal or project is determined.

It is important to recognize that payment of a monetary award for an individual contribution toward corporate goals is an essential element of suggestion systems. All successful suggestion systems have a monetary incentive as a basic element of the program. It is essential that no employee be accused of apathy on his or her part in a team effort or of being greedy because of participation in a suggestion program.

A group suggestion submission is a means to permit the entire team to share in a monetary award for a team idea. It is best to pattern a newly established suggestion system after existing successful programs. A manual is available from the National Association of Suggestion Systems (NASS) that is a very useful source of information.[7]

REFERENCES

1. Lawrence Munson, *How to Conduct Training Seminars*, McGraw Hill Book Company, New York, 1984.
2. Ernest Urbas, *Die Setters Training Manual*, Precision Metalforming Association, Richmond Heights, Ohio, 1978.
3. Jim Geary, *Die Makers Text*, Gearyco, Pleasure Ridge Park, Kentucky, 1984.
4. David A. Smith, *Die Design Handbook*, Society of Manufacturing Engineers, Dearborn, Michigan, 1990.
5. Shigeo Shingo, *A Revolution in Manufacturing: The SMED System*, Productivity Press, Cambridge, Massachusetts, 1985.
6. Jerry Claunch and Philip Stang, *Setup Reduction: Saving Dollars with Common Sense*, PT Publications, Inc., Palm Beach Gardens, Florida, 1990.
7. *The Suggestion System—A Total Quality Process*, National Association of Suggestion Systems, Chicago, Illinois, 1989.

13

SUPPORT REQUIRED FOR
QUICK DIE CHANGE TEAMS

SUPPORT IS NEEDED

The support responsibility required to get quick die changeover to work is illustrated in *Figure 13-1*. Without the support of these and other plant activities, the team's efforts may lead to needless frustration and even failure to achieve the goal of implementing setup reduction.

SUPPORT ACTIVITIES AND RESPONSIBILITIES

The following support activities must understand how their actions aid or hinder the goal of making quick die change a reality. All activities are vital to successful quick die changes.

Maintenance Support Responsibility. It is agreed that good maintenance is vital to the success of any stamping operation. This is especially true when diesetting.

Meet With Quick Die Change Teams. Maintenance department employees should understand how their actions can aid diesetting improvements. This can be done by attending a planning meeting of the quick die change teams from time to time. The head of the maintenance department should take time from his or her busy schedule to do so, and be prepared to involve the staff.

Keep Press and Automation in Good Repair. Maintenance problems are the basic reasons for delays in die setting.

Familiar examples of how maintenance problems can delay diesetting include: slide motors that require jumpers to actuate and self-moving bolsters that won't move under their own power.

As a general rule, good maintenance becomes increasingly important as pressworking equipment size and complexity increases. Poorly maintained transfer presses equipped for fully automatic five-minute die changes have at times required several days to exchange dies.

- *Building and Other Equipment Maintenance*. Good maintenance extends to all other equipment in the plant. Successful cost-efficient metal pressworking of metal requires that the physical plant be in good repair and that everything work correctly. Examples are:
  1. The compressed air pressure must be correct, dry, and steady.
  2. The electrical energy must be of the correct voltage, properly balanced

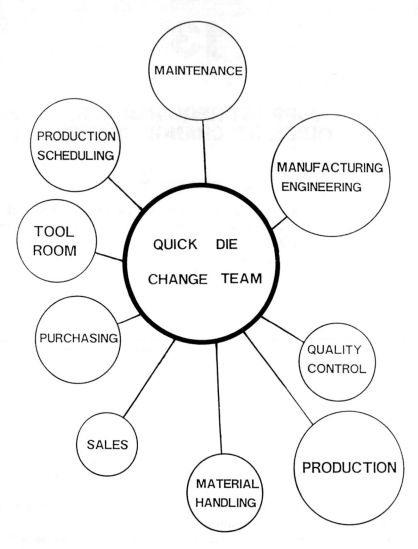

Figure 13-1. *To be effective, quick die change teams require the support of many other activities.*

    to ground, steady, and uninterrupted.

3. All systems for the delivery of stock and conveyance of scrap must work dependably.

4. The building must be in good repair, especially the roof which must not leak water to rust parts and stock.

5. Communications and computer equipment must function properly to avoid scheduling errors.

- *Maintain a Database of Equipment History and Preventive Maintenance Needs.* This is the best way to insure against scheduling maintenance by the occurrence of breakdowns. The database can range from a good card file system or a simple spreadsheet program used with a personal computer (PC) to an elaborate maintenance management program running on the plant's mainframe computer.

Several important requirements for a good functional maintenance database are:

1. A means is provided to accurately determine the maintenance department's capacity to do work.
2. A means is provided to prioritize outstanding work-orders (WO).
3. Work-orders accurately describing the nature and size of repair needed are generated whenever production or setup problems occur.
4. Preventative maintenance (PM) work-orders are generated as frequently as needed based on both elapsed time and amount of use.
5. Periodic PM inspections result in the immediate repair of small problems and the scheduling of larger repairs later.
6. Work-orders provide for the purchasing department participation in order to get needed repair parts and crib supplies.

Manufacturing Engineering's Responsibility

While the role of manufacturing engineering in a successful quick die change program may not be as obvious as that of maintenance, it is at least as important. The manufacturing engineering manager, or a representative, should meet with the quick die change teams frequently to help them solve their problems.

Standard Methods are Needed. It is important that standard proven quick die change methods be adopted on a company-wide basis. While the teams are very capable of devising numerous shortcuts (such as unique die locating and fastening methods), it is important that they not be randomly conceived, but rather, uniform throughout the company.

The diesetters need, and have a right to expect, engineering support on such matters as safe die handling and fastening methods.

Involvement in Continuous Improvement. Persons from manufacturing engineering should always consult with the toolroom, operators, and diesetters when evaluating process feasibility and capability. No one is better able to pinpoint the root causes of process problems than the persons directly involved in the press and dies setup and operation. Usually a problem that causes process variability also will cause setup and production problems. A unified whole-systems approach to problem solving can be both fast and effective.

The tendency for a quick die change team will be to want to set ambitious continuous improvement objectives and goals. The manufacturing engineering department can help keep these goals in clear focus. The manufacturing engineering department can provide engineering support as well as performance evaluation tools such as video equipment for task, time and motion study.

Material Handling Responsibility

There are varying degrees of involvement at all locations; activity is responsible for the success of quick die change, although the type of support varies from plant to plant.

At the newer integrated automotive and appliance assembly facilities, most aspects of both material handling and diesetting are under automatic control. Maintenance and scheduling are very important in accomplishing correct material handling.

Most contract stamping depends almost entirely upon the forklift drivers and/or crane operators for many services that are main diesetting activities. These often include:

1. Get the die and steel ready (pre-staged).
2. Put the die in press.
3. Get and place the scrap hopper, parts box, and stock table.
4. Put the die away.
5. Serve as a member of the quick die change team during a dieset.

It is obvious that the success of quick die change in many plants depends to a great extent upon the scheduling and cooperation of the forklift drivers. Providing key personnel—including the forklift driver—with inexpensive hand-held two-way radios is often a very effective way to aid real time decision making when scheduling the most effective use of time.

A means should be provided for these persons to attend the planning quick die change team meetings on a frequent basis.

Production Responsibility

Without the cooperation of the production operator who may be assigned to tend the press, the best efforts of the quick die change team will fail. In many stamping facilities, the operator tends two or more presses. This operator is responsible to assure that automatic feed detection systems are working properly. Quality control spot checks and entry of statistical process control (SPC) data often are tasks assigned to the operator.

The responsibilities of the operator should include:

1. Produce top quality stampings.
2. Assist with ongoing continuous improvement requirements.
3. Report process and equipment problems.
4. Assist the quick die change team during die change.
5. Suggest setup and process improvements.
6. Suggest ergonomic improvements.

In assisting with these activities and goals, the operator is actually enhancing everyone's job security in a very competitive market.

Production Scheduling Responsibility

Good scheduling goes hand-in-hand with careful planning. The production scheduling department often has the best potential opportunity toward quick die change and process variability reduction goals. All at practically no cost.

The Complexity of Scheduling. Many factors influence scheduling decisions. Diesetters do not have an understanding of job scheduling unless the factors behind the scheduling decision are stated. The scheduling activity should work closely with the quick die change teams if quality stampings are to be produced at minimum cost.

Cost Factors. Shipping costs are often a big factor for many stamping plants. The goal of scheduling is usually to ship full boxes, containers, pallets, trucks, or rail cars of parts to the customer. The cost of partial shipments often is billed as full shipments. The cost of shutting down a customer's assembly operation for lack of parts ranges from hundreds of dollars a day for small manufacturers, to over a million dollars a day for automotive assembly plants.

To avoid plant shut-downs, many stamping plants have helicopter landing pads on site to facilitate rapid shipments of small lots in an emergency. Such shipments certainly bring a new meaning to just-in-time (JIT).

Provide Advanced Notice. To accomplish pre-staging of external dieset tasks, it is important to provide as much advance notice as possible. This notice should be available to all other activities to insure that tooling, equipment, and production manpower are ready to run the job as soon as it is set.

Schedule Into the Home Press if Possible. Scheduling is much more important than is commonly realized. Even though the presses may be of identical size and made by the same machinery builder, subtle differences exist that will influence the process. Schedule the die into its original (or home) press, if possible.

There is No Scheduling Utopia. Scheduling must do more than determine the best lot size (as was explained in Chapter 6), and schedule accordingly. Unforeseen factors that are impossible to predict can cause a scheduling crisis at any moment. Factors such as:

- The customer can fail to order on time.
- Inventory can be misplaced.
- The shipment can be damaged in a train wreck.
- The truck driver can decide to go from Detroit to Louisville by way of Tazewell, Tennessee to visit a girlfriend.

These and other factors can cause orders to be issued to dieset and run production for emergency shipment as quickly as possible. The scheduling manager should meet from time to time with the quick die change teams to share concerns and determine ways to schedule more efficiently. When an emergency dieset is required, it is important that the quick die change team understand that someone isn't just "crying wolf."

Purchasing Responsibility

It is very important that Purchasing make sure that the correct material is available when needed.

Buy the Correct Material. Many quality and productivity problems have their origin in out-of-specification or inconsistent quality material. For example, coil stock camber problems can cause feeding difficulties in progressive and blanking dies.

Figure 13-2 illustrates a slit coil of steel with sweep or camber. This condition can result from poor slitting practices. However, often the cause is that the full coil from which it was slit had built-in stresses. These stresses were due to poor rolling practices.

An example of how this can happen is illustrated in *Figure 13-3*. This figure shows a full coil of steel with buckles in the center. This condition often is caused by the mill attempting to correct an excess thickness in the center of the strip too late in the rolling process. When it is slit, the coils that are produced will have sweep or camber. Only the strip cut from the center will be straight.

Figure 13-4 illustrates a full coil of steel with buckles on the edges. This condition can be caused by the hot mill over-compensating for roll deflection with the re-

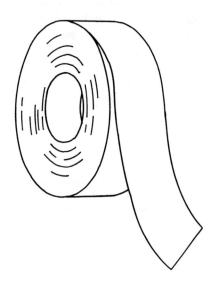

Figure 13-2. *A slit coil of steel with sweep or camber; a frequent cause of feeding and process variability problems.*

sult that the coil edges are thicker than the center. In the cold-finishing mill, the rolling process results in an increase of coil length only. There is very little change in width. The result of trying to correct for a uniform thickness in the cold-finishing mill is that the center of the coil will become shorter than the edges. When the full coil is slit, the coils that are produced will have sweep or camber. Only the center strip will be straight.

Return Out-of-specification Material. There is little advantage to having material specifications if out-of-specification material is not returned to the vendor. Should it be found that out-of specification material will make good quality parts, then the material specifications should be made less stringent. These less stringent specifications may result in a lower price.

The American Society for Testing and Materials (ASTM) has established

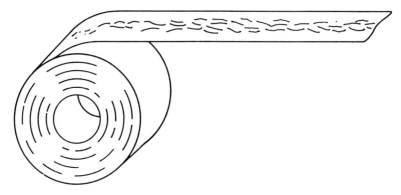

Figure 13-3. *An improperly rolled full coil of steel with buckles in the center that will have excessive sweep or camber when slit.*

generally accepted standards for thickness, width, length and camber for sheet steel. This information is available in a convenient pocket-sized booklet form.[1]

Vendor Certification. The procedure to establish a vendor certification program is beyond the scope of this book. Briefly, it involves establishing standards for material and component sources. These standards assure that suppliers can consistently meet the required specification and delivery criteria. Once a vendor is certified, incoming inspection is generally not necessary.

The purchasing department will generally work with the quality control department to establish certified vendors. In addition to the obvious quality improvement advantages, vendor certification can be a real aid to setup reduction and productivity improvements.

Quick Die Change Team's Responsibility

The supporting activities will want—in clear concise terms—the information

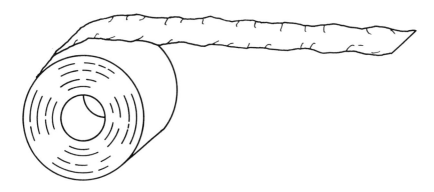

Figure 13-4. *An improperly rolled full coil of steel with buckles on the edges that will have excessive sweep or camber when slit.*

177

on how to help the quick die change teams. This means that the quick die change teams must be prepared to communicate their needs effectively. The needed information should be provided using accepted formats (such as short reports with Pareto charts).

Document Problems. Problems must be clearly defined and the root causes determined. The effect on the process must be documented.

Brainstorm Solutions. Possible solutions should be arrived at. The cost of correction should be determined where possible.

Provide Feedback to Supporting Activities. Prompt regular reporting of team activities to the supporting activities is an important way to keep their active help in solving the team's problems. The way of completing this process depends upon the size and structure of the organization.

Approach Problems as Continuous Improvement. Every problem is an opportunity for improvement. Continuous implementation of solutions to problems is the essence of continuous improvement.

Quality Control's Responsibility

The greatest supporter of quick die change teams in many plants is the quality control (QC) manager.

Present Scope of Responsibility. The QC manager was once mainly expected to be sure that the parts being produced and shipped met the customer's specifications. Statistical Process Control has changed that. The job now requires extensive record keeping, a careful analysis and follow-up, and correction of the root causes of the process variability that SPC reveals.

If correctly applied, SPC does not inspect quality into a part as much as it designs and engineers quality into the product. Quality is now planned. Planning for quality must be done in cooperation with all other plant activities.

Currently, many quality control managers are responsible to work with the purchasing department to certify vendors who can be depended upon to meet quality specifications as preferred sources of materials.

How the Quick Die Change Team Fits in. Chapter 15 explains how the setup repeatability that results from quick die change will reduce the variation in stampings. This is clearly shown in sample SPC data. Everything that the quick die change team does from how dies are handled and stored to where they are fastened in the press can and does affect the product. The team can count on quality control for support.

Sales' Responsibility

Customers usually consider the ability of a stamping supplier to change over presses quickly with consistent repeatability as an important qualification for certification as a top tier supplier of stampings. The sales manager should meet with the setup teams and explain the importance of documenting the quick die change team's defect prevention, repeatability, continuous improvement, and

JIT performance. This documentation would be done by the sales department for the customer.

Get More Work. Setup reduction can be expected to create additional press capacity. Sales must get new work to take full advantage of this increased capacity.

Tool Room's Responsibility

The quick setup adaptations discussed in this book will require the full cooperation of the tool room. Some companies have attempted to get the needed die retrofitting done in the tool room as "bootleg" projects without budgeting time and money for the work. This is a sure way to get less than optimal tool room cooperation.

Provide a Realistic Budget. Simple conversions from toe clamps to tee slot bolts can shave 10 to 20 minutes off of diesetting times at minimal cost. All that may be required is to drill bolt holes or mill slots for bolts in the die shoes. Even so, realistic amounts of time and money needed to do the work should be budgeted. Don't forget the need to lay-out the machine work needed on the die shoes while they are in the press. This step will assure accurate hole or slot locations.

Sources of Material. Often parallels and subplates need to be permanently attached to the dies to save setup time. While old dies can be a good source of surplus parallels and plate, there is usually a limit as to how much any shops junk pile can be relied upon as a source of material.

As discussed in Chapter 5, hot rolled steel plate is a good parallel material. The scrap dealer that buys the shop's slugs often can find a source of suitable plate at a good price.

Die Maintenance. Chapter 16 covers the relationship of die and press maintenance to achieving and maintaining the ability to change dies quickly. Ideally, all maintenance should be entered in some form of a database to track the work and control costs. Likewise, all preventative maintenance should be prompted from a database to assure that there are no oversights. Needing to do a great amount of die maintenance in the press defeats the purpose of reducing the time required to change dies.

REFERENCES

1. Data Pocketbook, *Tolerances for Dimensions for Sheet Steel*. The Iron and Steel Society, Warrendale, Pennsylvania. January 1988.

14

CONVERTING INTERNAL DIE SET TO EXTERNAL DIE SET

The Difference Between External and Internal Die Set

Figure 14-1 illustrates the difference between internal and external diesetting tasks. The strategy for improving diesetting speed is simply converting internal die set tasks to external die set tasks. Active employee team participation is essential to success.

Chapters 12, 13, and many other case studies point out that there should be no problem securing full employee and union cooperation. This occurs when management fully supports the quick die change conversion process and by addressing job security issues at the beginning of the implementation process.

VIDEO-TAPING PERMITS GROUP DISSECTION OF A DIE SET*

A portable video camera used with video playback equipment is an excellent means to document all tasks and the time required to perform them during a die set. Team acceptance is seldom a problem if the purpose of the video equipment is explained in advance. The Chapter 25 case study covers the use of a video recorder to record diesetting activities.

Desirable video equipment features required for taping diesetting activities include: operation without the need for auxiliary lighting equipment, a sturdy tripod, a zoom lens for flexibility of placement, and a clock displaying a second-by-second readout.

Analysis of Hit-to-Hit Time

The term *hit-to-hit time* is defined as the time that elapses between the production of the last part prior to die set and the starting time that the next good part is produced.

Figure 14-2 illustrates a worksheet developed by a quick die change team for their own use in analyzing their performance. The three-person team repeatedly

---

*The use of photography to perform time and motion studies had its origin in the extensive 19th-century studies of animals and human figures in motion by Eadweard Muybridge. A widespread North American understanding of motion picture time and motion studies as an industrial engineering tool can be attributed to the popular book and movie of several decades ago; *Cheaper by the Dozen* by Gilbreth.

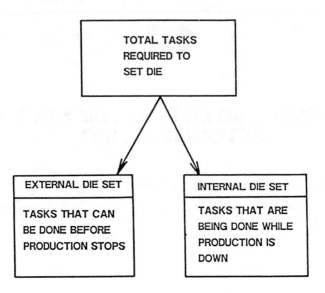

Figure 14-1. *To improve diesetting efficiency, as many internal die set items as possible must be converted to external die set.*

video-taped the same die set and used the worksheet as a tool to identify items for conversion to external die set.

Analysis of Major Delay Factors

There were three main causes of delays found when the team analyzed the first videotape. The forklift truck was needed to service production–a major cause of delays. The diesetters were required to service production while setting dies. Tasks such as starting coils and making minor adjustments to equipment interrupted them. Quality Control personnel were unavailable to approve the part.

Planning Strategy for Improvement

While investigating ways in which to reduce setup time, it was decided that one diesetter would be assigned to service the needs of production, leaving two diesetters to accomplish the die set without interruption.

The forklift truck was needed to get coils and move containers of scrap and parts. Analysis of these factors pointed out an opportunity for a big improvement in the shop.

The coil was brought from the coil storage area to the decoiler when needed. The coils were placed into the decoiler with an overhead bridge crane. A simple improvement to reduce the timing requirements was to provide an area under the crane way where several coils that would be needed within the next few minutes could be banked by the forklift truck.

HIT-TO-HIT ANALYSIS

PRESS NUMBER 8	PART NUMBER KC DeLove
DATE August 16, 89	TIME STARTED 1:07 PM
TIME FINISHED 3:58	TOTAL TIME 2:51

•TASK	•TOTAL TIME	•TASK TIME
UNBOLT DIE	1:14	7 min
WAIT FOR HI-LO	1:25	11
REMOVE DIE	1:30	5
CLEAN PRESS	1:36	6
MAKE SHUT HGT	1:39	3
WAIT FOR HI-LO	1:56	17
INSERT NEW DIE	2:01	5
SQUARE DIE	2:07	6
GET BOLTS, ETC.	2:16	9
FASTEN IN PRESS	2:28	12
BOTTOM DIE	2:31	3
LEAD CHECK	2:33	2
WAIT FOR HI-LO	2:47	14
GET COIL	3:00	13
PLACE IN DECOILER	3:05	5

•TASK	•TOTAL TIME	•TASK TIME
ADJUST DECOILER	3:09	4
FEED STOCK INTO DIE	3:12	3
ADJUST LEVEL ROLLS	3:16	4
ADJUST FEED TABLE	3:25	9
RUN SAMPLE PARTS	3:28	3
LEAD CHECK	3:30	2
INSTALL CHUTES	3:35	5
INSTALL AIR BLOW OFF	3:38	3
WAIT FOR HI-LO	3:52	14
INSTALL SCRAP TUB	3:55	3
INSTALL PART BOX	3:58	3
WAITED FOR QC		+CC
QUITING TIME		430
HAD to LEAVE		+06
to START COILS		on
OTHER PRESSES		

Figure 14-2. Worksheet listing the time required to perform individual tasks during a die set.

A further material handling improvement was to provide a chute with a deflector that could route the parts and scrap to a spare container. Where this was not possible, a hand-operated pallet mover was provided to permit the operator and diesetter to move the containers without the aid of the forklift truck.

The quality control approval delay was eliminated by training the diesetters to perform gage inspections of the finished parts. A final QC (Quality Control) approval was still required during the first 15 minutes of production. The QC inspectors were given copies of die set schedules so they could plan to be available on time.

Analysis of the First Round of Improvements

By eliminating the delays for the forklift truck and delays due to interruptions to service production, the setup time was reduced from two hours 51 minutes to one hour 11 minutes. This is a reduction to 42% of the former value. An improvement also was realized by getting the bolts prior to the start of setup. *Figure 14-3* illustrates the improvements realized.

Planning Strategy for Further Improvements

The team did not consider this improvement good enough. The next goal was to reduce setup time to under 20 minutes.

Since the dies are run on parallels, permanently attaching the parallels to the die shoe and providing a 2 in. (50.8 mm) ledge on the edges of the parallels provided a uniform clamping height. This provides for the use of the same clamps on all dies as was explained in Chapter 4.

An important benefit of having parallels attached permanently to the die is that the die can be handled by a forklift truck with excellent safety and speed. In this case, scrap chutes can be permanently attached to the die, further reducing setup time. This also aids in scrap shedding which reduces the time required to clean the press.

To permit locating the die in the center of the press, a keyway was milled down the length of the bolster to match with corresponding keyways in the parallels. This permits exact centering of the die. A word of caution: in the event cambered stock is encountered, either the die or feeder may need to be shifted to compensate for the camber problem.

Another improvement was to record the readings of an existing tonnage meter when the press was adjusted for optimum quality production. Repeating the tonnage values is an extremely accurate means of duplicating a previous shut-height value as is explained in a later chapter. This will eliminate the need to make repeated lead checks.

Since the die can be set with much greater ease because of the improvements, only one diesetter is required to insert and remove the die as well as bottom the press. The second diesetter then can simultaneously place the coil in the decoiler and adjust the decoiler.

HIT-TO-HIT ANALYSIS

PRESS NUMBER 8	PART NUMBER KC Dogbone
DATE Sept 15, 89	TIME STARTED 1:21 PM
TIME FINISHED 2:32 PM	TOTAL TIME 1 HR 11 MIN

•TASK	•TOTAL TIME	•TASK TIME
UNBOLT DIE	1:25	4
REMOVE DIE	1:30	5
CLEAN PRESS	1:35	5
MAKE SHUT HGT	1:37	2
INSERT NEW DIE	1:42	5
SQUARE DIE	1:46	4
FASTEN IN PRESS	1:52	6
BOTTOM DIE	1:55	3
LEAD CHECK	1:57	2
PLACE IN DECOILER	2:01	4
ADJUST DECOILER	2:04	3
FEED STOCK INTO DIE	2:07	3
ADJUST LEVEL ROLLS	2:10	3
ADJUST FEED TABLE	2:18	8
RUN SAMPLE PARTS	2:21	3

•TASK	•TOTAL TIME	•TASK TIME
LEAD CHECK	2:23	2
INSTALL CHUTES	2:27	4
INSTALL AIR BLOW OFF	2:30	3
INSTALL SCRAP TUB	2:31	1
INSTALL PART BOX	2:32	1

Figure 14-3. *Revised worksheet listing the time required to perform individual tasks during a die set after the first round of improvements. Continued on next page.*

Analysis of the Second Round of Improvements

The second round of improvements resulted in a setup reduction from one hour 11 minutes to 34 minutes—less than half the former time. The hit-to-hit analysis sheet is shown in *Figure 14-4*.

HIT–TO–HIT ANALYSIS

PRESS NUMBER 8	PART NUMBER K C Dog-bone
DATE Sept 22, 89	TIME STARTED 9:15 AM
TIME FINISHED 9:49	TOTAL TIME 34.0 MIN

•TASK	•TOTAL TIME	•TASK TIME
UNBOLT DIE	9:17	2.0 MIN
REMOVE DIE	9.18	1
CLEAN PRESS	9.21	3
MAKE SHUT HGT	9.23	2
INSERT NEW DIE	9.25	2
FASTEN IN PRESS	9.27	2
BOTTOM DIE	9.30	3
PLACE IN DECOILER	9.30	4 done while
ADJUST DECOILER	9.30	setting die 3
FEED STOCK INTO DIE	9:33	3
ADJUST LEVEL ROLLS	9:36	3
ADJUST FEED TABLE	9:44	8
RUN SAMPLE PARTS	9:47	3
INSTALL CHUTES	does Not APPLY	
INSTALL TUB & BOX	9:49	2

Figure 14-4. *Revised worksheet listing the time required to perform individual tasks during a die set after the second round of improvements.*

This did not meet the goal of a die set time under 20 minutes. Examination of the time required to set up the level rolls and feed table shows a total of 11 minutes — an area for potential improvement.

Another area offering great potential for improvement is adjusting all dies to a common shut-height that are run in the press (as was explained in Chapter 11.)

Planning Strategy for Another Round of Improvements

The feed rolls can be set very quickly by simply providing an adjusting scale and duplicating the correct figure from that of a previous run. This reduced the time for this task from three minutes to one. Adjusting dies to a common shut height was done in the manner explained in Chapter 11.

Through team analysis of the videotapes, it was observed that parts and scrap were run onto the floor when trial parts were being run. To correct this, the part and scrap containers were put in place before the sample parts were run. This reduced scrap and cleaning time.

Common shut-height improvement, together with exact die relocation in its home press, increased first hit capability. Nearly all first hits received QC approval.

Analysis of the Third Round of Improvements

The fourth hit-to-hit analysis sheet *Figure 14-5* shows that the 20 minute goal was surpassed. The actual hit-to-hit time was 18 minutes.

Further reductions are possible, but may not be cost-effective due to the law of diminishing returns. A reduction in hit-to-hit time from 171 minutes to 18 minutes (an 89.5% reduction) was achieved at a reasonable cost.

The most costly part conversion was the price of the steel parallels that are captive to each die. These are of standard design and can be reused as the dies become obsolete.

Potential Future Improvements

Die set operator involvement by assisting with cleaning and placement of the containers has the potential to reduce hit-to-hit time to 15 minutes. This should be done.

Further reduction of setup time will require substantial expenditures in hydraulic die clamps, die subplates, rollers, and die carts. This should be done only if shown to be cost effective.

HIT–TO–HIT ANALYSIS

PRESS NUMBER 8	PART NUMBER KC DogBone	
DATE Sept 25, 89	TIME STARTED 9:35 AM	
TIME FINISHED 9:53	TOTAL TIME 18 min	

•TASK	•TOTAL TIME	•TASK TIME
UNBOLT DIE	9:37	2 MIN
REMOVE DIE	9:38	1
CLEAN PRESS	9:40	2
INSERT NEW DIE	9:42	2
FASTEN IN PRESS	9:44	2
FEED STOCK INTO DIE	9:47	3
ADJUST LEVEL ROLLS	9:48	1
ADJUST FEED TABLE	9:51	3
INSTALL TUB & BOX	9:52	1
CHECK PARTS	9:53	1

Figure 14-5. *Revised worksheet listing the time required to perform individual tasks during a die set after the third round of improvements.*

15

PROCESS VARIABILITY REDUCTION

Many stamping executives see the main benefit of quick die change as a process variability reduction tool. The ability to know with certainty that a die can be in a given press and producing good parts in 20 minutes is more important to them than having the die in the press in five minutes and producing junk.

Some of the advice in this book may seem to be against the "competition class" diesetting that is presently receiving so much attention in the presswork-ing community. The tooling damage that can occur if the press is accidentally inched open with the die partly bolted-in can cost thousands of dollars to repair. If the part is critical and a large assembly operation is shut down, the damage can exceed several million dollars. With the present emphasis on inventory reduc-tion, avoiding tooling damage is more important than ever.

SPRINGBACK COMPENSATION

Figure 15-1 illustrates SPC control charts of a critical flange measurement when the same die is run in two different presses. The chart illustrated at *A* shows better stability than the one shown at *B*. The variation is press related.

Whenever metals are formed, some springback occurs. The springback cause is the residual stress that results from cold working metals. For example, in a simple bend, residual-compressive stress remains on the inside of the bend, while residual tensile stress is present on the outside radius of the bend.

When the bending pressure is released, the metal returns to the point that the residual stress forces are balanced by the material's ability to resist further strain. This is mainly a function of the material's modulus of elasticity. This is why materials with a high modulus of elasticity tend to *spring back* less than materials with a lower modulus but with equal tensile strength.

Some factors that increase springback are:
1. Higher material strength;
2. Thinner material;
3. A decrease in Young's Modulus;
4. Larger die radius;
5. Greater wipe steel clearance;
6. Less irregularity in part outline, and
7. Flatter part surface contour.

If a flanged part has sufficient irregularity with respect to either the outline or surface contour, the springback will be very slight.

189

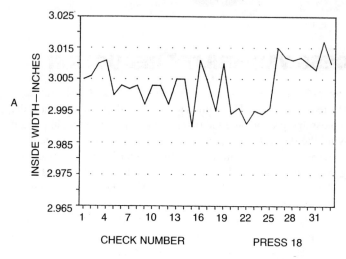

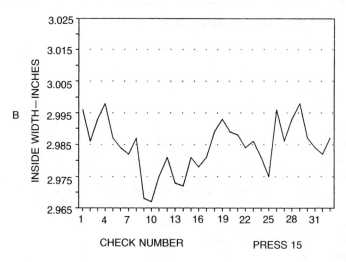

Figure 15-1. *How an SPC control chart differs when the same job is run in two different presses.*

Overbending to Correct for Springback

A common method to compensate for springback is to overbend the part enough to allow it to return to the desired shape. This method of bending also requires minimum tonnages for the work performed. Exact repeatability of ram travel is required to maintain close duplication of the bend-angle. Changes in

190

stock characteristics such as yield strength or thickness will cause a change in the angle-of-bend. Compensation for any change of condition affecting the angle-of-bend is easily provided by adjusting the ram travel. If other operations are performed in the same die such as embossing and coining, these will be affected.

Coining the Bend to Eliminate Springback

Coining-action eliminates the cause of springback which is tensile and compressive residual stresses. This is accomplished by bringing the entire thickness of the metal in the bend-area up to the yield point of the material.

This method has the advantage of producing sharp bends with less sensitivity to material conditions than is found with air bending. However, tonnage requirements are many times that of air-bending and die wear is accelerated.

The Effect of Die Wear on Springback

If a die for forming mild steel bends is ground to provide the compensating overbend for springback, the bend can be formed at tonnage values that agree with theoretical values. As the forming surfaces become worn, it may be found that the bends can still be made if the tonnage is increased to several times the initial value.

This can be accomplished as the additional tonnage will produce pressures on the thickness dimension of the stock that will exceed the yield point of the material. In this case, some areas of the part are actually coined. This relieves the residual stresses that are the cause of springback.

This same effect is observed in forming and reforming dies. As the dies wear, tonnage must be increased to produce a part of the required form. The die surfaces that provide the overbend are worn away. The die must then be used as a coining die to achieve the desired form.

Such high-pressures may exceed press capacity, and can result in accelerated die wear and possible die damage. The solution is to build the die of materials that will resist rapid wear on critical forming surfaces. The die should be reworked to restore the original form whenever higher than normal tonnages are required to form the part.

The Effect of Out-of-parallel Conditions

Off-angle flanges can result from a press or die out-of-parallel condition. *Figure 15-2 A* illustrates a section through a flange die. The wiper-steels go to the bottom on the bend to control springback. The desired shape of the finished part is illustrated in *Figure 15-2 B*.

Figure 15-2 C illustrates die closure with an out-of-parallel condition. The part *Figure 15-2 D* is mis-formed. The right flange is under-bent as the wiper-steel is not bottoming on the bend-radius to correct for springback. The

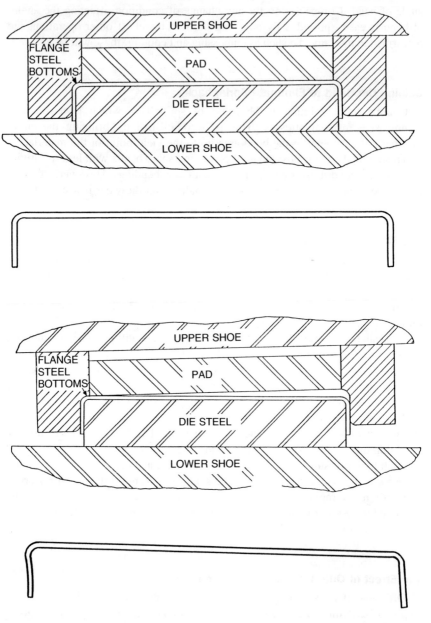

Figure 15-2. *The effect of press out-of-parallel conditions on the bend angle of a U shaped section. (Midway Products Corp.)*

left flange is both over-bent and exhibits side-wall-curl. The over-bending is a result of the wiper-steel going to the bottom excessively hard on the bend-radius, while side-wall-curl is due to the flange steel wiping too hard caused by the lateral forces generated by the out-of-parallel condition.

The solution to this quality problem is to maintain all dies in a parallel condition. A regular program of checking and adjusting the alignment of all presses also is required.

The Effect of Stock Thickness on Springback

To produce close-tolerance stampings, stock thickness variations should be held to a minimum. *Figure 15-3* illustrates the effect of thickness variations on the angle-of-bend. The stamping on the right is under-bent due to inadequate wiping and bottoming action, while the one on the left is excessively coined and subject to galling due to insufficient clearances.

The Effect of Pad Pressure

Pad pressure can have an effect on the exact bend-angle in a flanging operation. *Figure 15-4 A* illustrates a flanging die used to form two 90° bends in mild steel stock. The die is operated in an OBI press with an adjustable air cushion which supplies pad pressure.

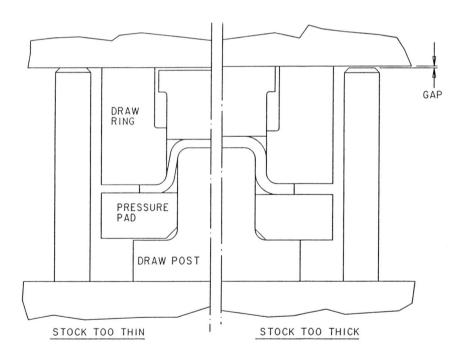

Figure 15-3. *The effect of stock thickness variation on springback. (Capitol Engineering)*

High-pad pressures result in less than 90° bends, while very low-pressures result in substantial overbending. In this case, a recoil condition occurs as the die closes and the bends are formed. In *Figure 15-4 B*, the bend is flattened when the pad bottoms, forcing metal into the bends. The metal involved in the recoil does not reach yield-point pressures.

Fine adjustment of pad pressure can vary bend-angles several degrees, permitting compensation for stock variations. This springback control method in conjunction with an on-line quality control program and can be considered part of a process-control feedback-loop system.

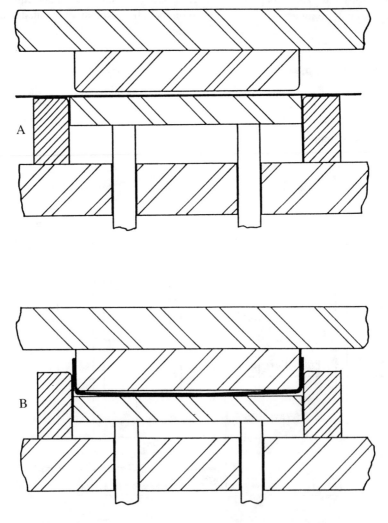

Figure 15-4. *Using pad pressure to make fine adjustments to a bend-angle. (W. C. McCurdy Co.)*

194

DETERMINING PRESS CONDITION

A major source of difficulty in metal stamping is maintaining good press alignment. Experience has shown that even badly worn presses produce high-quality work. This is provided that they are adjusted to be level under load when tested with calibration load cells. This procedure is illustrated in *Figure 11-4* and explained in detailed references in that chapter.

Testing Presses With Load Cells

The traditional method of checking parallelism is to sweep the opening from the slide to the bolster with a dial indicator and when the press is not running. This does not always consider the difference in bearing clearances. In those cases, where blocks or jacks support the slide, care must be exercised so that bending and defections are not created to mask the true alignment condition. Static checking of parallelism does not take into account the deflections that are a result of mass in motion. This creates forces found only when the press is cycling.

To determine the condition of parallelism under load, four calibration load cells are placed in the die space on strong supports. Shims are added under each load cell and the slide adjusted downward to obtain the desired loading when striking the load cells. The amount of shims needed in each individual load cell is equal to the amount of out-of-parallel condition at each load cell.

In the case of OBI or gap frame presses, it is important to recognize the angular deflections that occur in this type of press. Despite the lack of an industry standard for angular deflections, most press manufacturers use the approximate value of 0.0015 in. (0.038 mm) per inch (25.4 mm) of throat depth. Considering a nominal throat depth of 20 in. (508 mm), this could mean an angular deflection of as much as 0.030 in. (0.76 mm).

The tool may not allow misalignment of this magnatude. Guide pins and bushings cannot compensate for this misalignment.

PRESS BED LEVELING

The necessity of frequent large precision machine tools re-leveling is well-known and accepted. Like machine tools, press beds require periodic re-leveling to compensate for foundation settling.

Figure 15-5 illustrates a straightside with vibration isolating leveling devices installed. These devices allow easy adjustment to be made when leveling the press bed. These devices are available in sizes for all presses.

The larger sizes are equipped with internal hydraulic cylinders to permit the screw to be adjusted with ease. All sizes can be equipped with strain gages. The latter feature permits electronic weighing of each corner of the press to determine even weight distribution. A cut-away view is shown in *Figure 15-6*.

Figure 15-7 illustrates a press bed mounted on an uneven surface. While the twist or warpage may not be visible to the unaided eye, it is readily detected with

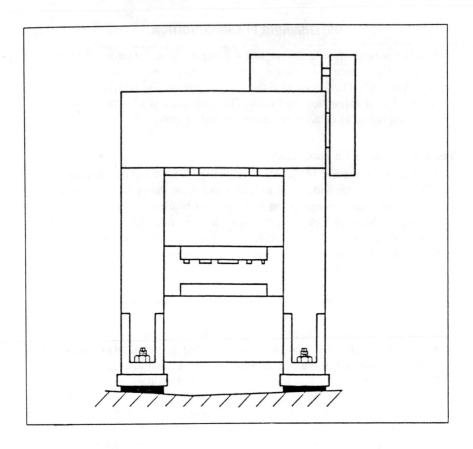

Figure 15-5. *Vibration isolation and press leveling devices installed under a straightside press on an uneven surface. (Vibro/Dynamics Corp.)*

a precision machinist's level. When the twist is removed from the bed, (*Figure 15-8*) the machinist's level will indicate that all four sides of the press bed are relatively level.

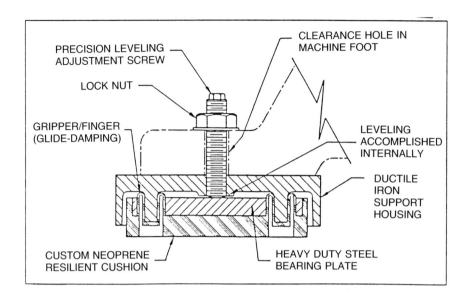

Figure 15-6. *Cutaway view of press leveling and vibration isolating device.*
(Vibro/Dynamics Corp.)

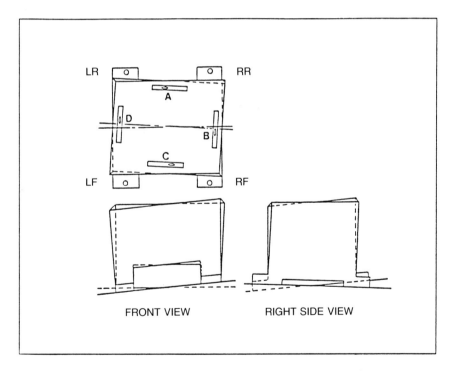

Figure 15-7. *Press bed warped and twisted by installing on an uneven surface.*
(Vibro/Dynamics Corp.)

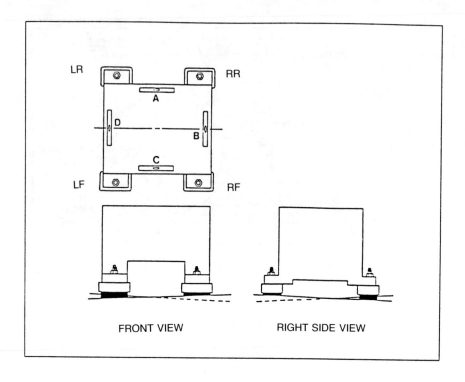

Figure 15-8. *Properly leveling a press bed eliminates warpage and twists.*
(Vibro/Dynamics Corp.)

REFERENCES

1. Michael Young, Vibro/Dynamics Corp., "Press Mounting Techniques for Improved Die Life", SME Conference Proceedings, Society of Manufacturing Engineers, Dearborn, Michigan, 1988.

16

MAINTENANCE REQUIREMENTS FOR QUICK DIE CHANGE

PLANNING DIE MAINTENANCE

To maintain quality production and forecast die repair requirements, there must be some method of planning die maintenance. The planning method can be as simple as a single individual in a small shop, such as the press room manager scheduling dies for repair,to a sophisticated computerized database for prioritizing and scheduling needed repairs. Any good system must take into account key planning factors:

1. Problems and their root causes must be identified.
2. Scheduled inspections and preventive maintenance are important.
3. The capacity to do the repair work must be known.
4. An accurate estimate of the time required to complete each repair is needed.
5. Production scheduling must be considered.
6. There must be a means to prioritize backlogged work.

A GOOD MANUAL SYSTEM*

Team Method of Stamping Die Maintenance. A Japanese automaker's integrated stamping and assembly plant in America depends upon a team approach to solving all die problems relating to quality and productivity. Team interaction is the key to the success of the system. The stamping shop has a total of five transfer press lines, an OBI line, and a blanker. Every die is assigned a home line and seldom runs in another line.

Making a Maintenance Request. The three-part Die Maintenance Request form shown in *Figure 16-1* is usually initiated by the transfer press or OBI line production team leader who sketches a description of the problem in space *1* on the form. After signing the form in space *2*, the person takes the form to the tool and die team leader for approval. The team leader reviews the problem with the production team leader and other persons having knowledge of the problem as needed. It is the leader's responsibility to plan the required maintenance.

*Based on material contributed by Ray Hedding and Eugene J. Narbut, Mazda Motor Manufacturing (USA) Corp., Flat Rock, Michigan.

DIE MAINTENANCE REQUEST   *INSPECTION / REPAIR / IMPROVEMENT*

PART 1

Part Number	
Part Name	
Press Line	
Die Number	
Defective Process	
Today's Date	1 Shift ___ 2 Shift ___
Number of Trial Parts/Blanks	
Unit Leader	

Description of Problem

①

Originator	②
Deadline for Modification	▲

Unit Leader Must Contact Planning Dept. for Dates |

DIE MAINTENANCE REQUEST

PART 2

Die Correction Date	D N	D N	Corrective Action	
Die Correction Time Required				
Trial Date	D N	D N		
Trial Time Required				
Die Maintenance Member	③			
Unit Leader				

CHECK THE FOLLOWING INSPECTION ITEMS	
Has Die Been Properly Cleaned?	
Are All Die Parts Secure?	
No Foreign Items On or In Die	
Proper Clearance	
Are Wear Plates Lubricated?	
Fingers	
Keeper Pins	
Lifter Tie Downs	
Has All Work Been Completed?	
Has Request Form Been Completed?	

Tryout Area	
Bench	
Tryout Press	
Production Press	

④

▲

After Correction, Die Maintenance Member Must Check These Items |

PRODUCTION

PART 3

		Results of Correction
Production Date	D N	
Unit Leader		⑤
Operation		

White: INFORMATION TO LINE AFTER CORRECTION
(Line → Die Maintenance→ Crane Operator/Die Setter By Mail Post → Line Must Check Results → Die Maintenance)

Figure 16-1. *Three-part form used in a manual die maintenance planning and tracking system. (Mazda Motor Manufacturing (USA) Corp.)*

Planning Maintenance

The tool and die team leader must determine the cause(s) of the problem and identify all dies that will require corrective action. The amount of time required to make the correction must be determined.

Only a two-day supply of any given part is usually produced at a time. Production of more than the usual run of parts may be needed to provide additional release time. The tool and die team leader coordinates the required release with the production planning department. When the plan is complete, the tool and die team leader co-signs the form in the blank space (3).

One of the three copies is posted on a cork board at the home line and the other two copies are inserted into a pipe attached to the die for that purpose. The required number of sample parts needed for evaluation and tryout are shipped to the dieroom together with the die(s) by the production team leader. The parts are identified and stored in a designated area.

Tracking and Prioritizing Requests

At the start and near the end of each shift, both the production team leader and the tool and die team leader meet to review problems including a review of all outstanding maintenance requests posted on the line's cork board. The outstanding requests are prioritized based upon the extent to which quality and production are affected. There are times when the entire correction needed cannot be made due to the size of the job and urgency of other requests. In such a case, the plan may be reduced to a partial correction, with a complete correction scheduled for a later date.

Correction and Follow-up

The diemaker making the repairs records the corrective action on the middle part of the form (4) and completes the list of inspection items. After the correction is completed, the second copy of the die maintenance request is filed in the die room records for that die and the first copy placed in the pipe attached to the die. When the die is returned to the press line, the first copy is placed in a plastic sleeve attached to the cork board.

The lower space on the form (5) is completed by the production team leader and line team leader after the success of the repair has been evaluated during a production run. The white copy is then retained in the die repair area as a part of the die's maintenance history.

Cooperation Required

The Japanese system of manufacturing places great emphasis upon each individual being part of a team responsible for quality and productivity. This maintenance system depends upon the cooperation of all employees.

AN EXAMPLE OF A COMPUTERIZED DIE MAINTENANCE SYSTEM*

Computerized Database Die Maintenance. A large automaker has improved quality and reduced cost by implementing a computerized die maintenance program in its stamping plants. The basic program strategy was to reduce the amount of breakdown repairs and increase the amount of planned maintenance to improve throughput and quality.

The approach revolves around six key steps in the die maintenance workcycle *Figure 16-2*. The work needed is identified and priorities set. The work is planned followed by scheduling and assigning. Progress is reported by each shift. At the completion of the workcycle, the work performed is evaluated and entered into the history file, by die number.

Daily Operating System. With this maintenance work cycle applied to a typical large tool and die department, a daily operating system has been developed *Figure 16-3*.

First, the work is identified by either preventive maintenance or operational symptoms. A work order is then initiated and entered into the maintenance management system (MMS) die backlog. Next, a daily planning meeting with personnel from maintenance, operations and production scheduling is held so that the work order can be planned, prioritized, and scheduled. This planning meeting is a key link in the communications process. Finally, the work is performed and entered by the planner into history. This provides a basis for analysis of maintenance costs, engineering capabilities and SPC data.

How the Data is Used. First, a daily work plan is printed for the supervisor to use as a management tool. It replaces hand-written reports that were formerly passed from shift to shift, and clearly avoids misinterpretation. It provides information such as part number, die number, work order number, a brief description of work to be done, date required, and a space for hours worked.

Next, there is a die history sheet which provides not only maintenance labor and material costs, but also signals repetitive problems.

Finally, reports can be generated from the database by cause code, type of die, a specific die, cause code as a percentage of the total work, and work location.

Additional Features. The MMS ties-in with the plant computer-integrated-manufacturing (CIM) system. Dieset schedules are prepared, based upon production requirements. The Dieset Scheduling System (DSS) provides reports for open and completed work orders on tooling scheduled for dieset. The DSS also can forecast future dieset schedules, an important planning tool. Reports on die and automation changeover-time performance are also generated to evaluating continuous improvement of manufacturing methods.

To further aid in reducing setup times, a Line-Changeover Performance System (LPC) has been developed. Computer-generated data reports documented problems that occur during diesetting, and any other problems that occur upon start-up of production.[1]

*Based on material contributed by Jeffrey Gordish, Management Technologies Inc.; Roman J. Krygier and Robert W. Prucka, Ford Motor Co.

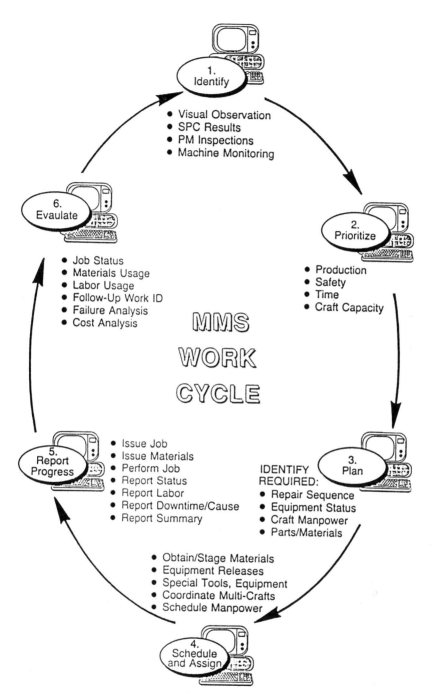

Figure 16-2. *Six key steps in a computerized die maintenance management system work-cycle. (Management Technologies Inc.)*

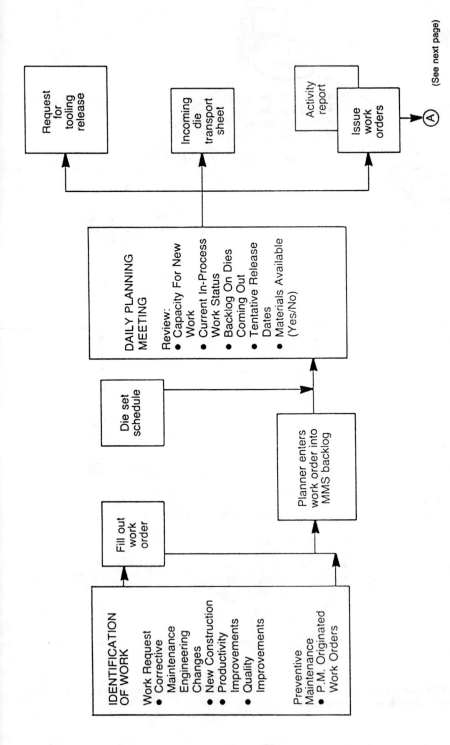

Figure 16-3. *Computerized die maintenance daily operating system flow-chart. (Ford Motor Co.)*

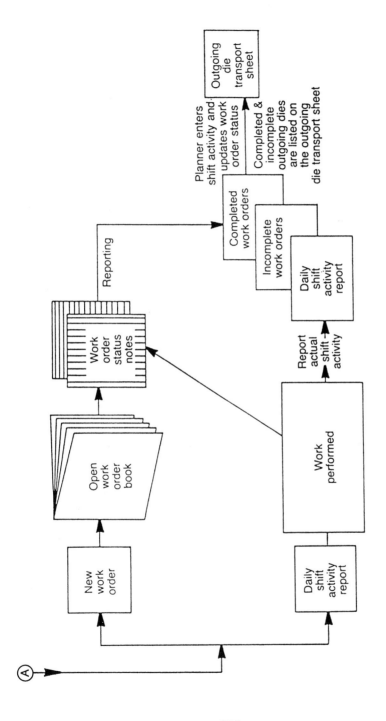

Figure 16-3. *Continued.*

205

Manual Versus Computerized Systems

Choice of Systems. Manual maintenance tracking systems have a limited capacity for information storage and retrieval. Reports on such factors as problem causes and labor hours expended are often needed for management decision-making. These can be very time-consuming to generate manually.

Manual systems generally work very well in shops having up to 15 employees in a repair activity. The actual number depends upon the degree of employee-management cooperative interaction. Manual systems that work well in very large shops often depend on reducing the maintenance activity into sub-activities having no more than 15 employees.

The manual system described in this section works well because of strong teamwork discipline and commitment to a high and ever-improving quality standard.

The information accessibility needed for wise resource management and efficient plant administration has resulted in computer-integrated manufacturing systems finding widespread application. Employee acceptance generally is excellent when they are involved in the early phases of the system implementation.

The use of a maintenance management database as part of a computer-integrated system can provide a means to improve quality, reduce cost, and bring about needed cultural change.

Choosing Maintenance Management Software

There are over 200 computerized maintenance management systems presently on the market. Chapter 27 explains the basic requirements for a good system and outlines a simple step-by-step, team-oriented procedure for selecting the computerized maintenance management system that is best for a company.

NUMBER OF MAINTENANCE CLASSIFICATIONS

The trend is for the multitude of skilled classifications to be combined into several basic core skilled trades. When this is done, considerable employee training may be required to teach all of the skills required by such a versatile skilled tradesperson. There is usually an advantage for personnel because long-term job security is improved by increasing both the profitability of the employer and the employability of the skilled worker.

The traditional skilled trades structure had 15 or more skilled classifications. Such a hierarchy of skills often made quick diagnosis and repair of a breakdown impossible.

How the Problem Originated. A widespread assumption is that labor unions negotiated the multitude of skilled trades classifications that presently exist. This is not entirely true.

For the most part, management "created a monster" with very little help from the union. In many unionized shops, seniority within a skilled trades classification is based upon date of entry. If management wished to hire a young skilled worker, rather than promote an older high-seniority worker, they would simply create a special classification for the worker that they wished to hire.

An Example From Years Ago. New pyrometer controlled furnaces were just installed in the heat treating department of a diversified manufacturer. The installers work for an electrical contractor who pays them $1.45 per hour,which is far below the union scale for Industrial Electricians.

Management is impressed with the skills of one of the pyrometer installers and wishes to hire him. The installer cannot qualify as an electrician because he does not have 10 years experience and did not serve an apprenticeship. Hiring him as an electrician would foster discontent and result in grievances being filed. This would not satisfy management's need to have a skilled pyrometer mechanic that they can depend on being available to keep the new equipment running. The new employee would be low man on the seniority list and hence, the first to be laid off. Management wishes to have him work day shift, and the lowest seniority electrician on day shift has 18 years seniority.

None of the electricians have training in the maintenance and calibration of the pyrometers. Several of them have expressed a dislike for the new equipment and stated that they will refuse to work on it. The union scale for electricians is $2.17. Management doesn't want to train them since considerable resistance to the adoption of new skills and procedures has been voiced.

Management approached the union representatives and discussed creating a new classification, that of pyrometer mechanic. Based upon a promise that another member will be added to the ranks of the union, the parties quickly agree. Restrictions on what a pyrometer mechanic can do, such as not installing conduit and working with wires larger than 16 gage are agreed upon. The new classification will pay $2.07 an hour, a dime less than industrial electricians earn.

The union is happy because they have another member. The pyrometer mechanic is very happy because he now has an easy job, fringe benefits, and much higher pay. The electricians are happy because the new classification pays less and none of them are embarrassed by not being able to fix the new equipment. Management is happy because they were able to place the man that they wanted in a protected classification on the day shift.

There Are Many Examples. The scenario above has been repeated countless times. Any number of classifications have been created in this manner strictly on management's initiative with the acquiescence of the union. It was seldom a problem because there was something in the arrangement that benefited both sides.

THE FORD WAYNE STAMPING SKILLED TRADES STRUCTURE*

There are shops that have streamlined skilled trades structures. Enhancement of problem solving capability is an important advantage.

*Contributed by Steve Cool and Robert W. Prucka, Ford Motor Co., Wayne, Michigan.

There are only three basic skilled trades groups: mechanical, electrical, and tool and die. This avoids the multiple "hair-splitting" work assignment practices of a traditional big three stamping plant.

The plant is located in Wayne, Michigan and is an integrated stamping and assembly facility. An important area of current Ford-UAW cooperation is in employee training. Classes ranging from basic math skills to advanced computer-aided equipment diagnositics are taught on-site.

Stamping Manager Robert Prucka says that computerized maintenance databases for both presses and dies are an important factor in the success of the Wayne facility. It is important not to let a particular equipment malfunction delay production repeatedly. A computerized database quickly determines the causes of any problem that repeatedly delays production or affects process variability.

Facility Engineer Steve Cool notes that maintenance plays a vital role in quick die change. Automated presses with dual moving bolsters and automatic die clamps are not new; such equipment has been in use for over 20 years. The lack of a systematic maintenance program together with sufficient employee skills and cooperation resulted in such systems falling into disuse in the past.

State of the Art Heavy Stamping Press Maintenance

Improved predictive techniques such as vibration analysis and tonnage waveform signature analysis are a key to avoiding unscheduled press downtime in heavy stamping operations. Several important predictive maintenance techniques are in regular use at the Wayne facility.

Important Preventive Maintenance Practices

Many stampers neglect the basics of maintaining optimal machine alignment because they are unaware of how important it is to treat a stamping press as a precision machine tool. At the Ford Wayne Plant, all press beds are periodically checked with a precision machinist's level to be certain that an out-of-level or skewed condition is not developing. Any discrepancy is promptly corrected following the methods outlined in Chapter 15 and references 2, 3, and 4.

A standard end-measuring rod with an attached dial indicator is available at each press line to use whenever an out-of-parallel or common shut height problem is suspected. This technique, when used with periodic load-cell testing, assures process repeatability. These techniques, which are outlined in Chapter 11 and references 5, 6, 7, and 8, maintain dies at a common shut height. They provide the means to insure quick die change and stamping flexibility between identical press lines.

Tonnage-waveform signature analysis using a high-speed chart recorder is another tool to spot and troubleshoot stamping problems. According to Prucka, this is a neglected technique that can yield a wealth of information about die and press conditions. Lack of training for interpreting the signatures is seen as the basic problem that must be overcome. In addition to the work being done at Wayne, important work is being carried out by Dr. Stuart P. Keeler and Mike Herderich at The Budd Company Technical Center in Auburn Hills, Michigan and by Joe Wise at Webster Manufacturing Company in Tiffin, Ohio. Chapters 28 and 29 as well as references 7, 9, and 10 provide data on this important troubleshooting technique.

At Wayne, press and die alignment maintenance is seen as the foundation of process repeatability. Alignment on 180 in. (4.572 m) wide tandem lines is routinely maintained within 0.008 in. (0.20 mm) total corner to corner. This is more than twice as accurate when compared to the industry standard of 0.001 in. (0.054 mm) per foot (305 mm).

This standard is typical of the high standards maintained in high-speed lamination dies and presses. As Prucka explained, "If you want to produce automotive body panels with the same burr-free condition and long die life attained in electrical lamination pressworking, the machinery must be aligned to the same standard."

Future Trends in Heavy Stamping Press Maintenance

Prucka states that the worst problem standing in the way of preventive maintenance on heavy presses is the amount of time required to dismantle, repair, and reassemble major systems or the entire machine. This has resulted in many managers accepting breakdown maintenance as the norm in spite of the warnings generated by the maintenance programs that may be in place.

Reducing press repair time is similar to reducing die change time. For example, changing the drive belts on a large press can take 12 or more hours. With proper prestaging of replacement parts, tools and crane equipment, this time should be reduced to under four hours. Application of the same discipline including the use of video equipment could reduce the time to under one hour.

This same principle, as outlined in Chapter 14, could also reduce the time required to dismantle and reassemble a large press from several months to well under 10 days. The presses are generally symmetrical, and identically trained teams could be assigned to each side to simultaneously accomplish the same tasks. The training requirements are that presses would need to be repaired using the team-oriented "Quick Press Repair" approach that Prucka envisions. This is seen as the best way to banish the "Breakdown Maintenance Mentality" that is still all too prevalent in heavy stamping.

REFERENCES

1. Roman J. Krygier, "Maintenance Management, a Review of the Program Installed at Body Operations Plants, Ford Motor Company", Presented at Dearborn, Michigan Aug. 25, 1989, Society of Manufacturing Engineers, Dearborn, Michigan.

2. Michael Young, Vibro/Dynamics Corp., "Press Mounting Techniques for improved Die Life", SME Conference Proceeding, Society of Manufacturing Engineers, Dearborn, Michigan, 1988.

3. David A. Smith, *Die Design Handbook*, Section 27, Society of Manufacturing Engineers, Dearborn, Michigan, 1990.

4. Donald F. Wilhelm: *Understanding Presses and Press Operations*, Society of Manufacturing Engineers, Dearborn, Michigan, 1981.

5. David A. Smith: "Adjusting Dies to a Common Shut Height", SME/FMA Technical Paper TE89-565, Society of Manufacturing Engineers, Dearborn, Michigan, 1989.

6. David A. Smith, "Why Press Slide Out of Parallel Problems Affect Part Quality and Available Tonnage", SME Technical Paper TE88-442, Society of Manufacturing Engineers, Dearborn, Michigan, 1988.

7. Donald F. Wilhelm: "Measuring Loads On Mechanical Presses", SME Conference Proceeding, Society of Manufacturing Engineers, Dearborn, Michigan, 1988.

8. David A. Smith: "How to Improve Hit-to-hit Time With a Tonnage Monitor", SME Technical Paper TE88-780, Society of Manufacturing Engineers, Dearborn, Michigan, 1989.

9. David A. Smith, *Die Design Handbook*, Section 4, Society of Manufacturing Engineers, Dearborn, Michigan 1990.

10. David A. Smith: "Using Waveform Signature Analysis to Reduce Snap-Through Energy", SME Technical Report MF90-11, Society of Manufacturing Engineers, Dearborn, Michigan, 1990.

17

SAFETY AND ERGONOMICS

SAFETY WHEN WORKING ON DIES IN PRESSES

A thorough discussion of personnel safety is beyond the scope of this book, but a few examples of how manufacturers strive to avoid injury to pressroom personnel will be pointed out. Almost all pressroom accidents are avoidable, and that must be everyone's goal.

Company Standards

Safe practices must be determined for each class of work that a stamping facility runs. The determination of how to make a die setup safe is very important. When formulating safety rules, such as a safe means of securing a die in a press, be sure to consult current government safety regulations. In the United States, the Occupational Safety and Health Administration (OSHA) promulgates and enforces power press safety rules which are subject to change.

Before training in safe practices can begin, good company standards for safe diesetting must be in place. Many factors should enter into comprehensive in-house diesetting standards. A few considerations are:

1. All statutory and administrative safety laws and regulations that apply.
2. A thorough analysis by the manufacturing engineering department.
3. Careful analysis of all fasteners in terms of both proper safety factors and resistance to fatigue failure.
4. Correct number, size and placement of parallels.
5. Avoidance of creating pinch points that can endanger the operator.
6. Provision of a safe means to block up the press slide if the dies are worked in the press.
7. Provision to lock out and dissipate stored energy (flywheels, surge tanks, capacitor banks, etc.) on any pressworking or automation equipment.
8. Good mechanical and human engineering practice in ''gray'' areas where no formal rules exist.

Safety Blocks

Extruded magnesium is an excellent material for blocking press slides in the open position. The material is very predictable in compressive loading, and has a good weight-to-strength ratio.

A few comments on their application:

1. At least two blocks should be used and placed across diagonal corners of the press.
2. Safety block pads may be provided in the die to simplify correct block placement.
3. An informal automotive stamping industry standard is to provide a minimum of two safety block pads having a closed height of 6 in. (152 mm).
4. The safety blocks are sized 4.5 in. (114 mm) longer than the press stroke.
5. Hardwood wedges are used to fill in the remaining 1.5-in. (38-mm) space, to prevent the slide gaining inertia before contacting the blocks.
6. The compressive strength of the blocks must be sufficient to support the weight of the press slide, attached linkage, and upper die, with a safety factor added.
7. Since the blocks are not designed to withstand full press tonnage, a safety plug which interrupts the press main run circuit is attached by a short chain. They must not be placed in the die-space with the press running.
8. If safety block pads are provided in the die, the compressive strength of the die in those areas must equal that of the safety blocks in any press into which the die may be set.
9. Since the length of the blocks is determined by the press stroke, the blocks should be conspicuously identified with the press number to prevent use in a press other than the one intended.
10. The blocks should be viewed as a lifeboat on a ship—they should be used for no other purpose.

Figure 17-1 illustrates safety blocks made from commercially available extruded magnesium stock. The aluminum end-plates are made from 6061-T6 aluminum plate. These plates become worn and mis-shaped with use and should be replaced. The screws holding the end plates should be secured with medium-strength thread-locking compound to keep the end plates securely attached and to avoid thread damage.

Safety Locks

When working on a die in a press, a method must be used to lock out the power source. Each employee must have an individual safety lock for this purpose. Multiple safety locks may be required to lock out the energy sources of automation equipment, if the unexpected movement of such equipment could endanger an employee.

Multiple lockout devices permit each employee assigned to the job to lock out the equipment, and must be provided.

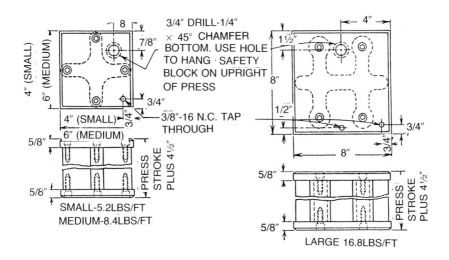

Figure 17-1. *Extruded magnesium safety blocks fitted with aluminum end plates. (Ford Motor Co.)*

Lockout During Diesetting

When setting dies, the press should be locked out while the die is manually bolted and unbolted. This advice may seem to be against all quick die change practices, but such a rule can save time and money in the long run.

The main danger is that someone may inch the press open with the die partly bolted in. This can easily happen if the diesetter leaves the job for any reason with only one side fastened, and someone assumes that the die is set. Catastrophic damage to both the die and press can occur. Such items as bolts, heel blocks, press gibbing, and pieces of iron castings have been known to fly considerable distances and seriously injure personnel.

Die Clamping

To prevent the possible shifting of the die shoe during the operation of the press, the die shoe should be securely clamped to the slide and bolster plate. Extensive information and many examples of good versus bad clamping practices are contained in Chapter 4.

COUNTERBALANCE AIR ADJUSTMENT

The correct adjustment of the press counterbalance air pressure is required for safe press operation. The purpose of the press counterbalance system is to offset the weight of the press slide and upper die. If the setting is too high, excessive clutch wear results. Low settings cause excessive holding brake wear and can cause the holding brake to overheat dangerously.

213

Figure 17-2 illustrates the components that make up a mechanical press counterbalance system. The main component is the pneumatic cylinder (*D1*) of the piston rod which both attaches to and counterbalances the weight of the slide and upper die. Some presses have two or more cylinders. Double-action presses have separate counterbalance systems for each slide.

A pressure gage (*D2*) and adjustable air regulator (*D3*) are provided on the press to permit accurate adjustment to the correct setting. Many regulators are of the self-relieving type in that they automatically bleed excess air when the pressure setting is lowered. Self-relieving regulators should have the pressure adjustment raised slightly—until air is heard entering the system—after bleeding the pressure to a lower value. Bleeding the system can be increased by opening the blow-down valve (*D4*).

Many presses have a chart that gives the correct pressure setting for various upper die weights. Dies should have the upper, lower, and total die weight clearly identified to facilitate both safe die handling and correct counterbalance setting.

Common Errors in Counterbalance Adjustment

Large presses have big surge tanks (*D5*) that take a long time to fill. A common mistake is to make big changes in the regulator setting. Sometimes a

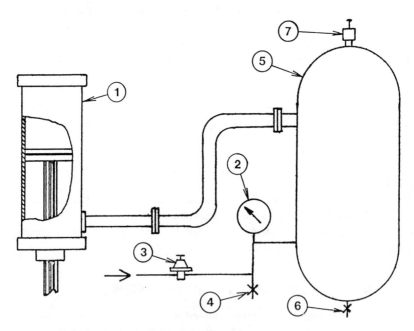

Figure 17-2. *Diagram of a typical mechanical press counterbalance system: (D1) counterbalance cylinder with a piston rod that attaches to the press slide (not shown); (D2) pressure gage; (D3) pressure regulator; (D4) blow-down valve; (D5) surge tank; (D6) water drain valve; (D7) safety pop-off valve.*

small change, followed by a wait of several minutes to allow the system to stabilize, is all that is needed.

A common source of incorrect pressure settings is inaccurate or missing gages. Press vibration and pressure pulsations can ruin the accuracy of a low-grade gage in a short time. To avoid this problem, only a high-quality liquid-filled gage with a built-in pulsation snubber should be used. Another good solution is to equip each press with a quick-disconnect fitting and use a portable gage of known accuracy. Special miniature diagnostic fittings are made for this purpose. The portable gages should be checked against a master gage periodically.

Some newer presses designed for quick die change feature automatic counterbalance adjustment based upon a computerized database of die numbers. In most cases, the correct pressure must still be determined and entered into the database. Failing to update the database and relying on manual adjustment after problems develop are common errors.

Setting Counterbalance Pressure with an Ammeter

Checking the drive motor current while the press is cycled is an accurate way to find the right air pressure setting. A reading that increases as the slide descends and drops sharply on the upstroke indicates that the pressure is too high.

Amperage readings that are high on the upstroke, and increase as the top of the stroke is approached, mean that the setting is too low. When ammeter readings are checked, allowance must be made for the fact that the press motor must supply the energy lost by the flywheel as the press rolls through the bottom of the stroke. A current surge is normal when that occurs.

Press stroke per minute indicators, that operate by measuring the RPM of the drive motor, flywheel, or crankshaft, can be used in place of an ammeter. If the press speed increases on the downstroke, the setting is too low. A loss of speed means the air pressure is too high.

Counterbalance Adjustment With a Dial Indicator

The dial indicator method can be used to establish correct counterbalance pressure if the press counterbalance adjustment information is not available. To use this method:

1. Stop the press at 90 degrees on the downstroke.
2. Follow proper safety procedure.
3. Exhaust the air from the counterbalance, but not the holding brake.
4. Place a dial indicator with a magnetic base on the slide so the tip of the indicator touches the slide.
5. Slowly raise the counterbalance air pressure until the dial indicator shows that the counterbalance has lifted the slide.
6. Make a record of this setting so that this procedure will not need to be repeated.

This procedure usually establishes a setting very close to that of the ammeter method.

Counterbalance Maintenance for Safe Operation

Water will accumulate in the surge tank(s) and must be drained by a valve (*D6*) provided for that purpose. Otherwise there will not be sufficient space in the surge tank, and excessive pressures will result in erratic press operation. In some cases, the safety valve (*D7*) will open at the bottom of each stroke, resulting in wasted compressed air.

The frequency of draining will depend upon the dryness of the air supply. Usually a weekly schedule is sufficient. Under conditions of high temperature and humidity, the compressed-air dryer may be overloaded and a daily schedule may be required.

Lubrication must be supplied to both the cylinder piston packing and the rod gland packing. Dry piston packing emits a characteristic sound best described as that of a cow mooing. If the problem is not corrected promptly, the packing will fail.

SAFETY GUARDS

Usually the diesetter is responsible for the safe installation of removable safety guards. If they are made especially for a single job, they must be stored in a designated location so that they are undamaged and quickly available prior to die change.

The Cannibalization Problem

Special safety guards that are not clearly identified, or incorrectly stored, are almost certain to be modified for use on another job. This modification is usually followed by a remodification the next time a special guard is needed. After several cycles of sledge hammers beating and cutting with oxy-acetylene torches, the special-purpose guard becomes nothing but a badly abused piece of scrap iron, and is tossed into the scrap bin.

The Dark Age of Diesetting

Years ago, setting a small hand-loaded die in a 150 ton (1.3 MN) OBI press could take days. Placing the die in the press with a fork-lift truck and bolting it in place took 10 minutes or less. Getting proper safety guards made up and in place was what consumed so much time. The complicated job assignment structure in some shops often contributed to the delay.

Avoiding the Problem Today

Safety guards should last the lifetime of the job provided that they are carefully stored and maintained. Storage systems for specialized pressworking

216

aids such as automation devices and safety guards range from high rise computerized storage and retrieval systems to brackets welded on the side of the press.

Storing the guards with the die is often not satisfactory because dies are often stacked. If wall space is available, hooks can be installed for guard storage. The space for each guard should be identified by job number. Painting an outline or a silhouette of the guard is an easy means to insure that everything is in its correct place. This system never fails to get favorable comments from visitors.

The widespread use of light curtain guarding systems has greatly reduced the guard storage problem in many shops. If all of the cost factors associated with the construction and maintenance of physical barrier guards are quantified, the cost of installing light curtain systems can be justified. An often overlooked cost factor is the time required to remove and install the barrier guards.

Ready-made adjustable guards are available from several suppliers. Because they are adjustable, the same guard may serve a number of jobs.

SAFE HANDLING OF LARGE DIES[1]

Large dies present a special handling problem because of their weight. A method preferred over chain slings is the use of double eye cable slings in sets of four *(Figure 17-3)*. The die is provided with four captive self-locking pins in each die shoe to permit safe lifting, opening, turning, and closing.[1]

Placing Threaded Steel Inserts in Iron Castings

Iron die castings are usually a one-of-a-kind item. The usual pattern material is styrofoam. This greatly simplifies both patternmaking and mold preparation because there is no need to remove the pattern from the mold prior to pouring the iron.

Figure 17-4 shows a method for placing an eye-bolt hole insert in a casting. The insert has a groove and flat which prevent the insert from turning or pulling out of the casting under extreme loading. Safe eye-bolt holes are available for handling the casting as soon as it is removed from the sand. The cost per finished hole may also be lower than that of conventional drilling and tapping.

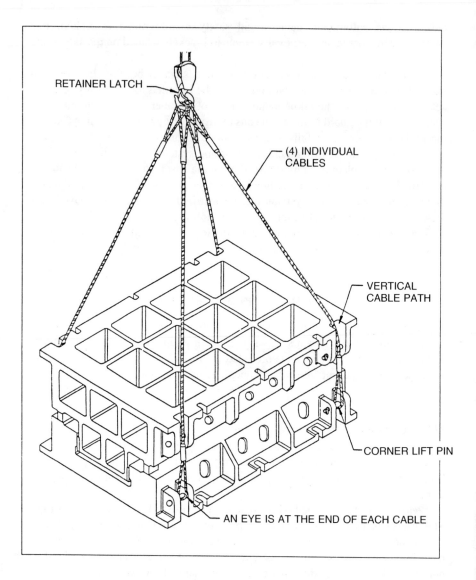

Figure 17-3. *Handling a large die with cable slings. (Ford Motor Co.)*[1,2]

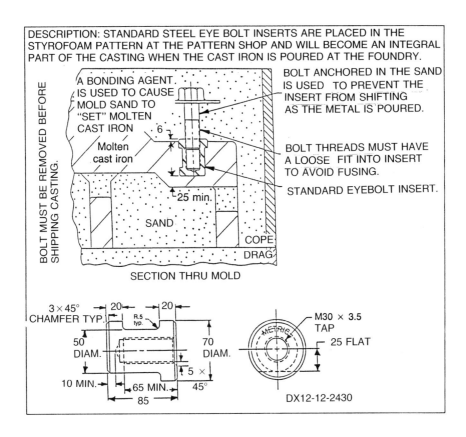

DESCRIPTION: STANDARD STEEL EYE BOLT INSERTS ARE PLACED IN THE STYROFOAM PATTERN AT THE PATTERN SHOP AND WILL BECOME AN INTEGRAL PART OF THE CASTING WHEN THE CAST IRON IS POURED AT THE FOUNDRY.

A BONDING AGENT IS USED TO CAUSE MOLD SAND TO "SET" MOLTEN CAST IRON

Molten cast iron

BOLT ANCHORED IN THE SAND IS USED TO PREVENT THE INSERT FROM SHIFTING AS THE METAL IS POURED.

BOLT THREADS MUST HAVE A LOOSE FIT INTO INSERT TO AVOID FUSING.

STANDARD EYEBOLT INSERT.

6

25 min.

SAND

COPE

DRAG

BOLT MUST BE REMOVED BEFORE SHIPPING CASTING.

SECTION THRU MOLD

3 × 45°
CHAMFER TYP.

20

R.5 typ.

20

50 DIAM.

70 DIAM.

M30 × 3.5 TAP

25 FLAT

METRIC

10 MIN.

65 MIN.

5 ×
45°

85

DX12-12-2430

Figure 17-4. *A threaded steel insert placed in a styrofoam pattern. (Ford Motor Co.)*[1,2]

ERGONOMIC FACTORS IN THE PRESSROOM

There is no reason why pressworking operations should inevitably result in human injuries. Nearly all modern stamping shops have impressive safety records for avoiding lost time accidents. Modern press controls, automation, and proper guarding of machinery have nearly eliminated the accidental amputations and severe lacerations that were once accepted as an inevitable result of pressworking operations.

The government-mandated hearing conservation programs have resulted in a remarkable reduction in hearing loss caused by the cumulative effects of exposure to high noise levels. There are other types of cumulative trauma injuries that can result from avoidable pressroom conditions.

Carpal Tunnel Syndrome

This is a common cumulative trauma injury to pressroom workers. It involves excessive pressure being placed on the median nerve where it passes through the wrist. The pressure is caused by a swelling of the tissue within the wrist. One cause of this swelling is repetitive wrist flexure. The result is numbness of a portion of the hand. If untreated, permanent loss of feeling and function can result. To help avoid this problem in the pressroom, a number of measures can be helpful. Changes in work rules may be needed in some cases. The measures include:

- Replacing mechanical switch-type palm buttons with newer types actuated by capacitive proximity switches or by interrupting an infra-red light beam.
- Designing the repetitive task so that the operator maintains a neutral wrist position.
- Rotating workers between tasks.
- Automating jobs where possible.
- Using sensors for die protection so the press does not need to be single-stroked by an operator.

Other measures can be quite innovative and improve the overall efficiency of an operation. For example, when a number of small knee or OBI press dies are required to produce a part, consider mounting them on common subplates and running the job in a straightside press. This will have the effect of varying the types of hand movements required. A second operator can also work on the other side of the press with the appropriate safety controls. This can have the added advantage of increasing productivity while eliminating the problems associated with work baskets and tubs in the process of completion.

Back Injuries

Industrial workers have been shown safety posters for decades which show the correct way to lift heavy objects. The proper way is to keep the back straight and lift with the legs. The object of correct lifting is to avoid a gradual deterioration or sudden failure of the disks in the spinal column *(Figure 17-5)*. Disk failures (herniation or rupture) are quite painful and can result in paralysis. However, improper lifting is not the only cause of back injuries. Some other causes are:

- Falls that place a sudden compressive shock on the spinal column.
- Lifting weights that are far too heavy.
- Excessive repeated forward bending.

Most press room injuries are avoidable and back injuries are not an exception. *Figure 17-5* illustrates a how the most common serious industrial back injury, a herniated disc, occurs. The *disk* functions to separate the bones known as vertebrae and provide flexibility to the spine. As shown in *B* the *disk* consists of a hard outer layer and a jelly-like core.

The hard outer layer must withstand the hydraulic-like pressure of the jelly-like inner substance. The pressure tends to be proportional to the loading on the spinal column. Extreme pressures caused by a fall or extremely heavy lifting can cause the hard outer layer to fail as is shown at *C*.

220

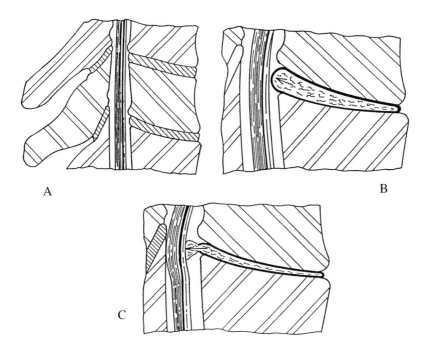

A
B
C

Figure 17-5. *Sequence of a disk failure in the human spine: (A) section through a portion of a normal human spine: (B) bulging disk caused by improper lifting, lifting excessively heavy weights and/or excessive bending; (C) a herniated (ruptured) disk placing pressure on the spinal cord or a nerve where it leaves the spinal cord.*

This is no different from the failure of a hose caused by the application of excessive pressures. Disk failures, like hose failures, occur because of extreme sudden overloading, chronic overloading, or excessive cyclical loading which is analogous to excessive repeated forward bending. The disks, like a rubber hose, deteriorate with age, so older workers are more susceptible to such back injuries than younger workers, all other factors being equal.

Avoiding Back Injuries

There are many ways to avoid industrial back injuries. For example, work rules must take into account the fact that certain classifications such as diemakers may occasionally need to use power equipment to move heavy objects, even though they are not classified as power equipment operators. The availability of hydraulic lift tables and battery-powered transporters, as well as the occasional use of a fork-truck, should be permitted for any classification needing them as an alternative to heavy manual lifting.

The education program should emphasize the mechanical function of the spine and associated ligaments and muscles. Avoiding sudden or chronic overload damage should be repeated frequently as part of the safety education program.

Implement Ergonomic Improvements

Ergonomic improvements should be implemented wherever feasible. Usually the improvements are simple and low in cost. The employee doing the work should be involved in finding ways to make the job easier. Apart from humanitarian concerns, making the job less stressful usually increases productivity.

Figures 17-6 and *Figure 17-7* illustrate simple devices that help press

Figure 17-6. *One type of air-actuated tilting platform designed to permit press operators to retrieve parts without bending over. (Webster Manufacturing Co.)*

Figure 17-7. *An air-actuated tilting platform similar to the one illustrated in Figure 17-6 in use on a pressworking operation. (Webster Manufacturing Co.)*

operators avoid bending over to retrieve parts from a container. An air control valve permits the operator to increase the tilt of the air-actuated platform which permits easy access to the parts in the bottom of the container.

REFERENCES

1. Ford Motor Company, Stamping Engineering, "CT-20 J/M Die Design Standards," Body and Assembly Operations, Dearborn, Michigan, 1989.
2. David A. Smith, *Die Design Handbook*, Section 13, Society of Manufacturing Engineers, Dearborn, Michigan, 1990.

18

QUICK DIE CHANGE AT LIGHTOLIER*

JUSTIFICATION

In justifying the investment of significant capital funds, engineering professionals tend to review the measurable quantitative elements in terms of current costs and expected financial benefits and/or inventory reductions. A project is considered successful when these goals are met and the auditors close their books.

At Lightolier an evaluation was made of the benefits realized through the implementation of a quick die change system within a fabrication work cell. The project implementation was evaluated and some qualitative aspects of quick die change and their impact on the company were reviewed.

This is illustrated by a process analysis of the quick die change project including: funding prior to its implementation, the actual processing of implementation, and a review of benefits derived after the quick die change system was established.

BACKGROUND

Lightolier/Edison, a division of Genlyte, is a lighting fixture manufacturer supplying the New York City area. The primary products are recessed fluorescent fixtures. The major components of these fixtures are made of sheet metal parts produced in the fabrication department.

Prior to 1985, the manufacturing equipment in the fabrication department consisted of presses and brakes running individual operations and dies. A typical part routing would have various operations performed on each part (Table 18-1).

To follow this routing, the fabrication department would have to set up two presses and three brakes, to produce the part. This task could be accomplished by either setting up five different pieces of equipment at the same time and running each operation simultaneously or running each operation on the same machine. In both situations, the plant faces 21 hours of setup time and .069 hours/piece of run time for each run. The routing times represent accurate figures developed through a time study by Industrial Engineers for use in the company's incentive system. The setup times on the other hand are best guess estimates without the benefit of time study. Both times are illustrated in *Figure 18-1*.

*By Ismael Vicens, Project Manager, Lightolier, Division of Genlyte, Edison, New Jersey. Presented at: SME/FMA Quick Die Change Clinic, May 2-3, 1989, Detroit, Michigan.

TABLE 18-1
ROUTING: CHASSIS RIGHT HALF

Operation Number	Description	Rate Hrs/Pc.	Setup Hrs/Run
1000	BLANK & PIERCE	.004	2.5
1100	PIERCE KO'S	.003	2.5
1200	FORM	.004	2.0
1300	FORM	.004	2.0
1400	FINAL FORM	.004	2.0
1500	PAINT BLACK	.050	5.0
1600	PAINT WHITE	.100	5.0
7 operations		.169	21.0

Upon first review, it would seem that the implementation of quick die change would yield excellent results. However, there was not a capacity problem in spite of the many setups required. There were quite a few brakes and presses which could be set up with enough lead time to meet the production schedule.

The cost of converting all of the presses and brakes to quick die change along with standardizing the dies would be prohibitive. In this situation, the cost of modifying dies and equipment did not provide good candidates for cost reduction. A decision was made to change the manufacturing method which would reduce the number of different operations needed.

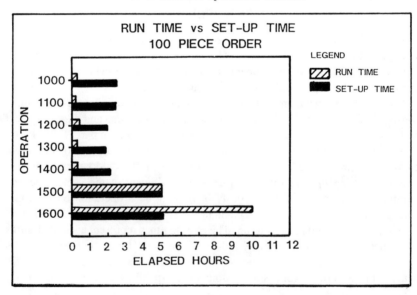

Figure 18-1. *Run time versus setup time for a 100 piece order before quick die change and tooling improvement.*

A QUICK DIE CHANGE OPPORTUNITY

The opportunity to improve the fabrication methods by eliminating many operations presented itself when the product was redesigned to take advantage of prefinished material. By using progressive dies, the run time involved in producing a finished chassis in 14 separate operations (including fabrication and finishing) to just one. *Figure 18-2* illustrates the change in routing after progressive dies were in use.

TABLE 18-2
ROUTING: CHASSIS RIGHT HALF (After Progressive Dies)

Operation Number	Description	Rate Hrs/Pc.	Setup Hrs/Run
1000	PRODUCT COMPLETE	.002	.25
1 operation		.002	.25

New Project Equipment Summary

To implement the new design and the progressive die technology the invested amount was over three million dollars in new equipment and included:
- Presses
- 600 ton (5.3 MN) press
- 250 ton (2.2 MN) press

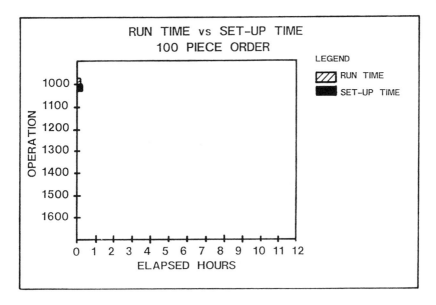

Figure 18-2. *Run time versus setup time for a 100 piece order after quick die change and progressive die tooling improvement.*

- Coil Feeds
- 60" DC feed
- 50" DC feed
- 60" straightener
- 50" straightener
- 12,000 lb (5455 kg) motorized reel
- 10,000 lb (4545 kg) non-motorized reel

Tooling

There were progressive dies for 17 different parts and they were produced from pre-painted steel or anodized aluminum. With this investment, the company offered an excellent product with very short lead times. This would seem to have solved the setup problems by simply eliminating most setups. This was not the case.

The problem was that these progressive dies would only run in the new presses. Press availability was limited. The company had over 17 dies, many of which had the capability to produce various versions of the same basic product.

Based on current projections, equipment utilization became a primary concern. The 250 ton (2.224 MN) press alone would have to run three shifts in order to keep up with demand if 2.5 hours were needed for setup between each run.

Fortunately, the equipment and dies were not yet ordered for this new project. This was the ideal opportunity to include quick die change technology into the plant. Facing the possibility of extended machine setup downtime, an investigation considered the options available in the field of quick die change. The evaluation included methods such as removable bolsters, auto-clamping, die-carts, lifters, etc. The most important discovery at this time was that the implementation of a quick die change system was far more complex than had been anticipated. There was a need to standardize items that were not considered.

ITEMS NEEDING STANDARDIZATION

The following items need standardization:
- Press height off the floor for the die cart.
- Bolster and ram tee slots for the clamps and lifters.
- Die pass line height to minimize adjustment.
- Die subplates to standardize for clamping positions and to provide "V-block" alignment in the press.
- Die shut height to minimize adjustment.
- Slug removal to standardize belts.
- Die centerline for coil positioning.

With so many variables, it was decided to utilize a turn-key supplier who could design and install the complete quick die change package. The selected supplier provided design specs for hydraulic, electrical lines and connections to the press manufacturer.

When the press arrived at the plant the installation was nearly 50% complete. Designs for subplates were provided to the tool vendors with instructions for die specifications relating to quick die change.

The die-cart was designed and specifications for tracks were supplied to the contractor installing all equipment. The quick die change vendor was prepared with clamps, lifters, and valves when the presses and coil feed systems were installed. The presses arrived with all controls for the clamps and lifters installed in the control panel which has greatly simplified their use.

When the tooling arrived most had been mounted to the standard subplates. Die cart installation was completed well within schedule and tests completed.

INSTALLATION

So it may sound as if this was a problem-free installation. In reality, the process was very challenging.

The press vendor was not accustomed to having a third party involved so intimately in press design and construction. This resulted in conflicts which required constant communication and at times some "refereeing." The traditional die vendors could not supply the large progressive dies for the project. The die vendors chosen were also unaccustomed to dealing with standard subplates, shut heights, pass line heights, slug removal and clamping locations. There was a mutual learning process involved which resulted in receiving the dies to specs and the die vendor being introduced to quick die change.

After successful installation of the equipment, a new problem emerged with methods development and personnel training. The quick die change systems were centered on each of the new presses. The 600 ton (5.338 MN) press would only have two major sets of dies requiring minimal setups.

The quick die change system which was installed to standardize the setup to handle large 15,000 pound (6818 kg) dies with die lifters with minimal effort. The exact location for accuracy of stock feeding and process repeatability was accomplished by means of installing "V-block" locators on the subplates as is illustrated in *Figure 18-3*.

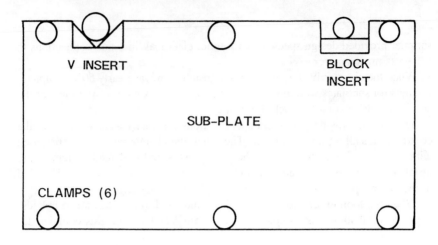

Figure 18-3. *Sub-plate used showing locating method and six hydraulic clamp locations.*

PRESS EQUIPMENT AND DIE CHANGING METHODS

600 Ton (5.338 MN) Press Equipment

The following quick die changing equipment is used on the 600 ton (5.338 MN) press:
1. Die lifters along bolster.
2. Removable hydraulic clamps on front.
3. Self-locating clamps on rear top.
4. Removable clamps on front of press.

Die Change Method for the 600 Ton (5.338 MN) Press

The following is the sequence of die change operations used on the 600 ton (5.338 MN) press:
1. Lower ram to bottom of stroke.
2. Release clamp pressure.
3. Remove top and bottom clamps to the front of press.
4. Raise ram to top of stroke.
5. Engage die lifters.
6. Position outriggers.
7. Retract die from press onto outriggers.
8. Remove die with truck and place in storage.
9. Place new die on outriggers.
10. Push die into press against "V-block."
11. Position bottom clamps.
12. Disengage die lifters.
13. Lower ram to bottom of stroke.
14. Position top clamps.
15. Engage clamp pressure.
16. Raise ram and load new material.

250 Ton (2.224 MN) Press Equipment

The 250 ton (2.224 MN) press would have the majority of dies and die changes. The decision was made to utilize more automation in the quick die change system for this press. Layout of the 250 ton (2.224 MN) press and associated quick die change equipment is illustrated in *Figure 18-4*. The following is a list of the quick die change equipment installed on this press:

1. Die lifters on bolster.
2. Swing clamps on top front and rear.
3. Removable clamps on bottom.
4. Two position powered die cart on tracks.
5. Four position die racks.
6. Outriggers as a bridge between press and cart.

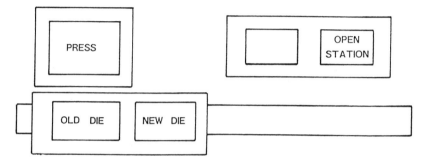

Figure 18-4. *Layout of 250 ton (2.224 MN) press and associated quick die change equipment.*

Die Change Method for the 250 Ton (2.224 MN) Press

The following is the sequence of die change operations used on the 250 ton (2.224 MN) press:

Prior to the end of current run:

1. Position next die on rack.
2. Position die cart in front of rack.
3. Load die onto second station in cart.

After the run is complete:

4. Lower ram to bottom of stroke.
5. Release clamps.
6. Raise ram to top of stroke.
7. Remove bottom front clamps.
8. Engage die lifters.
9. Position die-cart to first location.
10. Lock cart into position.
11. Lower die-cart pins.
12. Pull die onto die-cart.
13. Reposition die-cart and lock.

14. Push new die into press.
15. Move cart back to racks.
16. Lower ram to bottom of stroke.
17. Position bottom front clamps.
18. Disengage die lifters.
19. Engage all clamps.
20. Raise ram to top of stroke.
21. Load new material, start new run.
22. Position slug conveyors.

After the new run has been started:

23. Position die cart in front of empty rack.
24. Push die onto rack.
25. Inspect and store die.

Fine Tuning the System

These method descriptions reflect extensive work completed prior to the actual trial runs. During die trial runs, their location on subplates had to be fine tuned and then secured through pinning. Each die's shut height has been adjusted and noted on setup sheet so that fine adjustments can be made prior to lowering ram to bottom of stroke. All die parallels were permanently mounted for ease of slug removal. Die protection was standardized as were cam settings for pilot release.

Scheduling

Through the production scheduling department, a job list to be run must be prepared with sufficient lead time to allow for scheduling of dies in the press. An attempt was made to schedule common coil material from run-to-run to minimize coil changes. The purchasing department must now buy prepainted material which involve longer lead times.

RESULTS

When everything was accomplished, the new fixture was introduced to the sales staff. Rather than call them into a conference room and show a finished product, the equipment was demonstrated. All of the sales people and some of the corporate management gathered around the new work cell. The 600 ton (5.338 MN) press was producing a completely painted chassis at the rate of 25 per minute. The 250 ton (2.224 MN) press was producing one of the other parts.

A die change was then performed on the 250 ton (2.224 MN) press to demonstrate the ability to respond quickly to production shifts. The die change was completed in 10 minutes. The spectators, who had been used to 2.5 hour setups, were delighted with the demonstrated ability to meet the dates required by the customers.

Hidden Benefits

It has now been nearly four years since quick die change was implemented at Lightolier/Edison. Since then other plants in the corporation have also installed quick die change. The experience has shown some hidden benefits which quick die change has provided:

1. Die lifters have reduced back strain.
2. Setup personnel want quick die change everywhere.
3. Die design has improved dramatically.
4. New product justification is easier.
5. The delivery performance has improved.
6. Time standards are more accurate.
7. Die problems are solved out-of-press.
8. There is improved preplanning of projects.

Setup Personnel were Amazed

Setup personnel were amazed that they could move an 8,000 pound (3636 kg) die with one hand. Normally it would take two men to load and position a 2,000 pound (909 kg) die in the conventional presses. Setup personnel like quick die change at all presses for ease of handling dies and also because it simplifies their operation. In evaluating the need for reduced setup times, full shift observations of various setup operators were performed. The same die, set in the same press, with the same material, could delay from 1.5 hours to 3.5 hours in setup. This range was determined by various factors such as:

1. Which die had been in the press?
2. What type of tie-downs are needed?
3. Do the bolt holes need cleaning?
4. What was previous ram setting?
5. What press had die been on before?
6. Which die was worked on last?
7. Is another person available to help push the die into the press?

With quick die change none of these factors had a bearing on the time for setup. Because of the subplates, standard shut height and pass line height for each die is identical as far as die change is concerned. Since each die is on the die-cart or die-rack which includes die rollers, one person can easily move an 8,000 pound (3636 kg) die. The "V-block" inserts at the back of the die plate allow one person to properly position the die at the same time it is being placed in press.

Improved Planning and Scheduling

Prior to quick die change, the fabrication department would have to plan far enough in advance to set up three to four presses so that an operator would have a press to operate when the current job was completed. At times, the 2.5-hour set up would be complete when production control would change priorities and order a different job set. The press would then have to be reset with the new die at a cost of 2.5 more hours. This would create delays in production and also frustration of the setup employees and floor supervision. With quick die change, the next three jobs could be waiting on the staging racks. If production control changes priorities it is only a matter of positioning the die cart for the alternate choice. This flexibility allows for rapid production shifts without the incremental costs of setup hours.

Progress Since 1985. Progress has come a long way since 1985. The company developed from single hit dies in presses and brakes which required over two hours for each setup to progressive dies which can be changed in as little as 10 minutes.

The transition to a quick die change shop has been facilitated by including the change required by a new product introduction with new equipment and tooling. By taking advantage of the opportunity to implement quick die change within a new work cell, the company utilized the turn-key services of the quick die change vendor who would coordinate purchase and installation of quick die change items with other capital equipment. By introducing both the new product tooling and the quick die change equipment to the employees at the same time, the training of the setup personnel and staff was simplified.

The success in the new quick die change work cell allowed the company to expand quick die change to the conventional fabrication department. As new products are developed, all tooling will be purchased with the standards developed for quick die change built-in. In the not too distant future, the majority of products made will be produced on quick die change tooling and equipment.

19

DESIGN THE SYSTEM TO
MATCH YOUR NEEDS*

FACTORS TO CONSIDER

The cost of an idle and expensive stamping press can usually be considered a poor investment. It's true that when stamping parts, a method to reduce lengthy die changes and setups is essential. However, factors beyond stamping production parts can demonstrate the value of quick die change. Justification for a press line, even at the expense of having excess capacity, can sometimes depend on having quick die change capability. One such case surfaced at Inter-City Products while planning production of a new air conditioning line.

The need was determined by several underlying factors for purchasing a four-press automated stamping line. Without quick die change, the system would not have been successful. A comparison of earlier manufacturing methods and part costs were made with the automated system. This illustrates that a wise decision was made.

The quick die change system is directly responsible for part cost reduction. The justification for the system was based on this projected cost decrease.

Careful system planning and lay out is important to a successful installation. Possible future expansion is also considered in the design. Planning and setting up a new press line is a difficult undertaking. Problems will be encountered and planning for them is essential to keep a project on schedule. A workable system requires that both a preventive maintenance and thorough training program be in place.

A CHALLENGE TO REDUCE INVENTORIES

Introducing a newly designed product to the market place offers many opportunities for method improvements in all corporate divisions. The success of the product depends on all divisions meeting these challenges from marketing to manufacturing. Everyone has to perform as a team.

One such opportunity for improving the manufacturing method was provided by the introduction of a new air conditioning line. The need was to reduce the

*Based on SME Technical Paper MF90-120, presented at SME Quick Die Change Clinic, December 5-6, Nashville, Tennessee, by James H. Woodard, Manager, Tooling and Equipment, Inter-City Products Corporation, Lewisburg, Tennessee.

235

response time between the receipt of a customer order and building the unit on the assembly line. This would eliminate large stock quantities of each model in the warehouse. One outdoor unit is produced in more than 60 unique models.

To accomplish the objective, it was necessary to configure the assembly line so that a model change could be made without missing a single unit at the designed production rate. Model changes were made often with as many as five or six within one shift.

This presented problems in supplying manufactured parts and stampings to the line. All models fall within one of three basic chassis sizes. Each chassis' appearance is similar but each has a progressively larger foot print and height. Since the base and the top of each chassis are the two largest pieces of sheet metal in the unit, they also presented the largest problems for flexible stamping.

THE OLD WAY OF PRODUCING PARTS

Part Size Considerations

The three sizes of bases and tops, six parts in all, are formed as single piece parts. Each stamping required four operations. Past experience suggested that 24 dies would be required. Certainly a smaller number of dies would be desirable. Since the blank size of the largest base is 37 in^2. (940 mm^2), individual dies are more manageable.

Routing of Work-in-Progress

The old method of manufacturing would start by shearing the blanks and delivering them to the point of the first stamping operation. The second, third and fourth operations could be set up in additional presses if scheduling requirements would permit their availability. Often the same press may be used by changing dies between operations. Either way, the blanks would be hand-fed into the die. The operation was performed and the partially completed part would then either be placed on a skid or into a container and transported to either another manufacturing location or to storage.

For economic reasons, several thousand parts would often be stamped and stored for future use to minimize the effects of costly die changes and setups. This resulted in a large amount of work-in-process, lengthening the total cycle time for each part. At this point, operating costs, some of which are very hard to control, start accumulating rapidly.

Part Cost Factors

Sometimes several days will pass from the time a blank leaves the Shear Department until the part is used. During this time, the part probably would have

236

been moved and handled several times. Over-runs made it necessary to stock parts not used for weeks or even months. As partly completed stampings were moved from operation to operation, damage often occurred. Some damage could be reworked but such repair operations were very costly. If too many parts were damaged and scrapped, it was sometimes necessary to cut short a production run on the assembly line.

There was also the cost of returning both purchased and fabricated parts to inventory. Each time a part is handled without adding value, it adds cost. Each time a part is handled there is a risk of damage. It takes valuable factory space to provide adequate storage for all of the parts in various stages of completion. Not only can this type of stamping process be costly in direct labor, all of the contingencies add to the burden that is absorbed into the total cost of the product.

THE STAMPING LINE IS THE BEGINNING OF THE ASSEMBLY LINE

Basic System Requirements

Investigations seeking the most cost effective manufacturing process point out four conditions that should be satisfied:

1. The parts should be automatically transferred from one operation to the next.
2. The finished quantity of bases produced should equal the finished quantity of tops produced.
3. The bases and tops should be produced only as they are needed on the assembly line.
4. The parts should be delivered directly to the assembly line.

This suggests that the stamping line for bases and tops as well as the paint system be considered part of the assembly line. It further suggests that excessive change over time from one chassis size to another could not be tolerated.

Presses and Automation

The stamping system is compatible with systems either already in place or added to the system. It also satisfies the conditions desired. The line illustrated in *Figure 19-1* employs four 600 ton (5338 kN) presses, automatic destacker, a combined lube roll coater and loader, press-to-press transfers, and a quick die change system. Blanks are sheared and stored in a special rack near the crane saver and destacker. Enough blanks to run several hours can be stored in the rack, though it is not necessary. Stacks of blanks are transferred to the crane saver as needed.

A base and a matching top are produced simultaneously through the stamping system. Two blanks at a time, one for the base and one for the top, are fed into the first press from the destacker and lube roll coater. Parts are transferred automatically from press-to-press and an exit conveyor moves the parts a short

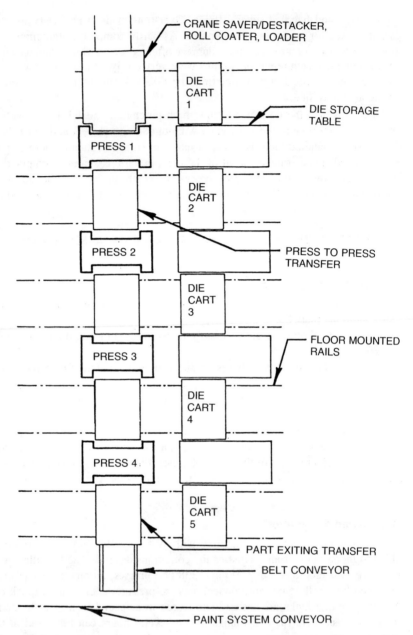

CRANE SAVER/DESTACKER,
ROLL COATER, LOADER

DIE
CART
1

DIE STORAGE
TABLE

PRESS 1

DIE
CART
2

PRESS 2

PRESS TO PRESS
TRANSFER

DIE
CART
3

PRESS 3

FLOOR MOUNTED
RAILS

DIE
CART
4

PRESS 4

DIE
CART
5

PART EXITING TRANSFER

BELT CONVEYOR

PAINT SYSTEM CONVEYOR

Figure 19-1. *Layout of automated four press line for producing air conditioner chassis bases and tops simultaneously, including quick die changing equipment and die storage tables.*

distance to the paint system's monorail conveyor.

Figure 19-2 illustrates the sequence of operations from blank storage to the

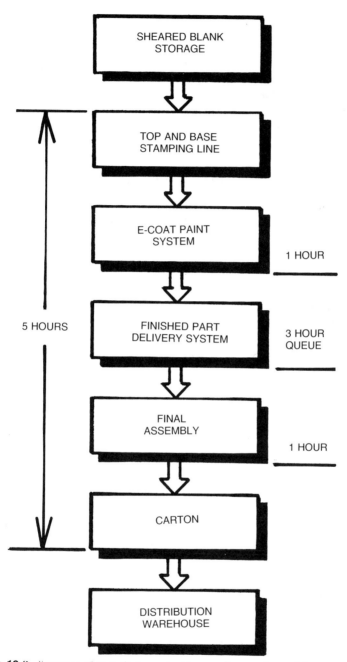

Figure 19-2. *Sequence of operations required to manufacture air conditioners. Illustrates the stamping line's integration with the total manufacturing system.*

239

warehousing of the finished units. The paint system requires approximately one hour. After leaving the paint conveyor, the finished bases and tops go to a special parts delivery system that holds approximately a three hour queue. Bases are delivered to the head of the assembly line and tops are delivered to their assembly station. The unit, after assembly and testing, is placed in a carton and taken directly to the distribution warehouse. A pair of sheet metal blanks fed into the first stamping press is completed in less than five hours as the base and top of a finished air conditioner.

THE QUICK DIE CHANGE SYSTEM

The need to change models quickly when dealing with 24 dies means that quick die change capability is a must. The entire manufacturing process would not work as planned without it.

Subplate System

The dies are divided into pairs with a base die and top die for each chassis size and operation mounted on a common subplate *Figure 19-3*. This reduced the number of units to 12. The 12 pairs of dies are segregated into four groups by operation. Each press then has three pairs of dies that must be stored, moved, and mounted.

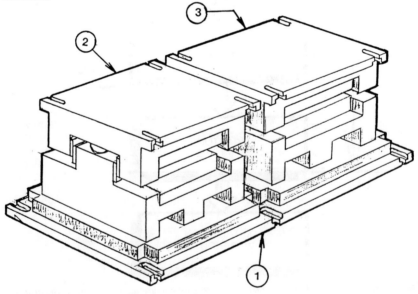

Figure 19-3. *Two dies mounted on a common subplate: (1) subplate with slots for automatic die clamps. (2) chassis base die. (3) chassis top die.*

Die Handling and Storage

Four die storage tables, each with space for two pairs of dies are located at the side of each press. Five die carts move on rails mounted in the floor and traverse from a position aligned with the presses to either of the two positions adjacent to the die storage tables. The rails extend beyond the presses and serve as guides for the press-to-press transfers and the part exiting. The crane saver, destacker, lube roll coater and loader are on a common wheeled frame. They can be moved out of the working position on a pair of rails running parallel and on the center line of the presses.

The four presses are mounted below the floor level partially down into a pit which runs under the entire line. Running the entire length, in the pit, is a scrap conveyor. At one end of the pit a scrap elevator lifts scrap out and into a mobile scrap container.

The three central die carts have dual latching mechanisms that engage brackets on the die subplates and reach into the press on both the front and rear of the cart. Up to five die carts have single latches toward the presses only.

To prepare for a die change, the next set of dies should be identified and loaded onto die carts. The carts are numbered two through five with the dies for press one on cart two, dies for press two on cart three and so on. When the current production run is complete, the system is cleared of parts through a special shut down sequence. The combination destacker and roll coater is moved back out of the way. The press-to-press transfer units and the part exiting the transfer unit are moved to the side where it will be out of the way. The die's air and electrical quick connectors must be disconnected.

Die Clamping

Each press is equipped with hydraulic die clamps. The lower subplate is secured with six special die clamp cylinders and eight clamps in each press ram secure the two top die shoes.

When changing dies, all presses are jogged to the bottom of the stroke. The quick die clamps holding the top die shoes are then cycled to release and retract. The press rams are then raised to top of stroke. The lower quick die clamps are now cycled to unlock and lower. At this point, each die is lifted a slight amount above the bolster plate by tee-slot mounted roller lift units.

Exchanging Dies

The number one die cart is moved into position and secured with an automatic shot pin. The die latch mechanism on the die cart is actuated and secured to the die subplate. The number two through five die carts are then moved into their respective change positions and secured in the same manner as number one. The second of the dual latching mechanisms of cart two, three, and four can be actuated to engage the subplate latches of the dies in presses two, three, and four respectively.

The first of the dual latches is already secured to the die subplate on each cart. The die unloader on die cart one is actuated pulling the pair of dies in press one on to the cart. The die loader on die cart two is energized removing the dies from press two and loading dies into press one in one movement. The loader on carts three, four, and five are likewise actuated so that all four pairs of dies are now in position in their respective presses and all die pairs being removed are on die carts one through four. The latch mechanisms can be disengaged and the five die carts can be moved back to the side.

Carts one through four are then moved to the empty spot adjacent to the die storage tables and the dies rolled on to the tables for storage until needed later. The tables have safety catches that will not allow the die to move unless the die cart is in place and the loader latches are engaged. The press tee-slot roller lifts are lowered when the bottom and upper quick die clamps are cycled after lowering the press rams.

Automation Setup and Adjustment

The air and electrical connections are then coupled and the part transfers returned to the operating position. The combined destacker and roll coater is then moved up and blanks of the correct size are placed onto the crane saver.

Fine adjustments are made to the part transfer units after they are moved to pre-selected locations and pinned. The stamping system is now ready to be placed back into production. The entire die change can be completed in 30 minutes.

PROJECT COSTS

The entire stamping line project cost amounted to approximately $6.2 million. The quick die change, including the die clamping supplied on the presses, was nearly $400,000 or about 6% of the total project cost. What must be considered though is the savings brought about by the quick die change capability. Each production change, with the automated system, requires two persons to spend 30 minutes changing dies or one labor hour.

Labor Costs to Change the Old System

Consider the old manufacturing process. The old system would require a die truck operator, a die setter and perhaps a toolroom technician. Twelve dies would be manually removed from the presses and returned to storage and then 12 different dies set. Adjustments would have to be made to support equipment. This could easily amount to 20 minutes per die change totaling four hours in actual time. With an average of two and one-half people this amounted to 10 labor hours. If one change per work day was performed, a total of 2,500 labor hours per year would be expended just for die changes. This increased nonproductive costs considerably.

Analysis of Direct Labor Costs

The direct labor comparison is equally unbalanced. The automated line runs at a speed of 10 strokes per minute. Two parts per stroke places the gross productivity at 20 parts per minute. With a conservative projection of 80% up-time, a net productivity of 7,360 parts could be produced in one eight-hour shift. Compare this with the process used in the past. Four operations in four separate presses per part could amount to a rate of 10 minutes per 100 parts total. To equal the output of 7,300 parts per shift for two operators, it would take four people approximately five shifts. This is perhaps a little misleading since the requirements do not approach the 7,300 parts per shift but what is important is that with the manual feed process the maximum output possible is about 1,300 tops and 1,300 bases per shift. That's very near the present requirements. This means any growth would require additional capital and tooling using the manual feed process. With the automatic stamping line, new capacity allows growth in output of finished products with no additional capital or tooling expenditure.

With all factors considered, it was estimated that the automated stamping line would result in approximately a half million dollars in savings per year based on today's volumes. The investment difference required was approximately three million dollars. The automated system was $6.2 million and the conventional one was more than three million for capital and tooling.

THERE WERE PROBLEMS

A large project such as the planning and installation of this stamping line is certain to require solving a few unanticipated problems. Contingency plans should be considered to avoid delays in the production start-up phase of the project.

Tooling and Automation Problems

The tooling itself required extra work to produce quality parts. This had to be accomplished while de-bugging all of the automation changes.

There was a problem of sensor failures located in the automatic die clamps. This was found to be caused by a chemical reaction between the stamping lubricant and zinc fines from the material being processed. This and many other problems were all solved. The resolution did take more time than was anticipated due to the complexity of the system.

Die Cleaning Problems

Another consideration was any special die cleaning problems. This should have been addressed at the conception of the project. The dies weigh nearly five tons (4536 kg) each. Two dies on their subplate approach a weight of 10 tons (9072 kg). It is difficult to move the dies to another location for cleaning. The zinc fines from the galvanized material are especially difficult to clean from the louvering dies. A special cleaning facility for such activities should have been considered and included in the project.

TRAINING REQUIREMENTS

Training is of great importance on a project such as this. Typically, training sessions for operators, maintenance, and supervisory personnel do not begin until a project such as this is near completion. This will not provide enough time for proper training.

Scope of Training

When a manufacturing process is planned and is much more complex than previous methods, it is necessary to begin training before the equipment installation is started. Training should be provided for anyone who is involved with the system. In this case, it included everyone from material schedulers to equipment clean-up people. Success is assured by making people aware that they are a part of the team that is responsible for a smooth start-up.

Preventive Maintenance Training

Because there is not a large inventory of parts ready to go to the assembly line, the stamping line cannot be allowed to break down. A preventive maintenance program carried out by well-trained people must have confidence both in themselves and in the equipment.

Sophisticated automation alone is not enough. Reliable and well-trained people are what make success possible.

20

QUICK DIE CHANGE AT GM BOC LANSING FABRICATION*

Lansing Fabrication is a major fabrication facility of the General Motors Corporation. The workforce comprises 3,000 hourly and 375 salaried employees. In addition to sheet metal stampings and assembly, composites also are produced.

Necessity of Quick Die Change

Quick die change began with the start of the GM-20 project to produce the "N" car starting with the 1984 Model Year. This basic body type was incorporated into the Pontiac Grand Am, Oldsmobile Calais, and the Buick Skylark.

This ambitious project resulted in the number of dies to be set from 998 to 1,664, a 60% increase. This project also entailed a 40% increase in total plant content and necessitated a three-shift operation.

Emphasis of Small Lot Sizes and Improved Manufacturing Methods

Goals for the GM-20 project included:
• World class manufacturing in terms of quality and cost.
• The ability to change dies quickly.
• First hit quality control approval.
• Realizing a savings by running smaller lot sizes.

IMPLEMENTING THE QUICK DIE CHANGE PROGRAM

Visiting Other Plants

Both hourly and salaried employees went to other U.S. companies and gathered information on their methods, organization, and equipment. Five Japanese automotive companies and six tool and equipment companies were also visited by the teams.

Scripts detailed work and of each person's responsibility during a changeover.

*Presented at SME Quick Die Change Clinic, May 2-3, 1989 in Detroit, Michigan by Robert I. Johnson, Director of Manufacturing Engineering, and Gary Cousins, UAW Uptime Coordinator, BOC Lansing Fabrication, General Motors Corporation, Lansing, Michigan.

Initial Improvement

With the support of many people in all departments, progress was continuously evaluated, and improvements made. *Figure 20-1* illustrates how many plant activities provide support for the die change cycle control program.

A plan for each of the elements involved in quick die change was developed. As a result, the setup time on the trial line had gone from over four hours to less than 30 minutes. *Figure 20-2* demonstrates the dramatic drop in the time required to die change-over. The script *(Figure 20-3)* was developed for the first trial operation which produces outer hoods on a four-press, 144 in. (3.66 m) wide Danly press line.

At this point, with a true success story accomplished, the program began to expand to other press lines and other work shifts.

Problem solving meetings were held by the teams. Problems were brainstormed with the aid of fish bone diagrams *(Figure 20-4)* and pareto charts. From this information, obstacle lists were formed. The hourly person familiar with the line recorded problems observed by fellow workers. Items requiring correction were assigned to the proper organization. The teams developed and implemented plans to reduce or eliminate obstacles.

At this point in time, the Japanese quick die change expert Shigeo Shingo

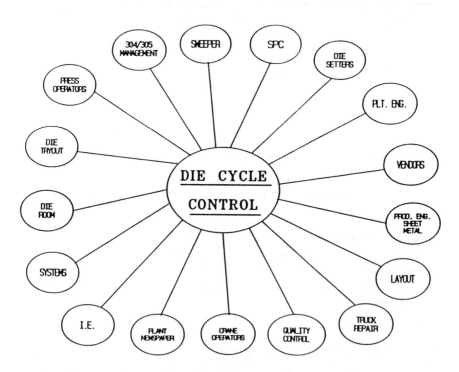

Figure 20-1. *Many plant activities provide support for the die change cycle-control time-reauction program. (General Motors Corp.)*

DIE TRANSITION IMPROVEMENT TRIAL LINE

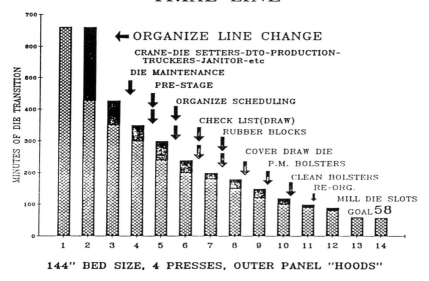

Figure 20-2. *An illustration of the dramatic time decrease for change-over in a trial line during the initial phase of a quick die change program. (General Motors Corp.)*

visited the Lansing, Michigan facility.

Mr. Shingo is a consultant and in-plant training expert who reviewed the front-body hinge-pillar manual-press line to see the program's accomplishments in reducing the die change cycle. He stated the importance of video filming the die changes for people to critique their own moves and methods. Mr. Shingo also emphasized the need to continually move internal actions to the external portions of the die change.

By using video equipment to record and critique, the diesetting operations showed many opportunities to increase the performance in setting dies without the use of automatic equipment.

After an initial benchmark was established, several rounds of improvements were made based on the conversion of internal dieset tasks into external dieset tasks. Where possible, tasks were eliminated. The emphasis was on streamlining all aspects of the setup operation.

Continuous Improvement

Refining the execution of every required task was emphasized. The Shigeo Shingo visit gave renewed interest and confidence toward reaching this goal. Areas for employee involvement were identified and quick die change teams formed.

247

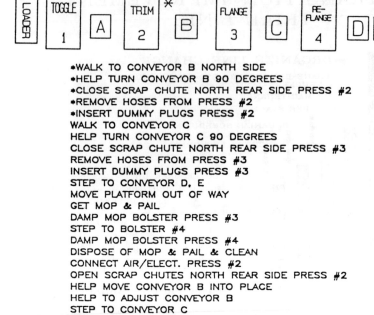

* WALK TO CONVEYOR B NORTH SIDE
* HELP TURN CONVEYOR B 90 DEGREES
* CLOSE SCRAP CHUTE NORTH REAR SIDE PRESS #2
* REMOVE HOSES FROM PRESS #2
* INSERT DUMMY PLUGS PRESS #2
WALK TO CONVEYOR C
HELP TURN CONVEYOR C 90 DEGREES
CLOSE SCRAP CHUTE NORTH REAR SIDE PRESS #3
REMOVE HOSES FROM PRESS #3
INSERT DUMMY PLUGS PRESS #3
STEP TO CONVEYOR D, E
MOVE PLATFORM OUT OF WAY
GET MOP & PAIL
DAMP MOP BOLSTER PRESS #3
STEP TO BOLSTER #4
DAMP MOP BOLSTER PRESS #4
DISPOSE OF MOP & PAIL & CLEAN
CONNECT AIR/ELECT. PRESS #2
OPEN SCRAP CHUTES NORTH REAR SIDE PRESS #2
HELP MOVE CONVEYOR B INTO PLACE
HELP TO ADJUST CONVEYOR B
STEP TO CONVEYOR C
OPEN SCRAP CHUTE NORTH REAR SIDE PRESS #3
HELP MOVE CONVEYOR C INTO PLACE
HELP ADJUST CONVEYOR C
STEP TO CONVEYOR D, E
HELP MOVE CONVEYOR D, E INTO PLACE

NOTE: * MIGHT BE DONE BY DIESETTERS

Figure 20-3. *The script for the die change on 1010 line. (General Motors Corp.)*

Factors that Contributed to Long Changeover Times

Employees developed a list of factors contributing to long die transition times. Solutions to the problems also were identified. Some examples of problems and solutions are:

Problem: —Long mechanical portion of the tool changeover.
Solution: —Elimination of adjustments.

Problem: —Lack of die readiness to make a good part.
Solution: —Last part analysis, a die tracking system and a die maintenance system.

Problem: —Lack of press readiness to perform after die change.
Solution: —Form a separate press preventive maintenance (P.M.) group and form a P.M. Program for each line; one week per year.

Problem: —Lack of ability to verify part quality.
Solution: —Provide captive tryout presses for die verification.

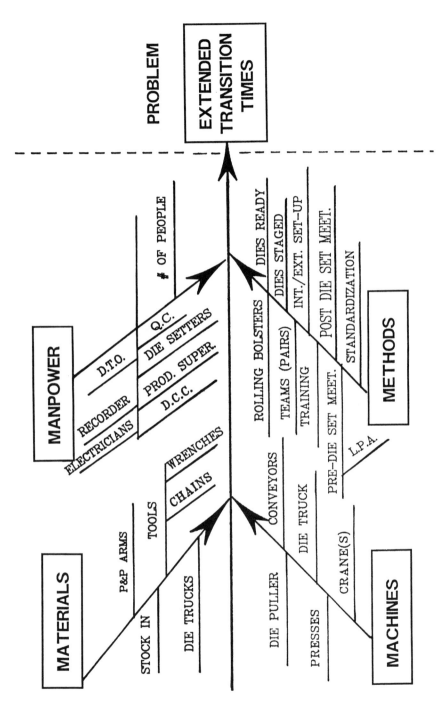

Figure 20-4. *A fish bone diagram used by quick die change teams to analyze the problem of excessively long die transition times. (General Motors Corp.)*

Problem:	—Poor communications with people concerning time-related problems with die transitions.
Solution:	—Properly trained workforce: training in all aspects of quick die transition.
Problem:	—Housekeeping concerns.
Solution:	—A place for everything and everything in its place.

WITH THE "FACTORS" IDENTIFIED—WHERE TO GO FROM HERE?

After identifying many issues to address in the task analysis, two views were taken. The first was to obtain the necessary capital to correct those problems that only money could fix. The second, was to implement several needed programs in which hourly people could assist in developing, and later run.

Hardware Solutions

First, money was allocated for revision to the existing dies to standardize shut height so that press ram adjustment would be eliminated during die change. This would save valuable time during the die transition. Also, other machining work was done to the dies so that it was possible to position them in the press exactly in the same place every time.

Second, press revision money was allocated for the installation of positive locators in the press bed. Digital shut-height indicators were installed on some presses. Another important press modification was to equip the inner ram of all of the double-action toggle presses with automatic die clamps. This was a very cost-effective time saver.

Third, new lightweight part handling conveyors were obtained for the medium press group. Previously, it took six people to remove and replace the conveyor used between the presses during a die change.

The fourth expenditure was for several 10-ton (889-kN) gantry cranes in the die repair facility. This eliminated the problems of skilled die makers waiting for the large overhead crane to assist them in removing die pads and small die details when working on dies. An electric die cart was purchased, which runs through the plant, to shuttle or transport dies coming and going to the die repair facility and storage.

Human Resource Solutions

The second direction was "people-related programs." Human resource utilization needed improvement to attain the goal of accomplishing world-class die transitions.

The die tag program is a good example. One hourly person per shift tracks the movement and maintenance activities of over 1,000 dies. They update a computerized database from the information on the die tags, which contain the latest maintenance requirements or work completed on any one of the dies. With the aid of a computer, all of the dies can be tracked for their location and status.

RESULTS AND CONTINUED IMPROVEMENTS

The *Automotive Industries* Die Change Challenge

An accomplishment that is the pride of BOC fabrication workforce, is the outstanding reduction of changeover times. This was shown in the battle of the quick die change teams sponsored by *Automotive Industries* magazine. The classes of lines for change-over in the competition included a manually set line, a semiautomated line with sliding bolsters and manual clamping, and a line equipped for automated changeover with sliding bolsters and automatic clamping. The changeover reduction times are illustrated in *Figure 20-5*.

Comparing Quick Die Change to Slow Die Change

Figure 20-6 illustrates the remarkable reduction in line changeover times that a disciplined team-oriented workforce can accomplish. Many improvements in methods such as separating internal from external dieset and operating the dies at a common shut height have contributed to making this possible.

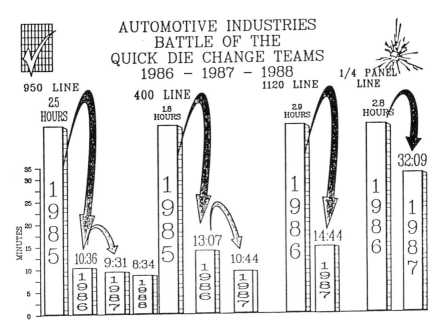

Figure 20-5. *Continuous improvement of changeover time in the Automotive Industries magazine sponsored annual quick die change competition. (General Motors Corp.)*

251

QUICK DIE CHANGE VS. SLOW DIE CHANGE

1. Production stops
2. Rams come down
3. Clamps come off dies
4. Rams go up
5. Bolsters slides out of presses
6. New bolster slide in
7. Rams come down
8. Clamps go on dies
9. Automation changed (if needed)
10 Production resumes
11 Overhead crane takes dies to storage

TOTAL TIME: 5-10 MINUTES

1. Production stops
2. Rams come down
3. Workers look for wrenches
4. Clamps come off dies
5. Rams come down
6. Bolsters slide out
7. Overhead crane takes die to storage
8. Break time: 10 min.
9. Die spotter looks for new dies in die storage room
10. Overhead crane brings new dies to press line
11. Die setters start bolting dies to the bolsters
12. Lunch time: 30 min.
13. Bolsters slide into press
14. Ram height adjusted for new die
15. Workers look for other wrenches
16. Clamps go on dies
17. Automation is changed
18. 3-4 panels run through draw die; if not ok, call die repairmen
19. Break time: 10 min.
20. Run more panels, adjust dies and automation accordingly
21. Production resumes

TOTAL TIME: 6-10 HOURS

Figure 20-6. *The sequence of events of quick die change versus slow die change. (General Motors Corp.)*

A rigorous preventive maintenance program also is required. Without a top-notch maintenance program, the many hydraulic and electro-pneumatic systems required on any press equipped for automatic quick die change will deteriorate and fail.

Future Plans

The continuous improvement process that the teams have in place refine the process even further. The "successes" are being expanded to other areas of the operations.

Obtaining a quality panel after a quick die changeover is a vital aspect of maintaining a high level of up-time or capacity utilization.

The joint process of continuous improvement and process variability reduction is necessary to make the plant remain competitive in a world class market. To do this, process performance is measured to gain control and improvement.

Business depends on the ability to produce high-quality parts when the customer needs them, at a competitive price. Die cycle control will help meet that challenge.

21

AUTOMATIC DIE CHANGE AT MAZDA*

INTRODUCTION

A challenging new market demands that manufacturers search for innovative methods of reducing costs and achieving higher quality standards. One method which obtains these goals is automatic die change (ADC).

An Example of Automatic Die Change Equipment

To illustrate the concept of automatic die change, one stamping line at Mazda Motor Manufacturing (USA) Corporation has been selected as an example. It is known internally as A Line, and is the most intricate and complex line within the stamping plant. It includes a blank de-stacker, a double action press with a mechanically linked loader and extractor, a turnover segment and a 2649 ton (23.565 MN) transfer press. An illustration of this line is shown in *Figure 21-1*.

Elements of Automatic Die Change

Automatic die change is the result of four elements working in coordination with one another. These elements are the facility layout, computer integrated manufacturing, external staging, and employee integration. The interaction between, and coordination with, each of these elements produces effective and efficient automatic die changes. The short time required to set the next dies makes small lot size production runs economically feasible.

FACILITY LAYOUT

One of the first items which must be considered to achieve successful automatic die change capabilities is the facility layout. The goal of any layout for a process should be to maximize the efficiency of that process. Effective facility layouts utilize the available human resources to their fullest potential and provide efficient material flow. This can be realized through careful planning and thoughtful consideration of the tasks which the employee must complete.

Efficient Die Handling

An example of an automatic die change facility layout is illustrated in *Figure 21-2*. Two obvious advantages in the layout as compared to many older

---

*Contributed by Ray Hedding, Stamping Plant and Area Manager, and David D. Couch, Stamping Plant Staff Member, Mazda Motor Manufacturing (USA) Corporation, Flat Rock, Michigan. This case study is based on the paper, "Automatic Die Change: Success Through The Integration of Teamwork and Technology." The paper was presented at the SME Clinic "Effective Techniques and Tooling for Quick Die Change", December 5-6, 1989, Nashville, Tennessee.

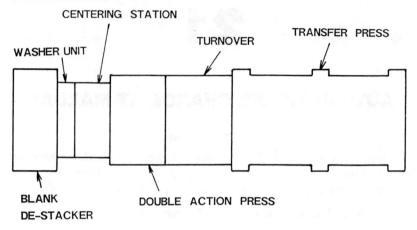

Figure 21-1. *Block diagram of transfer Line A. (Mazda Motor Manufacturing (USA) Corp.)*

automotive stamping plants can be noted. First, the overhead service crane is located in the same bay as is the die storage area and presses. This layout permits the straight transfer of dies between the die storage area and the moving bolsters without any intermediate trucking.

Moving Press Bolsters

Two moving bolsters are supplied for each operation. These operations include the double action press, turnover, and both slides of the transfer press. This layout allows the external staging of each operation while production is still running. Once a die change is required, the moving bolsters simultaneously move the new job into the press as the old job moves out *(Figure 21-2)*.

Automated Blank Storage and Transportation

The flow of material is controlled by an automatic guided vehicle (AGV) system which features both automatic storage and retrieval. This system offers quick response times and high repeatability. Repeatability is a measure of the capacity of an operation to achieve the same outcome of events under similar conditions. In this example, *high repeatability* refers to the AGV system capacity to control the position of the pallets with very little variation in their location.

An automatic stacker crane stores material after it has been blanked and until it is required for use by a line. When a line requests the material, it is done so through a terminal at the line. This terminal is directly linked with the automatic guided vehicle system's control computer. The computer then locates the material in the storage system where it is picked up by the automatic stacker crane and delivered to the line by the automatic guided vehicle carrier.

Upon delivery of the full pallet, the carrier will also retrieve the empty pallet from the blank de-stacker and return it to the system. A block diagram of this system including the material ordering communication network is shown in *Figure 21-3*.

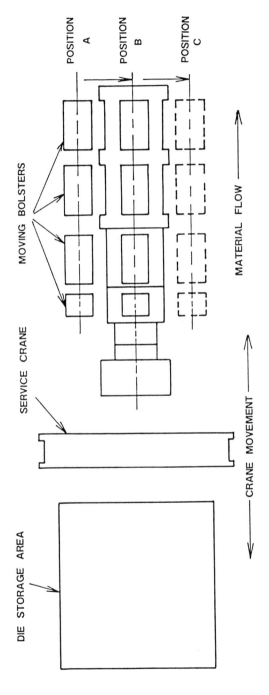

Figure 21-2. Layout of die storage area in relationship to transfer press line equipped with air moving bolsters. (Mazda Motor Manufacturing (USA) Corp.) As the bolsters at position A move into the press, the bolsters inside of the press (position B) move out of the press to position C. The die change is completely automated, and requires less than five minutes.

257

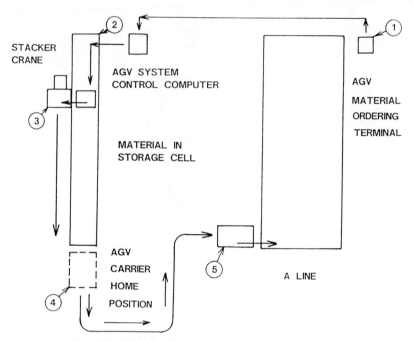

Figure 21-3. *Block diagram of material ordering communications network showing sequence of stock retrieval events: (1) AGV material ordering terminal where the stock is ordered; (2) AGV system control computer locates the material; (3) material is loaded onto the stacker crane and placed on the AGV carrier; (4) the material is transported to the line; (5) the pallet is unloaded from the AGV carrier to the blank destacker. (Mazda Motor Manufacturing (USA) Corp.)*

COMPUTER INTEGRATED MANUFACTURING

Computer Terminals at the Line

Each line has a production scheduling terminal at a convenient location. The job priority level for each line is displayed on this terminal. Each job is listed in priority according to their inventory levels and usage rates by the Body & Assembly Plant. This information permits the line operator to determine which blanks should be ordered through the automatic guided vehicle system prior to the start of an automatic die change.

The Programmable Logic Controller Network

A network of programmable logic controllers (PLCs) and a personal computer at each line makes it possible to arrange preset data files for each part. This type of computer integration into the manufacturing environment greatly enhances productivity, diminishes the possibility for human error, and reduces the time required to perform an automatic die change. These data files contain the process parameters which must be adjusted during a die change to compensate for the different part sizes and configurations which may be produced. The individual part files are downloaded into the programmable logic controller registers from the personal computer before an automatic die change is executed. Programmable logic controllers then automatically adjust the process variables to their predetermined settings for that part.

MAJOR FUNCTIONAL GROUPS CONTROLLED BY PLCs

Four major functional groups are controlled by the programmable logic controllers. These are the blank de-stacker, double action press, turnover segment, and the transfer press.

Blank De-Stacker

During production, the blank de-stacker unloads material from pallets one sheet at a time. The pallets of blanks delivered by the automatic guided vehicle (AGV) are unloaded and indexed, into position, and centered within the blank de-stacker.

Special blank fanning magnets known as magnetic floaters are automatically positioned to contact the material on the pallet. These magnets serve to separate the individual sheets of material to allow easy pick-up by the vacuum cups.

The vacuum cups are extended downward until they contact the material. The material is raised upward until it is attracted to an overhead magnetic conveyor. The material is released by the vacuum cups and the magnetic conveyor indexes the material into the washer unit. Upon exiting the washer unit, six adjustable motor driven gages center the material on a roller table from which the blank is then loaded into the double action press.

Sequence of Operation During an ADC. There are three pallet stations within the blank de-stacker. The first station holds the material when it is unloaded from the AGV carrier until the pallet at the second station is empty or finished. The second station is where the actual destacking takes place. From the second station, empty or finished pallets are indexed to the third station where they are picked-up by an AGV carrier and returned to the automatic storage/ retrieval system.

Before an ADC, the second station is left empty with the next part's material waiting in the first station. This material is automatically indexed to station two, centered, and lifted into position upon the start of the ADC. This assures that the correct material is in place for the next job.

The vacuum cups, magnetic floaters, and centering gage positions are computer selected from the ADC data file. The vacuum cups are computer selected from a four by ten rectangular array. The cup selection is determined by the blank pattern.

The magnetic floaters are selected from a bank of nine. The number selected and their location is dependent upon the sheet size, weight, and pattern.

The centering station gages center the sheet accurately before it is picked-up by the double action press loader. The location of these gages is adjustable and is dependent upon the sheet size and shape. The accuracy of gage adjustment at this station is critical to assure accurate blank loading into the double action press dies.

Double Action Press

The double action press is used exclusively for drawing material. This press features two separately acting slides called the inner slide and outer slide, or blank holder.

Sequence of Operation. The material is loaded via a mechanically interlocked loader. This loader picks the material up from the roller table and places it in the die. The press cycles, and the part is removed by a mechanically interlocked extractor.

Sequence of Operation During an ADC. First, both the loader and extractor are fully retracted and locked into position to avoid any interference and the die cushion is lowered. The upper slides are lowered to bottom dead center and the upper die clamps are released. The upper slides then rise and the computer selected die height adjustments begin.

The die height adjustment data is contained in the ADC data file. The accuracy of adjustment is ± 0.004 in. (0.10 mm). The loader mechanism cups and jaws are also selected automatically.

Next, the moving bolster unclamps and the safety gates rise. Once the safety gates are locked in their up positions, both moving bolsters with dies in place simultaneously move out of and into the press. The bolster is clamped hydraulically to secure its position inside the press, all pneumatic lines are pressurized, and the safety gates close.

The upper slides then automatically lower to the present die heights and stop at bottom dead center. Motor-driven, hydraulic upper die clamps move forward within the tee slots to clamp the inner punch to the inner slide. The clamps move forward until a proximity switch on the clamp is activated signaling that the die is present and in position to be clamped as shown by *Figure 21-4*. These die clamps are rated at a 7.9 ton (70.28 k N) lifting force and a 10 ton (88.96 k N) withstanding force. The outer slide clamps swing into position to secure the binder to the slide. This type of automated die clamping requires that the die locating slots be standardized within close limits.

The upper slides then are raised to the home position and both the loader and extractor are unlocked. Finally, the die cushion is pressurized, bringing it to the operating height. This completes the automatic die change sequence for the double action press.

Part Turnover

The turnover operation inverts draw panels which are removed from the double action press. This is required before they can be loaded onto the first die in the transfer press.

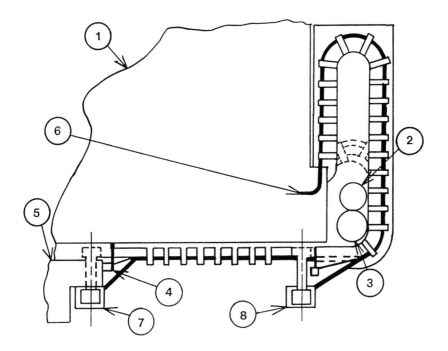

Figure 21-4. *Automatic die clamp attached to upper press slide: (1) upper slide; (2) motor with gearhead; (3) driving sprocket; (4) proximity switch; (5) die; (6) hydraulic pressure source; (7) clamped position; (8) unclamped position.(Mazda Motor Manufacturing (USA) Corp.)*

Sequence of Operation During Production. The part is removed from the double action press via the extractor. It is then placed onto the panel-receive lifter. This device actuates vertically to meet the part at the same level as the double action press die. The part is then lowered while on the panel-receive lifter to the shuttle fingers. These fingers are simply metal brackets formed to match the contour of the part and to hold the part as it is transferred. The shuttle advances one pitch and the lifter rises upward to lift the part off the shuttle. The shuttle then retracts one pitch. The lifter descends to allow the part to rest on the next shuttle fingers. Again, the shuttle advances one pitch as the process continues to advance the part forward until it reaches the turnover station.

The actual turnover process is completed by two elements: the turn-arms and receive-arms. When the part reaches the turnover, it is clamped with pneumatic jaws attached to the turn-arms. The turn-arms have the rotational capability of 160 degrees and are driven by an A.C. servo-motor system. The part is inverted, the jaws open, and the part is dropped onto the receive-arms which rise 20 degrees upward radially to meet the turn-arms. The receive-arms then lower the part onto the lifter which is at the transfer press work level. The transfer feeder bar then catches the part and advances it towards the transfer press.

Sequence of Operation During an ADC. At the start of an ADC, the panel receive lifter automatically lowers and the turn-arms open to their maximum width. Then the turnover moving bolsters simultaneously move out of and into position. The turn-arms width spacing is automatically adjusted to the computer selected preset value when the moving bolster is in position.

The turn-arms width adjustments are used according to the required width for each part and have a range of 24.6 in. to 77.75 in. (625 to 1975 mm) with an accuracy of ±0.012 in. (0.30 mm). Next, the turn-arms height adjustment take place. The turn-arms heights are also adjustable with a range of 59 in. to 66.93 in. (1500 to 1700 mm) and an accuracy of ±0.012 in. (0.30 mm). Both are driven by an A.C. servomotor system.

Two other turnover process variables, the turn-arm speed and panel turn, can also be adjusted based upon the information stored in the ADC data file. The turn-arm speed can be selected from either low, medium, or high speeds. The panel turn can enable or disable the turnover process by toggling on and off states. This alternative is for parts which do not require the turnover process.

Transfer Press

The transfer press features tri-axis transfer feeder bars for indexing the parts within the transfer press. An illustration of the transfer feeder bars and their motion is shown in *Figure 21-5.*

Sequence of Operation During Production. The transfer feeder bars are mechanically linked with the slide motion. The fingers inserted into the transfer feeder bars hold the parts during indexing. Only the first pair of fingers use

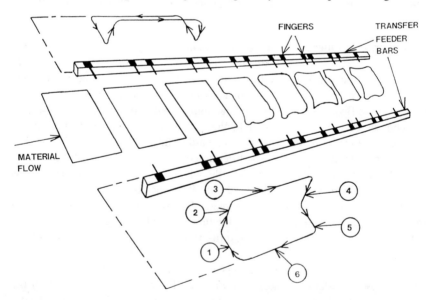

Figure 21-5. *Transfer press feeder bars and fingers showing motion diagram sequence: (1) clamp (catch part); (2) lift up; (3) advance; (4) lift down; (5) unclamp; (6) Return. (Mazda Motor Manufacturing (USA) Corp.)*

pneumatic jaw clamps. The other fingers rely upon gravity.

Sequence of Operations During ADC. The first operation to take place at the start of an ADC is the automatic lowering of the die cushion and die lifters. The transfer feeder bars are then moved to their maximum width setting, disconnected, and lowered to a rest stand for solid support during bolster movement.

Each transfer feeder bar can be separated into six pieces. Three of these pieces, known as *bar connectors*, are in the area between the uprights of the press. They cannot move outside of the press. The other three pieces move in and out of the press on the moving bolsters for each slide. *Figure 21-6* is a graphic representation of A Line with the transfer feeder bars highlighted. During production, parts must move through these areas between the uprights; therefore, there must be fingers and arms ready to support these parts at these locations.

To compensate for this problem, additional equipment has been installed in sections 1, 3, and 5 of the transfer feeder bars. The transfer feeder bar mechanisms installed are known as *idle fingers* and *idle skid arms*. The idle fingers travel within a tee-slot between the transfer feeder bars and the bar connectors and are driven by a pneumatic cylinder. They are retracted onto the transfer feeder bars during bolster movement. Once inside the press with the bolster secured, all pneumatic lines are pressurized, and the idle fingers are advanced onto the bar connectors.

The idle skid arms are also driven by pneumatic cylinders. These arms have a 90 degree radial movement. When retracted, they are flush with the bolster and avoid the upright during bolster movement. When extended, they are in line with the material flow. These idle skid arms provide support for the part during transferring in the area between the uprights.

After the transfer feeder bars are disconnected, the upper slides automatically lower to bottom dead center allowing the upper and lower die clamps to release.

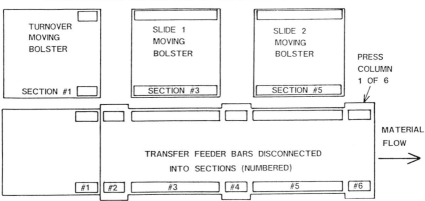

Figure 21-6. *Top view of transfer press layout with transfer feeder bars highlighted. (Mazda Motor Manufacturing (USA) Corp.)*

The counterbalance pressures start to automatically adjust at this point in the die change sequence. The slides then rise and the die height adjustments begin. The moving bolsters are unclamped, the scrap chute doors close, and the safety gates ascend.

The moving bolsters with dies in place begin to simultaneously move out of and into the press when the safety gates are locked in the up positions. Once in place, the moving bolsters are hydraulically clamped into position and secured, the press scrap chute doors open, and the safety gates close. The upper slides having been automatically adjusted to the correct shut height then close to bottom dead center. The transfer feeder bars are connected with the automatic bar connectors and then clamped together. The dies are also clamped using the motor driven hydraulic upper die clamps similar to the inner slide on the double action press in *Figure 21-4*.

Both the idle fingers and idle skid arms are extended as the upper slides move to their home position. The transfer feeder bars are raised from the rest stands and the width adjusted to the preset data file value. Finally, the die cushion and die lifters assume their operating heights.

OTHER ADC DATA FILE PARAMETERS

Several other parameters are downloaded during an ADC. Some of these include the die cushion pressure, miss grip sensor selections, die pin lifter strokes and patterns, tilt finger automation, and die automation selection.

Die Cushion Pressure. The die cushion pressure is adjusted during an ADC to a present value with an accuracy of $\pm$ 1.44 psi (0.1 kg/cm2). This allows optimal performance of the draw dies which require die cushions to actuate the draw ring. Each die station in the transfer press also has at least one finger with a limit switch installed. This limit switch is known as a *miss grip sensor*. If a panel is not transferred correctly to the next die station, the miss grip sensor will not detect the panel as present. This will result in an emergency stop of the press to avoid any possible die damage. The ADC data file allows the operator to select an ON/OFF state for each sensor also; however, these sensors are always in the ON state during production.

Die Lifter Timing. The die pin lifters are located in the bed of the press. The die pin lifters raise products into a position which the transfer feeder bar fingers can catch. The pin lifters are servo-motor-driven and allow the operator to preset the stroke and timing of each lifter during the ADC data file. The stroke is the vertical displacement exhibited by a die lifter: the timing denotes when the lifter will ascend based upon the slide angle. This timing value is derived from a digital rotary cam electronically interlocked with the slide.

Tilting Transfer Fingers. Some finger stations also feature a tilt finger automation. This automation tilts the finger radially to orientate the part to the part to be picked up horizontally level at one die and, as it is transferred to the next die, to be tilted 10 degrees clockwise around the axis of the part for the next die. This angle of orientation for the part may be required for optimal performance of that die.

Compressed Air Timing Flexibility. The die automation controls the flow of air to the dies which operates such devices as the punches. The air can be turned ON and OFF at preset slide angles using the digital rotary cam. The air can be preset to operate every cycle, every other cycle, or continuously.

EXTERNAL PRE-STAGING

Items That Make Up the External Dieset

Without the ability to externally pre-stage the moving bolsters, automatic die changes would not be possible. There are four elements involved in externally pre-staging A Line: (1) installation of the die locating pins, die cushion pins, and die lifter pins, (2) setting of the dies and the lower hydraulic clamps, (3) installation of the fingers, and (4) installation of the turnover fingers.

Locating Pins Correctly. Each moving bolster face is composed of a rectangular array of locating holes. These holes are then filled with the locating pins, die cushion pins, and die lifter pins. The location of these pins varies from die to die.

Every die setting team has this information graphically detailed to insure quick and correct pin placement. With all pins in place, the dies are lowered onto the locating pins which establishes their correct location with respect to the bolster.

Hydraulic Clamping. The lower hydraulic die clamps are installed manually and pressurized. In order for the clamps (which have a fairly short stroke) to function properly, it is necessary that both the height, slot width, and exact location of the lower die shoe clamping locations be machined accurately.

Double Checking a Correct Setup Electronically. A die identification box is attached to each die. An electrical pin connection is made between this identification box and the programmable logic controller. The programmable logic controller then checks this data against the part number for the next ADC to insure that the dies are correct and in the proper sequence. The material for the next ADC is also electronically cross referenced between the programmable logic controller and the AGV system's computer.

Transfer Finger Storage. As an additional time saver, the fingers associated with a die are stored with the die. Also, each finger is inscribed with a number and painted one of two colors: orange or blue. The matching number to the finger can be found on each locating slot for the finger on the transfer feeder bars. The risk is further reduced by painting all fingers on the north side of the moving bolster, blue and those on the south side, orange. The die setters have the additional responsibility for the limit switch electrical connections and all pneumatic connections.

Turnover Pre-staging. The last element to be completed is the turnover pre-staging. To eliminate confusion, all the turnover shuttle and lifter fingers are

265

kept grouped by part. When a die set is necessary, the appropriate storage cart is located and the correct fingers used. As it was on the transfer feeder bars, each finger has a matching number on the turnover shuttle as well as the two color code system.

EMPLOYEE TRAINING AND INTEGRATION

General Training

Great emphasis is placed upon employee training. People are a company's most important asset. Proper training and education can and does improve the quality and efficiency of any manufacturing process. Through the use of program work sheets, abnormality operations, and point guidance operations; employees are taught what to recognize, understand, and what to be cautious about.

Program Work Sheets basically outline the sequence of work elements to be performed to achieve a task. Abnormality Operations Sheets are used when an unplanned occurrence or condition arises which requires physical interaction but is not covered in the Program Work Sheets. This generally relates to some form of mechanical or electrical problem encountered. Point Guidance Sheets provide very specific details on how to perform each work element.

Every employee is, or will be, thoroughly trained to operate and diagnose problems with all equipment within the stamping plant. Class instruction and examinations are given to prove competency before an employee is certified at a given job. Extensive training programs such as this will provide a company with a well-trained, educated, and versatile work force and provide the flexibility needed to achieve success within the automotive marketplace.

Specific Automatic Die Change Training

To improve the success of an automatic die change, each employee's job tasks during automatic die change are analyzed and any waste is eliminated. This is done on a regular basis to achieve continuous improvement. Each task during an ADC is outlined as a sequence of work elements to complete that task. These elements help guide the employee to maximize his or her efficiency and that of the automatic die change. The following is a partial list of the work elements performed by two employees of A Line prior to an ADC.

Employee A:
1. Place last panel from last run on quality check fixture.
2. Remove part from the quality check fixture.
3. Rack the part.
4. Calculate production counts.
5. Record results on quality check sheets.
6. Locate program work sheets and quality check sheets for next part number.

266

7. Fill out missing information on new quality check sheet.
8. Exchange old program worksheet with new program work sheet.
9. Place old program worksheet into file.
10. Adjust exit conveyor width.

Employee B:
1. Push cycle stop and advance conveyor.
2. Push the start ADC button.
3. Push the PF-5 key on the production computer.
4. Push the lot report button on the central control panel.
5. Disconnect the air hoses to the jaws and clamps.
6. Turn the turnover to auto and check the data.

Clearly spelling-out work elements defines the interaction between man and machine necessary for a successful automatic die change.

CONCLUSION

Four major functional groups have been outlined in this section for success using automatic die change techniques: (1) facility layout, (2) computer-integrated manufacturing, (3) external staging, and (4) employee integration. These techniques can and do offer effective and efficient means to achieve their common goal but one is no more important than any other. Automatic die change is a system and should be approached in such a manner.

22

RETROFITTING EXISTING PRESSES/SYSTEMS SHOPS AND SETUPS*

Job Shops

Job shops throughout the United States handle all types of stamping. These shops are small in size compared to other shops in the auto industry. They do not specialize in one type of stamping and variety is what keeps them in business.

Standard cold formed tank ends from 4 in. (101.6 mm) in diameter to 72 in. (182.9 mm) in diameter can be made in these shops. They are considered medium to heavy job shops. Products are made from materials 0.02 in. (0.5 mm) to 0.75 in. (19 mm) thick. A variety of products include custom-designed stampings of heavy gage materials.

Die Setups

Multiple die setups are a common practice to produce finished products. Press sizes range from 400 tons (3.56 MN) to 2,000 tons (17.8 MN) and bed sizes from 3 × 4 ft. (.9m × 1.2m) to 8 × 16 ft. (2.4 m × 4.9 m). Single and double-action straight-side presses manufacture the products and there are some unique problems related to die setup methods used in this type of job shop.

BACKGROUND

Years ago, most job shops of this type had long production runs generally ranging from 5,000 to 15,000 pieces. Because of this, the cost per piece for setup was very small. The need for improvement of die setup times did not motivate many shops until the early 1980s.

Other needed changes were being made in these job shops. Improvements in material flow, tool storage facilities, handling methods, and better systems for performance data collection were being installed. Statistical Process Control (SPC) for improvements in the product also enabled these shops to perform more efficiently. All of these improvements helped reduce labor costs.

Due to foreign competition, customers needed to reduce inventory costs.

*Presented at SME Quick Die Change clinic, May 2-3, 1989 in Detroit, Michigan by Mr. Ralph Meyers, General Foreman, Machine Shop & Maintenance, Commercial Intertech Corporation, Youngstown, Ohio.

Customer orders decreased to smaller quantities of 100-250 pieces, although these orders were repeated more often throughout the year. The increased runs caused more setups and as a result, a higher cost per piece.

Actual production run time became less than setup time for the tools. Competition has increased the need to find ways to decrease setup times, also. The task to identify elements that prevent faster setups is presented in this chapter. A case study is provided in detail. It shows applications of new methods and concepts.

Job Shop Problems

There are many problems related to actual setups. Four of the major problems are discussed here.

Old Presses

The average age of presses used in American shops is 40 years. This equipment was built prior to World War II or shortly afterward. Most presses were not constructed with quick die changes in mind. The maintenance required on this equipment must be considered before attempting a quick die change program. Requirements for more up-time is essential to the program so efforts must be made to improve press performance and preventative maintenance prior to starting a quick die change program.

Old Tooling

Tooling that was built years ago is still in use today. Most of these tools were built with little or no thought given to making them load or unload quickly in presses.

Production Requirements

The requirement of production presses has changed drastically over a short period of time. Customers want several size products shipped at the same time to control shipping costs. As a result, several presses will be running various size products during the same period. If job shops do not work under this system, they will be forced to warehouse finished products and to provide shipments to customers. This raises inventory costs.

Methods

The methods used in the setup of dies has not changed much since the beginning of most job shops. The handling equipment is the same, and it is not very easy to make changes. The presses are very large and have foundations under them that cannot be changed without large expense. As a result, some changes that could improve setup times are not justified. Overhead lifting of tools and loading them into presses is very slow; the tools cannot be put directly into place. Dies are loaded by skidding, pushing, and prying into place. These methods are dangerous to perform and result in damage to many tools. Therefore, the repair cost rises to maintain dies.

Improvements

With an understanding of the problems to be faced, one must make improvements that will lead to quicker die changes. The critical manufacturing points must be determined. There are many different applications through the shop. Priorities must be set. Some companies can afford to assign people to work on these problems full time. If this is not the case, the person assigned to the task may not be able to devote more than two hours a day to the project. The following points should be considered when setting up goals for a thorough study:
- What present handling methods load and unload tools in presses.
  1. How efficient are they?
  2. How safe are they?
  3. What equipment is available and what is the cost?
  4. Check available space requirements.
- What changes are needed to tools to adapt them to quick die change?
  1. What are their sizes?
  2. How frequent are they used?
  3. Can alterations be made?
  4. Are new tools required?
- What changes can be made to fasten tools more quickly and precisely?
  1. How efficient is the present system?
  2. How long does it take now?
  3. Do bolsters need changing?
  4. Do press slides need changing?

GETTING STARTED

It is assumed that the survey of these factors is to be a part-time duty of a skilled, experienced person. Because this person has other job duties to perform and can only spend a couple of hours a day investigating for possible improvements, it is better to start on a single die setup. This type of setup utilizes a press that only accommodates a single die set in the center to make the product.

Get the prints of standard tools used in the press and make a sketch of how the whole setup will look in the press. Someone in the Engineering Department might assist with the drawings. Get a thorough understanding of how each component works to produce the product. This can be accomplished by spending time around the press. Ask operators and helpers how components work in setup.

After becoming familiar with setup process and how these parts work in setup, take time to list them in the order that they are put into setup. Check with the operator and helper again and explain what you plan to do. Many times, they are glad to help, if they know their job has a chance to become easier. Record the component again on another list. This time, leave enough space to record work performed on each component during setup.

If a video camera is available and the persons doing setup are comfortable being on camera, then it can be taped for study later. However, if the setup is taped, the elements must be broken down on paper for review. Also keep in mind that most people act differently if they are being filmed. Check the listing of components with the operator to make sure nothing has been forgotten.

CASE STUDY

This study discusses a setup for a standard tank head. This press is used 95% of the time for this type of work. The setups are about the same for tank heads from 12 in. (305 mm) to 24 in. (610 mm) in diameter. The tools are different heights and die shoes are different sizes. The bolster has tapped 1.125 in. (28.58 mm) holes on various centers. The dies are drilled to match these holes on four corners.

All punches are fastened with a 4 in. (102 mm) screw through a spacer where a wedge is driven tight to hold it. The second action holds the blank in position and applies pressure during forming.

Automation removes the part from die, turns it over, and conveys it through a washer. The automation is easily removed from the back of the press to allow personnel to work.

The operator and helper assemble the die components at the press and are responsible for die setup and production. A one-ton (8.896 kN) jib crane is mounted on the front of the press so the tools can be handled from the storage rack and lifted into position in the press. The punch holders, 4 in. (102 mm) screws, spacers, cushion pins, and blank nests are stored at or near the press. The second action slide and main slide spacer remain in the press 95% of time. The form die, blank holder, punch rings, punch pads, and die pads are brought to press via lift truck and overhead crane.

Components to Setup a Die to Form Tank Heads

Figure 22-1 illustrates a sectional view of an unmodified assembled die used to form standard tank heads. This die is assembled in the press with interchangeable components.

The components include the punch pad which must often be changed whenever a different tank head is to be produced. The punch ring also requires changeover.

The punch holder is kept at the press. Sizes are available for 12 in. (dia) (305

272

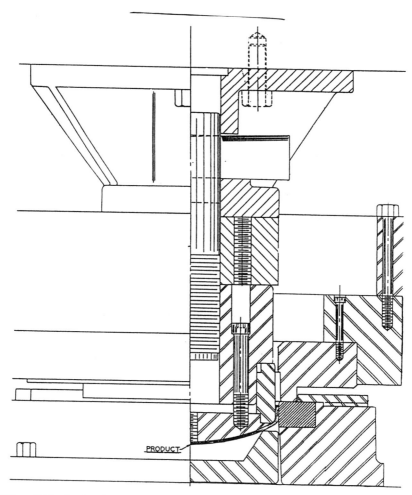

Figure 22-1. *Sectional view of a typical die for forming large tank heads before modification to reduce setup time.*

mm) through 24 in. (dia) (610 mm) heads.

Other components include the die pads, large central screws with wedges, forming dies, blank holder rings, blank nests, cushion pins and die nests.

These are considered standard form die components and are all used to manufacture a variety of tank heads. The sizes of the component required will vary according to the size of product, but the basic configuration remains the same.

Record Component Changes

Careful records of component modifications should be made to document all changes. This provides a good cross-check to be sure that nothing has been

273

20 mins.	1. Punch pad: Select proper shape for product and lift from rack and set on floor.
8.0 mins.	2. Punch ring: Locate punch ring and lift out of rack lowering onto register of punch pad. Check fit around register.
20.5 mins.	3. Punch holder: Pick up proper punch holder and lower into hole in punch ring, align bolt hole with rod in punch pad. Get proper length bolts from rack and thread into punch assembly. Use impact wrench and tighten six bolts.
2.5 mins.	4. Die pad: Get proper die pad and lift onto bolster.
45.5 mins.	5. 4 in. (102 mm) Screw: Locate and thread proper screw into punch assembly. Lift and load onto die pad on press bolster. Bring slide down and locate 4 in. (102 mm) screw into punch spacer hole. Push drive wedge into slot of 4 in. (102 mm) screw into punch spacer hole. Push drive wedge into slot of 4 in. (102 mm) screw. Tap until snug but not tight. Return slide to top position. Pull out die pad and place on floor. Put three roller rods on the bolster to roll die into press.
25.5 mins.	6. Place die: Secure sling through the die hole and lift to set on roller rods on bolster, push the die to the approximate center of the bolster. Lift front and back with a pry bar and remove rollers. Get bolts and thread through the die into the bolster but leave it loose.
40 mins.	7. Blank holder ring: Pick up proper blank holder ring with sling and with aid of blocks, slide on to the top of form die. Center ring around the register. Bring slide down until second action slide is close to blank holder ring. Align bolt hole with rod and put three bolts in tight. Bring slide back to top.
5 mins.	8. Cushion pins: Measure height of die above bolster and die pad height. Select proper pins (four) and insert into holes in bolster.
3 mins.	9. Blank nest: Go to rack and select proper blank nest and load onto form die register. Check fit.
2 mins.	10. Die pad: Pick up die pad and lift onto nest. Slide into form die hole and onto cushion pins.

Stop: The tooling has been loaded and now the die and punch must be set and tightened into place.

1. Secure shims and set four equally spaced shims around the die.
2. Block second action slide and bring punch into die hole until shims are inside the hole; thus setting die clearance.—Stop.
3. Get wrenches to the front and back of the press and tighten the die down.
4. Operator takes drive bar and drives wedge tight. Return press to top again. Take blocks out from under second slide.
5. Locate lift table in front of press. Get 2 cranemen to setup material on it.
6. Put the drawing compound on the die and load the blank. Put the compound on top of the blank.
7. Operator checks pressure required for the blank holder and adjusts if necessary. Helper checks the cushion pressure and adjusts.
8. Mark the part and check for high/low condition.
9. Call the foreman and quality control technician for approval.
10. Install automation equipment and make adjustments required to pull out part.
11. Check stencil for proper information.
12. Complete job.

Figure 22-2. *Changeover analysis prior to making the improvements.*

overlooked. Record the work done on each component as it fits into the setup. Space must be allowed to record any forgotten elements.

Analysis Of Elements

A review of a setup card enclosed in the production schedule will show serial numbers of tools to be used for given job. Caution must be used to select the correct tools for job. The time required for each identified task is recorded for analysis for areas of possible improvement.

Figure 22-2 illustrates a record of the time elements required to changeover a typical job prior to implementing the improvements.

This type of setup permits the use of form die, blank holder, and blank nest for another product. They are usually left in the press to run other tank heads that are the same size but different gage material. The only part that must be changed is the punch ring assembly. The wedge that holds the punch assembly is driven out and the 4 in. (102 mm) screw is removed. The punch is then hooked with the jib crane and pulled out from under the second action slide. It is disassembled and a different gage punch ring is assembled and loaded back into press for the next run.

From the element sheets on this setup, it can be seen that there is a lot of work involved. The standard time allowance for this setup is two and one-half hours. The time allowance for change over to another gage is three-quarters of an hour. Because of the shorter time when only the punch assembly is changed, production scheduling will run as many orders as possible before changing the entire setup. Another significant point with this setup involves the time allowance to remove the entire setup in one and one-half hours. This occurs because the overhead crane must skid the die parts out from under the slide.

Develop a Plan

After a thoughtful review, develop a written plan and cost estimate. Sometimes the cost of a change will be high, but it also might be the only way to achieve an improvement. Justification of cost can come from the reduction of setup time.

If you find that expensive alterations are needed for the press, get at least two estimates on it. When talking to outside sources for estimates, make sure they can do the work on a timely basis.

Example of Needed Changes

This setup revealed many opportunities for improvements. The following is a list of items that were done.

Inner Slide Modifications. A 4 in. (102 mm) hole was bored into the center of the inner slide platten. This modification assured that the spacer is mounted in the exact center of press. The spacer was altered to mount a locator in the center of it to fit the hole within 0.005 in. (0.127 mm) clearance. The spacer also was bored and sleeved so that 4 in. (102 mm) screw would fit to 0.015 in.

(0.38 mm) clearance. This assured proper alignment of the entire punch assembly. To facilitate ease of clamping, tee slots were cut into the face of the slide at a 45° angle starting at the corners.

New Bolster Design. A new bolster was made for the press. The tee slots bolt the die down at a 45° angle starting at the corners. One-inch diameter pin holes were provided, front to back, on a number of centers to provide locators for the dies in the press. Provision also was made to install the hydraulic die lifters needed to roll the dies into position.

New Sub-bolster Design. A new sub-bolster was made with the same tee slot pattern as the main bed bolster. It also has provision for hydraulic lifters. This sub-bolster draws the deeper heads that are shoved out of the bottom of the die. A cut out in the center allows automation to pull the heads out after drawing. Two fillers adapt it to various sizes of form dies.

Outriggers With Rollers. *Figure 22-3* illustrates a sectional view of the press showing the bolster, sub-bolster, upper die and the lower die placed on roller equipped outriggers and in position to be shoved into place in the press. These outriggers can be removed once the die is in place.

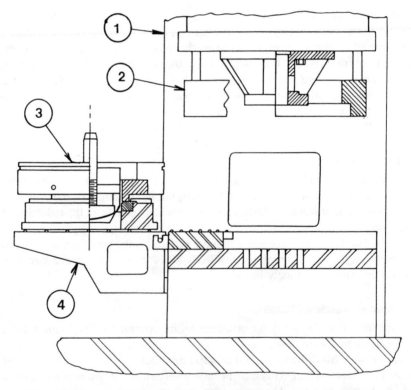

Figure 22-3. *The press and die after modification: (1) double action press with new bolster and sub bolster; (2) upper die attached to the press slides; (3) lower die pre-staged and ready to place in press; (4) removable outriggers equipped with rollers.*

276

Lower Die Locating Method. The form dies require alterations. A one-inch hole is drilled in them, front and back, to match the locator holes in the new bolster. The old bolt holes drilled in the form dies were slotted out to provide four places where tee bolts can slide into place. Since the parts being formed are symmetrical, and the die components precisely located, there is no need for guide pins or heel blocks.

Punch Modifications. The punch pads were converted to a solid assembly by welding them to a plate with a 4 in. (102 mm) tapped hole in the center and two 0.750 in. (19.1 mm) tapped holes to fasten it to the punch ring. A plate was made the same as the punch holder and provided a clearance hole for the large center screw. These changes allow the punch assembly to be made up in about three to four minutes.

Blank Holder Ring Improvements. The draw rings were modified by turning a 0.750 in. (19.05 mm) wide by 0.5 in. (12.7 mm) deep groove around the circumference. This allows the ring to be fastened into the upper blankholder by four horizontal screws tapped and threaded into the the the upper blankholder.

This change permits the correct draw ring to be fastened in place much faster and with greater operator safety. The operator and helper no longer have to reach under the slide to tighten the three bolts that held the rings.

Results

The changes made to the press and tools were substantial. These tooling alterations are still being made as an on-going project. Because of the number of tools to be modified is large, conversions of this type take considerable time to complete this step. The conversion method permits the use of both styles of tooling, and has no adverse effect on press up-time due to the on-going changes.

When the tools that have been altered are used, the time required to do a setup is from 10 to 20 minutes. Both the operator and helper continue to contribute valuable suggestions toward further reduction of setup time.

SETUP RECORDS

A good setup record system is important to the operations in any job shop. Shops usually run two or three shifts and use the operators and helpers on the large presses to setup dies.

Setup cards are made and maintained by the operators. *Figures 22-4* and *22-5* illustrate the two sides of a setup card. Left to their own, each individual operator may not set up the job the same way. It is important to have a standard system or procedure for all shifts to insure process repeatability and a uniform product. Once a setup is made and approved by the foreman, the card is signed and kept at the press. The new operator will then do the same thing as the previous worker. This prevents extra work if dies are changed after the setup.

#225 PRESS

DIE SET-UP CARD

ENGR. PT. NO. _____

BY: _____

DATE: _____

PAGE: 1 OF 2

REFERENCE FORM A

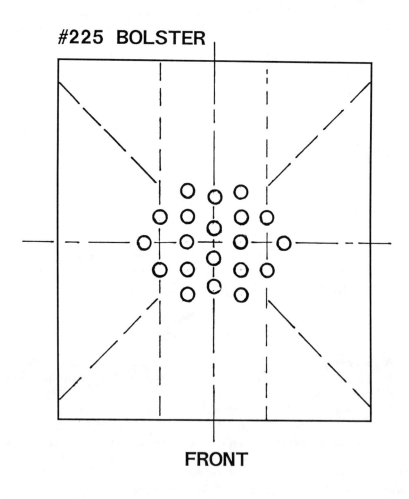

Figure 22-4. *Setup card used to inform operator and helper of how to setup a job correctly.*

```
#225 PRESS                    ENGR. PT. NO.  _____

  DIE SET-UP CARD             BY:  _____

                              DATE:  _____

                              PAGE:  2 OF 2


HEAD SHAPE: D.D., F.O., F&D, with horiz., ASME F&D,
            Hi-Crown. Ellip.

DIE S/N                    _____

PUSH THRU                  _____ yes _____ no _____
DOGS IN DIE                _____ yes _____ no _____
LIFT OUT PAD               _____

PARALLELS UNDER DIE        _____
K. O. CUSHION PINS         Lg. _____ Qty. _____
HOLD-DOWN YOKE             _____
HOLD-DOWN ADAPTOR          _____
HOLD-DOWN SIZE             _____
NEST                       _____ yes _____ no _____
PIN GAGES                  _____ yes _____ no _____

PUNCH HOLDER SIZE          _____
PUNCH RING                 Gage _____ S/N _____
PUNCH PAD                  Gage _____ S/N _____ Shape _____
PUNCH SPACER SIZE          _____
FILLER SIZE                _____

K.O. PRESSURE              _____ PSIG _____
HOLD-DOWN PRESSURE         _____ PSIG _____
TONMETER READINGS          _____ TONS _____

PRODUCT DEPTH              _____

AUXILIARY EQUIPMENT        _____
                           _____
                           _____
                           _____
                           _____
                           _____
                           _____

  D. Petro

  2/89                                          FORM A
```

Figure 22-5. Reverse side of the setup card illustrated in Fig. 22-4.

Setup records are important to the overall reduction of setup times also. The cards have notes on them that tell about the spacers or shims used on each die. These can modify tools to standard shut heights where multiple die setups are made in a press.

Cost and Payback Period

The cost of the changes reviewed in this chapter was $25,000. The savings per setup were enough to pay these costs back within one and one-half months. The old setup times were from two and one half hours to three and one half hours. Standard cost per hour is $112.00. Two die sets were made per shift at $560.00 per day. This amount for a one month period would be $22,400.

APPLYING THIS INFORMATION

This case study deals with some typical setup problems related to a medium to heavy job shop. While a good approach was suggested, there is no single absolutely correct way to proceed in implementing quick die change. The person leading this project had many years of experience with the press operations. The latter factor is often vital in successfully implementing setup reduction methods in the older job shop environment.

An excellent way has been offered to get started toward improvements in the die setup area. Some improvements may seem small but they do improve overall performance.

As newer equipment and systems are designed and installed, quick die changes become easier to achieve. The methods described in this case study are in use today alongside old methods. With many of the tools being over 60 years old, a total quick die change conversion should not be expected to happen overnight. The standard method and procedure that was instituted has resulted in more profit and customers.

The future of small job shops becomes more and more secure as improvements are made in this area. No matter what products are manufactured, there is always a way to make quicker setups. They may be harder to find than this one, but they are still there.

23

EMPLOYEE ACCEPTANCE AT FORD MOTOR COMPANY*

STEADY EMPLOYMENT

The quick change of dies in a stamping press not only has an impact on a company's bottom line, its quality, and its competitiveness, but it impacts the plant workers as well. Consider the case of Ron Lake. Lake is a Machine Repairman at the Ford stamping plant located in Maumee, Ohio. He is a member of the United Auto Workers and works on the midnight shift.

As part of the preparation of this volume, Local UAW President Gary Smotherman talked with Lake for his opinion of quick die change or "hit to hit" as it is known at the plant. Hit to hit is the amount of time the press is idle during job changeover. Put another way, it is the time that lapses between the last hit in a press production run and the time that the operation is set to the next job. "Being able to make quick die changes," noted Lake "has given me steady employment. When Maumee Stamping became successful with quick change die sets, it allowed the company to bring in more work. "I came from a plant that had closed," Lake told Smotherman, "now, I'm working at Maumee and without the hit to hit program, I would not be here."

BACKGROUND

This chapter presents a case study of quick die change at the Maumee stamping plant. The plant was established in an existing facility in April 1974. It was established as additional stamping capacity was needed quickly. Thus, the plant was designed around available equipment rather than long-term efficiency. In many ways, the problems associated with setup time reduction at Maumee are much like those of a contract stamping shop.

The plant handles a wide mix of work. On the one hand, it includes large, deep-drawn, automotive body panels produced on seven major tandem lines each having a double-action lead press. It also produces medium-sized stampings on smaller single-action straight-side tandem lines. Several straight-side presses are equipped with decoilers, stock levelers, and stackers for cutting the needed blanks. Many plastic parts also are produced. Maumee was faced with closure

*Contributed by Mr. Gary Smotherman, President UAW Local 1892, Maumee, Ohio. Mr. Enoch Nelson of the Body and Assembly Division, Dearborn, Michigan also provided background for this chapter.

during a recent economic downturn. To secure the future of the plant, the facility should be established as the stamping supplier of choice. Producing stampings at the lowest possible cost was the challenge. Quick die change was the key in meeting that challenge.

MAUMEE STAMPING HIT TO HIT STORY

The story of hit to hit at Maumee is a story of competitiveness, success, and growth through the cooperation of union and management. The hit to hit program at Ford's Maumee facility began as a discussion of competitiveness.

Competitiveness is a term used far and wide today from government offices to factory floor to the members of the mass media. But remaining competitive—or increasing competitiveness—means two important things to the workers of a factory who, in this case study, are members of United Auto Workers Local 1892. First, it means job security. By doing the job to not only produce a higher volume but with higher quality as well, workers realize that they play a large part in securing their own futures. Second, it means the creation of more jobs as work that is brought into the plant increases.

The hit to hit program was viewed as a key to Maumee competitiveness. Previous to the installation of the hit to hit program, the lines took between four and eight hours to set. Following management/union discussion, hit to hit was installed in three steps.

Three Steps Toward Progress

The first step was to secure agreements from all parties that die setup time was too long. The second step involved more direct implementation. This involves team building on the factory floor. It is important to think out who will do what task during the die change. It is also important that the area be adequately staffed and equipped at the time of die change.

During this implementation process, the lines were turned over to the workers on the floor. *Involvement* is the key. At Maumee, production workers stayed on the lines through the die sets and they helped in any way possible to facilitate the change-over. During this second phase, there needs to be a strong management involvement as well. It's called *incentive*. Commitment needs to come from management that additional work will be arriving at the plant gates if the quick change of dies is in practice. At Maumee, setup times initially decreased with no resulting increase in competitiveness as the line was idle following the die set. Then, fulfilling their part of the bargain, management brought in 17 new jobs, loading the pressroom with work for three shifts. The additional work also required the plant to do some hiring. Workers who were laid-off from other Ford locations were transferred to Maumee.

Success

At Maumee, that growth continues every day. Three years ago, when the program began, only two of the seven major tandem lines were equipped for automated part transfer between the presses. Now all seven major lines are automated. It is the feeling of the union that this addition of new equipment is an indication of Ford's interest and faith in the capability of Maumee. Even with the addition of automation, new employees were hired to help handle the additional work.

At this writing, the most time needed for any line to set is two hours. Some lines can be set in 30 minutes. The lines which are set in 30 minutes produce outer skin panels, a task with a high-quality requirement. There are six presses on this line. There are, however, no automatic clamps. Die setters unbolt and bolt down the new tools. The work groups have overcome every problem by working together. Today, hit to hit teams film their die sets and review the tapes seeking further ways to improve the process.

"I think hit to hit has been a very good tool for our plant," notes Don Trainer, a Machine Repairman. "It has given us more jobs. It has given us more job security and it has helped the employees to work together as a team, which, in turn, makes one feel better about his or her job. It has made the plant more efficient. I also think that it will promote better quality parts." The comment sums it up. The Maumee involvement in quick die change benefited everyone involved and contributed greatly to that very key concept in today's economy. That concept is called *competitiveness*. At Ford's Maumee Stamping facility quick die change provided plenty of impact.

24

STEPS LEADING TO AUTOMATED
QUICK DIE CHANGE *

DEFINITION

Quick die change is defined as the interval that occurs between the end
of one job and the beginning of the next. More specifically, the time that elapses
when the off button is pushed on the previous job to when the start button is
pushed on the newly set die or tool.

AVAILABLE TECHNOLOGY

The technology that can help accomplish quick die change is immense. It can
range from completely automatic die changing with minimal time in minutes or
seconds to a coordinated team effort of skilled people making the change. The
required capital investment will vary in proportion to the basic state of the art.

The Appropriate Starting Place for the Job Shop

It should be noted, that in the job shop setting lacking state-of-the-art
equipment, much time can be saved without any capital investment. In some
cases, savings can be 75% of the setup time. Savings can be accomplished by the
proper use of external and internal dieset methods. Therefore, the first step in
quick die change—before any capital expenditure—should be analysis of the
external and internal methods. Once fine-tuned, the next step can be in capital
investments such as rollers in bolsters, hydraulic clamps and entry rollers.

Quick die change falls into two different categories: The first being the job
shop with no rolling bolsters or real state-of-the-art equipment and the second, a
highly automated category specially designed for certain dies and the rapid
change of dies or tools (rolling bolsters).

The First Category. The area that needs to be addressed is the first category
(a job shop with no rolling bolster or real state-of-the-art equipment). In this

---

*Contributed by Philip E. Laven, a metal stamping consultant located in Wyoming,
Michigan and Director of Manufacturing, Trumark, Inc., Lansing, Michigan.

category, a company usually has been in business for a long time and it has a diversity of older presses. Usually economics has not allowed a large-scale conversion to newer, hi-tech equipment. If the equipment is not adaptable to rolling bolsters or if the dies don't adapt well to standardizations, we must then ask ourselves what the job shop is supposed to do (if anything).

Certainly, no one has the luxury to put his or her head in the sand and ignore what is going on. Therefore, each of us must react to modernization and make improvements. There are two general areas to investigate:

- the external area, or
- the internal area of die setting methods.

In the external area, much can be accomplished. Everything from material-production control (management) to the nuts and bolts for the dies is a candidate for improvement.

External Dieset. *External* relates to what happens before the die is set into the press. Has a die (large or small) ever been set into the press only to find that the stock to run the die has not come in yet or has been rejected and is not available? Has a die been set for a rush job only to find that the rush job tool is still out for repair or still being worked on in the tool room?

What can be done about this?

The old method of planning die setting followed a sequence which often started when the operator finished the production order. He or she then either went to the lead person and said, "what is next?" and the reply was, "I will let you know," or "go run X press."

With external preparation, the foreman or scheduler lines up the next job for a specific press ahead of the previous job's completion. This step allows time to the lead person or the assigned die setter to check the availability and readiness of the stock. Is the die ready and available and will it be moved to the press before the other job runs out? Has the die been checked out?

A good identifying method uses a red tag. The tag is placed on the die after completion of the last part and the web. Mark the tag by stating any functions that needs to be corrected or changed. The tool room, along with quality control, evaluate the red tag descriptions and the tool room makes proper corrections. When this setup is completed, the die, now with a green tag, is placed into the storage rack. When production is anticipated, the press room lead person or setup person checks the rack to see if the die is in the die rack and if there is a green tag indicating the die availability.

Next, determine if you have the shop order, setup sheet, and SPC data sheets. Determine if the setup sheet indicates any changes in ram height, lubricant, bolt lengths, and air pins. If so, prepare now to make the change. Is quality assurance aware that you are changing a die so that they can be at the press for the initial approval? What about containers?

This generally covers most of the external preparation and these few smart steps will save a large amount of setup if the preparation is done properly and ahead of time. There is no additional cost as the setup was an eventual necessity.

Internal Dieset. *Internal* means that the right tools and staff are ready at the conclusion of a job, remove the old die out and replace it with the new one.

On a coil fed press, the setup team might have one person in front of the press to loosen and tighten bolts etc. In the rear, there should be another bolt person. This same person (at the rear) can clean and mop the bolster, push slugs out and clean the floor. A third person places the steel on the reel and gets it through the straightener and into the feed rollers. The front person can operate a forklift. The fork-lift removes the dies and sets them on the floor next to the press. It then picks up the next die (usually next to the press) and inserts it in to the press. Next, the bolts and clamps are attached and the ram adjusted. Remember, safety must come first and everyone must know when the ram is moved up or down. When the die is set and the area cleaned, the old die is put away and all the players except one assigned person go back to their normal daily responsibilities.

The assigned person then gets the production approval, sets the probes and gives the operating instructions to the press operator.

It should be noted that basically the same principles that apply to the coil fed machines apply to hand fed dies.

Employee Involvement and Acceptance. Many companies have plenty of machine capacity and quick die change should not be looked at as a method to get the setup people to work harder or faster.

There are key points that must be addressed in the quick die change process with the foreman, setup people, engineers and material-production control personnel.

First, establish a quick die change team and include some of each of those people. Next, establish the main purpose of quick die change (better quality and less inventory). For example, if the lot size is smaller, related problems are caught much sooner. The production of large amounts of defective parts to scrap or rework is avoided. This is especially true with down stream operations or processes.

Also the inventory carrying cost is greatly reduced and a financial advantage can secure more opportunities in the market place. Less inventory means less clutter and better, neater looking facilities with less parts and more accurate inventory.

Each team member must understand and agree with the reasons for the quick die change team to be successful.

A work center designated as a pilot must be chosen to launch the quick die change efforts. This is best done by the material-production control people to avoid rapidly setting a press that will function at far less than the daily capacity. As might be expected, the setup people will say, ''what's the hurry?'' Therefore, choose a work center that has a normal workload to begin the quick die change pilot.

Next, establish a standard reference using the old methods and times. This will provide a baseline for measurement of improvement once improved external and internal procedures are in place.

Meet weekly to discuss ways to improve procedures. Do not spare the compliments. After a couple of weeks, success should become visible and the material people may begin to cut the lot size by perhaps 25% of the normal lot size.

Wait for several weeks to see the results. This is now a very critical time to judge the capacity and again gage the success of what you have done. If success is there, proceed to your goal, but go slowly.

One work center pilot is manageable and can be enlarged from the point of some initial success. But success is the key. Publish and praise the little successes because they will build and compound.

Evaluate the Results. To this point, not a dime has been spent, other than for group meeting time. Effective communication is the purpose for this meeting.

The quick die change team is critical and should be lead by the foreman, the industrial methods engineer, or another key person. The leader must have output and change-time figures for the past week as well as current status and a set of goals. A bar graph of progress should be posted and brought to the team meetings. The Vice President of Operations should also be aware of progress.

Future Improvements. Following the development of the external and internal functions of quick die change, investigate adding bolster rollers, entry levers, hydraulic clamps, and so forth.

25

COST EFFECTIVE QUICK DIE CHANGE AT WEBSTER MANUFACTURING COMPANY*

Webster Manufacturing Company produces engineering class chain and the side bars for the chain are produced in the Punch Press Department. Economic factors requiring an increase stamping productivity and the company's background are expressed in Chapter 29.

Establish a Benchmark

The recommended first step toward undertaking a quick die change program is to establish a reference point from which to measure improvement. Webster Manufacturing Company established a series of accounts to track the activities of the Punch Press Department. The accounting summary was then established as a reference point from which improvement could be measured. The important goal is that a specific set of account definitions accurately and consistently record activities in the department well before, during, and after the quick die change implementation process.

To chart improvement and determine the cost-effectiveness of quick die change expenditures, a total of 11 accounts were established.

Presenting the Program to Diesetters and Operators

The Quick Die Change Training program was presented to the punch press personnel by the Quality Control Manager who was selected as project leader by top management. The summary that was given included the need to react to various production demands. Many of these demands required the ability to respond to short production runs. Some jobs had a longer setup time than production time. The punch press personnel began to view this training program as a form of job security by insuring the company's effort to remain competitive in the market place.

Selecting the Quick Die Change Team

Top management made the decision to form the team both for hourly and salaried personnel. A decision was made to have pressroom management lead

*Based on SME Technical Paper TE90-290, by Joseph L. Wise, Punch Press and Metals Treating Manager, Webster Manufacturing Company, Tiffin, Ohio. This paper was presented at the SME Precision Stamping and Die Technology clinic, October 30-November 1, 1990, Schaumburg (Chicago), Illinois.

diesetters with tool and die makers analyzing their needs and determining their own methods. The years of setup experience were a valuable asset in determining the best methods to be used. Cooperation and team spirit made individuals comfortable during this learning experience.

The following individuals were selected:

- Two diesetters from each shift.
- One tool and die maker from each shift.
- The head of the Engineering Department.
- The head of the Quality Control Department.
- The head of Production.
- One Punch Press Department Supervisor from each shift.

Getting Started

Once the needed training materials were compiled, training of the team was begun in quick die change techniques. The team met monthly on a Saturday morning so individuals from all the shifts could meet at the same time. No production was scheduled in the Punch Press Department on meeting days so there would be no interruptions during the training sessions. Each meeting lasted approximately two hours with a 10 minute break. The meetings were held in a conference room where all individuals were supplied with copies of the training material for their own use. Periodically, the team separated into smaller groups to analyze individual portions of current setup methods. Then a spokesperson from each smaller group presented their methods and recommendations to the team for discussion.

Using A Video Camera to Study Current Methods

The quick change team discussed methods to document individual events that occurred during a setup. One suggestion involved a group time study conducted by the team in the press room. After further discussion the decision was made to use a video camera to tape the current setup method. The use of a video camera gave the team the ability to review the setup several times. Additionally, individual segments could be viewed and reviewed to accurately record written details of each segment. During review of the video, individual portions of the setup were time studied. On screen digital clock display simplified the timing process, especially when the team began defining and separating individual elements of the setup.

Securing Operator Cooperation In Video Taping

The quick change project manager met with the punch press operators from each of the three shifts to discuss use of the video camera. Care was taken to present the use of the video camera as an educational tool. In no way was the video camera presented as the big eye of management sent to spy. The use of the video camera was well-accepted by the press operators and diesetters in this union shop.

The diesetters were always informed when a routine setup was to be video taped. The team selected a setup to be video taped that included changing of die sets and bar material. The diesetter and operator involved were encouraged to proceed as they normally would when setting dies. Often individuals perform differently when video taped.

Team Study of Current Setup Methods

The first setup that was video taped lasted just over one and one-half hours from the last production part on one run until the first production part on the next run. The change-over was performed completely by one diesetter which was the normal procedure then. The operator did not participate in the setup.

The team first viewed the video in its entirety so that the overall concept of the setup could be seen. Then the team began to dissect the video and define segments that could be separated into individual tasks. These individual tasks were written on note cards in addition to the time taken to perform them. Later the note cards would give the team the opportunity to rearrange the individual tasks to provide for a more efficient setup.

Team Discussion of Quick Die Change Techniques

Information was provided to the team showing some of the many commercial products available to improve the ability to set up punch presses. The decision was unanimously made to first concentrate on refining the current techniques before purchasing any of these products.

Discussion was held concerning some of the tasks that could be performed while the press was still running production prior to the change-over. These tasks included transporting the next die set to the press, moving an empty die cart to the press to place the old die set, and moving the diesetters tool cart to the press. Some of the tasks obviously had to be performed while the press was not running production. These tasks included unclamping and removal of the old die set, cleaning of the press bolster plate, placement and clamping of the new die set in the press, and final ram adjustment. Other tasks could be performed after the change-over once the press was back in production. These tasks included transporting the old die set to the bench area, moving the diesetters tool cart to the bench area, and returning the die cart to its designated location.

ANALYZING CURRENT METHODS AND DEFINING NEW ONES

Based on the video, individual tasks were documented, defined and timed. The team defined and timed the individual tasks and video taped them in the exact order in which they occurred in the setup. Next, this documentation was used to create a script of the video.

The team determined that all of the elements fell into three basic categories:
1. Work that can be performed when the press is still running production.
2. Work that must be done when the press is down for setup.
3. Tasks that can be done when the press is back in production.

During this first setup video, all the activities occurred while the press was down for setup. After thoroughly examining the individual tasks, the team began to separate the tasks into the three categories listed earlier. Some tasks were eliminated all together.

The team determined what tasks should be performed by the diesetter and what tasks should be performed by the operator. The team decided that the new setup or change-over method should be performed by one diesetter and one operator instead of just one diesetter. The tasks were assigned in such a way that individual tasks could be performed simultaneously by the two people without one interfering with the other. The task work loads were balanced so both the diesetter and the operator completed their portion of the change-over at approximately the same time.

The Team Determines What Tools Are Needed

Now that the press change-over techniques were refined, the team was ready to investigate the purchase of equipment that would further improve change-over time. Every team member's suggestion was analyzed for cost-effectiveness.

The following suggestions were the ones that the team found to have a cost-effective potential for quick die change improvement.

Standardize Manual Clamping Devices

The items needed to fasten the dies in the presses were kept in a storage table that housed many drawers in which the different size clamping devices and bolts could be stored. To simplify the maintenance of clamp and bolt inventory, the table was placed in a central location.

It was time-consuming to walk from the clamp and bolt storage table to the press where the setup was performed. Often a diesetter had to make more than one trip for bolts or clamps.

The quick die change team decided that the same size clamps and bolts should be used on each press. Using the same size nuts in every setup to clamp the die set to each bolster plate saved time. The diesetter could use the same wrench throughout the setup without going back to a tool box to get another size wrench. The team decided to purchase standardized die fastening items for each press. All of these items are identical from press to press and enough of each item was purchased for each press to cover the maximum quantity required during setup.

Design Standard Tool Boxes for Each Press

After discussing several possibilities, the team decided to define the criteria of the tool box that they needed. The team wanted to place the tool box in a permanent location as close to the press as possible without being in the way. Another requirement was that all items should be available for reach between waist-high and shoulder-high for the average diesetter. To save time, drawers or doors were not wanted. Each item was to have a designated place in the box. To discourage placement of items that did not belong in the box (such as left over production parts, empty coffee cups, etc.) there were to be no shelves.

The team's final design was a vertical tool box in which to hang the items to be purchased for each press. All items stored in each tool box were positioned to minimize space requirements. The tool box was to be four feet square and one foot deep. These boxes were built from steel plate heavy enough to support pegs. The pegs were welded to the inside of the box. The designated tools were hung on the pegs. Identical boxes were made for each of the seven presses involved.

The team painted the inside of the boxes white with a solid black silhouette of the tool to be hung on each of the pegs. This allowed the diesetter to quickly locate the correct peg when placing an item back in the box. Additionally, a quick glance at the tool box indicated what items were in use in the press. The boxes were fastened to the columns of the building near each of the presses. Since all the boxes were the same, after a short period of time, it became second nature for the diesetters to reach for items in the box because the tools were always in the same location.

Purchase an Air Wrench for Each Diesetter

Air tools were purchased for each diesetter to use to remove or to screw on nuts or bolts. Instruction was given to manually tighten each nut or bolt properly after snugging it up with an air wrench. Also, nuts and bolts were to be started by hand before using the air wrench.

Place Overhead Retractable Air Lines at Each Press

An overhead retractable air line was fastened to each press on a press column high enough to walk under but low enough to reach the end of the air line. This eliminated having air hoses laying on the floor that had to be moved when a lift truck or die cart had to cross the area.

Purchase a Motorized Die Cart

The company owned one die cart that could handle the smaller die sets. This die cart had to be pushed to the press. It did have hydraulic lift with a roller conveyor attached. However, to this point, the larger die sets had to be transported by a lift truck. A self-propelled die cart that would handle most of the larger die sets was desired. This would leave only a few very large die sets that would still require the use of the lift truck. An electric die cart was purchased and equipped with a roller conveyor mounted on its hydraulic lift. Another useful feature is a cable hoist mounted above the roller conveyor to pull the die sets out of the press onto the conveyor.

Fire Proof Solvent Cans for Each Press

A four-gallon solvent can with a lid and approved safety linkage was placed at each press under the tool cabinets. This eliminated the time wasted looking for a solvent can.

Two-Way Radios

A two-way radio was placed in the bench die setup area to call the lift truck when lifts had to be made. The two-way mobile unit on the lift truck was permanently attached.

Move The In-floor Scrap Conveyors

The old punch press lay-out provided for all the scrap or slug conveyors to exit the presses in the floor. Exiting toward the aisle facilitated removal of scrap containers by a lift truck. This meant that the aisle side of the press could not be used by the die cart to put die sets in the presses. The press side where die sets could be placed was also the side where the steel racks were located. These racks held the bundle of steel bars to be punched and cut-off in the press and the roller conveyor guided the individual bars into the press. Those racks and conveyors had to be moved every time a different die set was to be placed in the press.

The quick die change team decided the scrap conveyors and scrap hoppers should be located beside the press so the die cart could load a die set from the aisle side of the press. This was an expensive improvement because it involved concrete foundation work. The change was cost-effective because 20 minutes were saved on each change-over.

DIESETTERS AND OPERATORS STUDY FINAL VIDEO

Pre-and Post Change-over Analysis

The last change-over video was taped. This change-over video involved the same change-over of die set and bar stock as the first video. This set up took 20 minutes as compared to the 90 minutes consumed by the first change-over video. In both cases, the time was measured from the last production part on one run until the first production part on the next run. This video was studied by the team. Team members agree that this new video and scripts will be the standard for future setups. The team trained the operators in new setup methods using the third change-over video and script as both a training tool and a written basis of the new standard setup procedure.

26

ELECTRONIC SENSORS
AND CONTROLLERS

INTRODUCTION

This chapter is based on a paper[1] presented by George Keremedjiev at a recent SME Quick Die Change Clinic. Keremedjiev, a recognized die sensor and electronic die protection expert, favors the use of electronic sensors over mechanical switches and mechanical contact probes.

Additional information on electronic die protection can be found in the *Die Design Handbook*.[2] Sensor manufacturers' catalogs also have detailed information on sensor selection and installation.

Keremedjiev, who has a great deal of experience in high-speed stamping sensor applications, states that electronic sensors often are cost effective in slower applications, when compared to mechanical switches and probes.

SENSOR REQUIREMENTS*

Basics

Quick connect/disconnect termination for the in-die sensors can dramatically enhance the importance and cost-effectiveness of quick die changes.

The sensor functions can encompass the monitoring of mechanical pilots, part position and dimension verification, scrap level detection and part ejection verification. Sensors are best implemented in the quick die change environment through the use of efficient interconnection devices. With the monitoring electronics for these sensors located elsewhere on the press, it is paramount to have a centralized approach to the wiring both within and outside of the dies.

In earlier presentations[3], numerous reasons are listed for the use and justification of placing electronic sensors in metal stamping dies. Although the purpose of this paper is to address the electronic sensor interconnection needs of the quick die environment, it is nevertheless important to summarize two of the benefits for using electronic sensors versus mechanical probes in dies.

Advantages of Electronic Sensors

The first and most important fact is that electronic sensors, when properly

*Contributed by George Keremedjiev, President, Tecknow Education Services, Inc., Bozeman, Montana.

handled and mounted, offer a singular advantage over their mechanical counterparts: no mechanical wear. Once buried deep within a die, a sensor (such as an inductive proximity type) will perform its detection duties with a lifetime generally limited only by human mishandling. Since there is no wear and the sensor makes no mechanical contact with its target, its useful lifetime can be viewed as the failure rate of its electronics. The longevity of electronic inductive proximity sensors, in many cases, will be several times that of its mechanical counterpart.

Second, the very quick response speed of electronic sensors wastes very little press stopping time. Since the primary point of using sensors is to detect a flaw in the stamping process, it makes sense to use devices that offer as little obstruction to the stopping time of the press. Once the problem within the die is detected, the sensor issues a warning to the die protection controller at electronic speeds. An example of this would be use of a mechanical probe whose misfeed detection would be translated against a mechanical switch, which in turn would then issue the alarm signal. An electronic counterpart includes the use of an electronic inductive proximity sensor to detect the misfeed without making contact with the strip. As soon as the misfeed is detected, the sensor would issue an electronic signal to the die monitoring circuitry. The latter's response time can offer several milliseconds of additional time for the press to stop.

Standardized Approaches

Once the decision is made to use electronic sensors for standard and quick die setups, the most important challenge is not electronic. Initial attempts in the use of in-die electronic sensors has led some to disorganization and randomly conceived wiring schemes. Instead of cabling routed by chance from the die to the control cabinet on the press, one can use available electromechanical devices such as connectors and junction boxes and have an efficient routing of the sensor cables.

All electronic sensors should have quick disconnect connectors when used in the quick die change environment. The sensor cabling should not require an electrician to hardwire the sensors to the control cabinet with each new die setup. Do not create an environment that reduces the quick die change rate.

Die Design Considerations. The most effective time to decide where and how to place sensors in a die is at the die design stage. Although some argue that one can best choose a sensor after a die is made and run, a die house that routinely uses sensors will find it beneficial to design the die around the sensors. In those design areas that use computer-aided design (CAD) hardware, it is recommended that commonly used sensor types be digitalized into the component libraries for easy retrieval. Thus, as the die is being conceived and an area for sensing arises, the designer can quickly have the sensor drawn into its appropriate area within the die. Particularly in the quick die change environment, where speed and efficiency are paramount, the designer with sensor experience will find his or her tooling designs will take on a different style. The designer will generate with each successive generation of tooling, more sophisticated and efficient designs with sensors as part of the design arsenal.

The routing of sensor cables within the die is again best thought of at the time of the die's design. One can machine snaking channels for the cables around various die components. With a CAD system, one cannot only visualize the sensor within the die, but also route its wiring on the computer monitor.

Retrofitting Existing Dies. If one chooses to retrofit existing quick change dies with electronic sensors, the task can be rather challenging.

This in part is due to the possible lack of provisions for the extra required space for the sensor and its cable. However, it is recommended that all quick dies be viewed as potential candidates for electronic sensing. The time spent retrofitting an existing die will be more than justified with the first die crash prevention.

Methods of Using Quick Disconnect Connectors. A common approach to the routing and interconnecting of sensor cables is the use of individual quick disconnect connectors on each sensor cable. If, for example, a given die has four sensors buried inside of it, the four sensor cables would each have a miniature connector attached to the ends of the cables. The lengths of these cables would be sufficient to reach a central junction box which would be mounted elsewhere on the press. In our example, the cables exit the die and are bundled into a single harness with four sets of electronic connectors at its end. An alternative to this approach allows a single multipin connector to eliminate the need for four separate miniature connectors. In this approach, the harness with its four individual sensor cables would terminate in a quick disconnect central connector. This central connector includes enough pins to accommodate the several individual wires which compose each sensor cable.

The obvious advantage to this approach is that with a single twist of the wrist, the die setup operator can quickly attach the sensor harness to the junction box on the press. Its primary disadvantage surfaces when the need arises to replace one or more of the four sensors. Since all four sensor cables are hardwired to the one connector, one would have to desolder the wires from the sensors which needed replacement and resolder the wires from the new sensors. If, on the other hand, there was a separate connector with each sensor cable, it would then be possible to have spare sensors in the stockroom with individual connectors pre-attached. Thus in replacing sensors, the setup personnel could simply:

- loosen the harness,
- remove the sensors from the die,
- replace them with the off-the-shelf sensor,
- rebundle the harness, and
- plug in the four connectors into the junction box.

Both approaches (the one with individual connectors on each sensor cable and the one with a single harness connector) are time-saving devices that are required in the quick die change environment. They both require that the press mounted junction box have readily mating connector terminations mounted to accept the connector(s) from the sensor cables.

Interfacing Cables With Junction Boxes. If a shop has dies that use individual sensor cable connectors as well as other dies that incorporate a single harness with its one connector, it is recommended that the press junction box have provisions to accept both types. Whether one builds the junction box or chooses to purchase a commercially available model, the importance of having a disciplined approach to the routing and terminating of sensor cables cannot be overstated.

A third possibility for dealing with the electronic sensor cabling is the mounting of a multipin, oil-tight connector right on the die itself. In this approach, the cables from sensors buried in the die are routed internally within the die to this central connector and their conductors permanently soldered unto it. This centralizing connector can be mounted directly on the surface of the die or on a small junction box that is then attached to the die.

In this arrangement, when the die is placed in the press, a single multiconductor cable is then directly attached to the die from the press sensor junction box via the die's centralized connector. Since oil is one of the worst environmental problems for electrical and electronic interconnections, special care must be taken to avoid contamination of the die connector with oil from parts, the die itself, or through human handling. Otherwise, false sensor signals may be generated or legitimate ones blocked by the intermittent signals emanating from the oil contaminated connector.

Universal Quick Disconnect Sensor Junction Boxes. It is useless to have sensors in a quick change die and not have a centralized quick junction area on the press. As was pointed out in the April 1990 *Manufacturing Engineering* magazine: The sensor interface junction box, when properly mounted on the press, will probably last the lifetime of the press itself barring any human mishandling. Mounting the sensor interface box high and away from oily areas stops oil mists or oil migrations on the sensor cables from entering.[4] The mating receptacles which accept the connector(s) on the sensor's cables are mounted on the bottom of the box to further prevent oil migration. Additionally, by having the sensor interface junction box mounted well above the normal working area, one can help to avoid unnecessary tampering with the interconnections.

The size and particular design characteristics of the junction box, as well as the proper wiring and mounting are left to the qualified electrical or electronic design personnel in each stamping facility. The following features are recommended for the sensor interface junction box:

- *Sufficient Connectors.* Enough connector receptacles to accept the maximum projected number of sensors to be used in dies running on that press.
- *Status Lamps.* Incandescent lamps, neon bulbs, and light emitting diodes (LEDs) often show the status of each sensor. These indicators can be mounted on the cover plate or door of the box. Since the sensors are often buried in the die, it is impossible—in most cases—to see the indicating LED on the sensor. By having external indicators on the sensor interface box, the sensor status can be readily determined. This is particularly useful in die setups where the activity of the sensors can be crucial in determining a good

setup.

- *Switches to Configure the Type of Input.* Normally open and normally closed selector switches to allow for quick sensor output determination without the need for rewiring is a desirable feature. Many sensors offer both types of outputs and this selector switch can easily assign the particular die protection channel a N.O. (Normally Open) or a N.C. (Normally Closed) function.
- *Use Rugged Enclosures.* Specify a good NEMA rating on the sensor interface junction box. This specification insures that the box can withstand the rigors of the metalforming environment. The quality of the materials used in the sensor interface box must not be compromised. The metalforming environment is simply too harsh to permit the use of poor quality enclosures.
- *Commercially Available Enclosures.* At least one manufacturer is currently supplying a commercially available, off-the-shelf sensor interface box specifically for the stamping environment. It incorporates a low-voltage DC power supply for the sensors.

Sensors Used in Advanced Diesetting Systems

Basic Sensor Types. There are two basic outputs from sensors. The first reads on and off for the detection of the presence or absence of a target. The second provides analog output for the precise measurement of the distance between the target and the sensor. By using a combination of these, it is possible to detect the proper installation of dies in the press. It is also possible to detect the shut height.

The sensors can be mounted in strategic areas, including the ram, in dies and in bolster plates, to name just several applications. Sensors can measure critical setup parameters which now are done with feeler gages, rule of thumb, or simply "eyeball" methods. The analog sensors offer an electrical output that is proportional to the distance between the sensor's sensing surface and the target.

Memory Modules. There are sensors available which are miniature memory modules. These sensors can be mounted on each die. These memory "buttons," as they are sometimes called, can store not only the identification number for each die, but can also contain such setup parameters as feed length, die protection timing, and limit switch angles. To read the information, a reading sensor is mounted on the press in such a way that it would read the memory modules mounted on all of the dies that are to be run on that press.

Thus, with these sensors tied to a small programmable logic controller and/or personal computer and a handful of peripheral equipment, one can have digital readouts. The display includes variables such as shut height directly in units of length, determining correct die installation, and correct area position in the press. Each die's setup parameters can be directly downloaded to the appropriate electronic hardware on the press.

Monitoring the Stamping Process

Additional uses for analog output sensors in the quick die change environment are limited only by one's imagination.

If each die has memory modules mounted on it which contain critical tolerances on measurements of strip thickness, feed length, maximum press run speeds, etc., then it would be essential to have additional sensors that also can be mounted both in and out of the die to monitor these parameters automatically as well.

Noncontacting Material Sensors. Production variables such as strip material thickness and feed length can be easily monitored with noncontacting electronic sensors. One can monitor strip thickness with inductive or photoelectric (including laser) sensors. The outputs of these sensors are sent to comparator modules. These modules then derive the thickness by measuring the distance between the surface of the sensor and the strip material as it enters the press. Various approaches include using a single sensor above the strip with a set of rollers to maintain the strip in tension or using two opposed sensors (one sensing below and the other above the strip.)

Contacting Sensors. Additionally, one can use a contacting sensor which has moving components that are attached to rollers and move in proportion to the strip's thickness. Sensor output, as with the noncontacting variety, is analog in nature thus providing an output proportional to the strip's thickness.

Monitoring Feeders. Feed length can be monitored easily both with analog as well as the on/off variety of sensors in the die. By critically placing these sensors, one can monitor hole locations or solid strip features for the proper feed length. Additionally, sensors can be mounted on the feed mechanism to monitor gripping and sliding motions on air feeds or similar mechanisms on mechanically coupled feeds. Variations in the material loops can be monitored with ultrasonic sensors as well as analog output photoelectric types. In this way, the entire feed cycle can be carefully monitored.

In the quick die change environment, the variations from die-to-die mandate that quick monitoring approaches be implemented. If one can eliminate as much of the time-consuming human-based measurement and malfunction detection approach, one's quick die change philosophy then takes on added meaning and reality.

Care and Handling of Sensors

No amount of well thought out electronic sensing in the quick die change environment can replace good personnel training. It is not enough to simply saturate the press and die with sensing and monitoring devices. One must take the time to train the shop floor personnel as to the delicate nature of electronic components when compared to the much more rugged mechanical hardware where the components are installed.

In the quick die change environment, the point is to be quick and efficient. No time should be wasted in the removal and replacement of dies.

Consequently, in this atmosphere charged with an urgency for speed, it is possible to overlook certain basic electronic housekeeping practices. With good training, shop floor personnel can be taught to handle sensor cables and harnesses with rapidity and respect. Well-routed cabling that is properly terminated with quick disconnect connectors can make quick die changes a reality. Taking the time to train the shop floor, design and managerial staffs to appreciate the advantages and special care requirements of using sensors cannot be overemphasized.

With sensors buried in and out of the die, quick die change is further enhanced by having the troublesome variables fully monitored. This allows for fully automated runs with little, if any, human monitoring or intervention. After all, the purpose for quick die change is to increase productivity and enhance competitiveness. There is no better way then to have a fully automated process that regulates itself through the use of electronic sensors.

REFERENCES

1. George Keremedjiev, "Using Electronic Sensors and Controllers in Quick Die Changes" SME technical paper TE89-512.
2. David A. Smith, *Die Design Handbook*, Society of Manufacturing Engineers, Dearborn, Michigan, 1990, "Die Protection Systems," Section Number 26.
3. George Keremedjiev, "Selecting and Implementing Miniature Sensors", SME Technical Paper TE89-183.
4. Kurt Miska, "Changing Dies Quickly," *Manufacturing Engineering* Vol. 104 No. 4 April 1990, p. 45-49.

27

SELECTING MAINTENANCE SOFTWARE*

QUICK DIE CHANGE REQUIRES A GOOD MAINTENANCE PROGRAM

To achieve the optimal conditions for quick die change, process variability must be reduced significantly. Typically, setup adjustments and fine tuning comprise 65% or more of the time requirements before a setup reduction program is instituted.

The key to eliminating adjustments is to provide a variability-free environment in which to execute quick die change procedures. The cornerstone of variability-free performance is doing everything right the first time.

Employee Involvement is Necessary

To approach the goal of zero breakdowns and zero process variability, operator and setup personnnel involvement is mandatory. However, responsibility at the operator and setup level is not sufficient to guarantee success.

Operators and setup personnel, together with specialized maintenance support employees, must have access to the tools necessary to accomplish the task. Additionally, these individuals should share in the responsibility and authority for the selection and application of these tools. Just as a multi-disciplined team must be formed to select the tools and methods for reducing setup times, a similarly combined group should select the tools to support a comprehensive preventive maintenance (PM) program.

COMPUTERIZED MAINTENANCE MANAGEMENT SYSTEMS

One effective maintenance management program is the development and continual enforcement of Computerized Maintenance Management Systems (CMMS). However, with over 200 potential suppliers, the process of determining which source can provide the right hardware, software and support for the business can be extremely complex and confusing. The best approach to successful system/software selection is the multi-disciplined team approach. The following pages present a generic representation of the process which will provide the best opportunity for success.

* Contributed by Philip D. Stang, Vice President, Professionals for Technology Associates, Inc., West Palm Beach, Florida.

Maintenance Management Software Selection Process—Summarized

1. Form a Maintenance Employee Involvement team to manage selection and implementation of the system.
2. Analyze and evaluate the current operation of the maintenance function.
3. Define the goals that are expected from the new system.
4. Review available software options.
5. Develop the "Probable" list and invite selected suppliers to visit your facility.
6. Contact references and/or visit existing user companies.
7. Analyze all accumulated information, match requirements and select the supplier.
8. Begin the training and implementation process.

FORM A MAINTENANCE EMPLOYEE INVOLVEMENT TEAM

The Process—How It Should Function

A Maintenance Employee InvolvementTeam should be formed to manage selection and implementation of the system. The team approach is necessary so that the appropriate people and functions are involved and in agreement with the goals and final decision. All of the following tasks should be performed collectively by the team. A typical team might composed of, but not limited to:

- Finance Representative
- Maintenance Planner
- Maintenance Supervisor
- Production Superintendent
- Operator and/or Setup Person
- Maintenance Mechanic
- Dieroom Representative
- Plant Engineer
- Storeroom Person
- An independent observer—someone to ask, "why?"

Selecting a Team Leader

One of these individuals should be elected as team leader. It's ideal if the same person can be the team leader for the selection and the project leader for implementation. The selection of the team leader depends on the skills of the individual, but it should be someone who is very project-oriented and able to grasp the scope of the project and how it fits in with long term overall company goals.

ANALYZE THE CURRENT ORGANIZATION OF THE MAINTENANCE FUNCTION

What is Currently Being Achieved?

Evaluate the maintenance function's organizational structure and determine what is currently being achieved. Determine if a manual work-order system is in place. What is the status of preventive maintenance? How is the storeroom organized? Where are the worst maintenance downtime problems?

The manner in which the maintenance function is organized will affect which software package is most appropriate for the company. Two important considerations are: whether the maintenance planners are to remain in the organization and whether a centralized or decentralized maintenance approach is used. Another organization concept that is becoming more common is the self-directed workforce/team approach. Not all maintenance software functions well with this approach.

Define the Goals Needed to be Achieved by the New System

By evaluating the current condition of the maintenance function, areas for improvement can be identified. System goals should certainly address those areas and then address any other specific goals that are critical to the facility. Goals should relate specifically to the maintenance department, such as implementation of preventive maintenance, reducing stock-outs in the storeroom, or improving productivity. Other goals may be more global, such as interfacing with the general ledger or purchasing systems, operating on specific hardware configurations, or the receipt of machine data from on-line production systems.

This step is critical, because later steps require clear definition of goals. Intelligent decisions can be made on option selection and tradeoffs.

REVIEW AVAILABLE SOFTWARE OPTIONS

Sources of Information for Maintenance Management Software

Plant engineering trade shows generally include numerous maintenance software vendors and are one of the best sources for identifying systems. Generally, meet with representatives of the company and review some of the software function. One or two days at a trade show should give a fairly good insight into the systems that should be considered.

Trade journals such as *Plant Engineering*, *Manufacturing Engineering*, *Engineers Digest* or *Maintenance Technology* have listings of maintenance software vendors who will provide information on available modules, prices, hardware platforms, and addresses of suppliers. From a listing, detailed literature can be requested from vendors. Trade journals also provide case studies of systems currently working in plants. In addition, as the interest in CMMS expands, major publications include impact studies on the topic (e.g., *Industry Week*, February 5, 1990).

A survey within the company should be conducted to determine if other facilities are currently using a computerized system. The company may even have a corporate agreement with a supplier which may enable it to receive a discount on the system.

DEVELOP A LIST OF "PROBABLE" SUPPLIERS

Tasks Required to Evaluate Suppliers

Develop a matrix of key required functions, key features, hardware preference, and budget guidelines. Weigh the factors in the matrix to meet the priorities, and rank suppliers based on the matrix. Suppliers' literature can be used, as can discussions with their representative, to collect this data.

Prepare a Standardized Request for Proposals

Preparing a standard request for proposals or a request for information to submit to suppliers tends to enhance the objectivity of the selection process. This document details the requirements of the system with adequate background for the supplier to clearly understand the company goals. It is generally laid out in such a way that the supplier can respond to each requirement in detail. Pricing should be required at this point. This will be time-consuming both in preparation and in awaiting responses, but because the requirements will be very specific, the time is worthwhile.

From the team's investigation of suppliers and with careful consideration of the company goals, cut the list to three or four suppliers that come closest to meeting the objectives.

INVITE PROBABLE SUPPLIERS TO VISIT THE SITE

Invite the selected suppliers to visit the facility and to present their product offering. Expect this visit to take between a half day and a day per supplier. Plan to share with them as much information about the company's objectives as possible and expect them to demonstrate how their product and/or services will meet those goals. Often a tour of the facility will help clarify the goals. All of the presentations should be conducted within a relatively short time period, ideally one week. This will help insure objective consideration of each product.

KEY AREAS FOR SUPPLIER EVALUATION

Functionality

Obviously, function is extremely important. The best way to evaluate function for the plant is to have goals clearly defined and to make sure that the product meets those goals. Features like resource balancing of labor, defect analysis, a menu-driven report writer and preventive maintenance tracking are good signs of a functional product.

Ease of Use

Most users of maintenance systems have little experience with computers, so ease of use is very important. Look for a fully menu-driven system (including report writers), pop-down pick lists, the ability to pick and put information on data entry, on-screen searches utilizing wildcards, and integrated graphics.

Integration With Other Systems

In today's era of information processing it is unacceptable to handle data more than once. Consequently, integrating systems is very important. Today maintenance systems can be integrated with purchasing, general ledger and CIM applications. Allow for expansion for other needs in the future.

Existing Hardware

Hardware requirements are sometimes set by existing equipment. The size of the operation may also dictate hardware requirements, however that is usually not the case. Generally, it's recommended that *the hardware decision is based on the software* that will best meet the need.

Customer Support

Check with the vendor and expect the following customer support:
- A full-time toll-free user-support phone line available in the company's time zone.
- Support personnel who are either programmers or engineers with plant maintenance experience.
- Training classes.
- On-site implementation assistance if needed.

Check the Company Background

The following points should be verified:
- How long has the company been in existence?
- What percentage of their business is devoted to maintenance software?
- How many installations of their system are in use?
- What is the background of their key people?

Contact References and Visit User Companies

Once a tentative selection of a system is completed, verify that decision by contacting existing users of that system. The supplier should be able to provide numerous references. Areas to consider when checking references are:

- How long has their system been fully operational?
- What industry or type of operation is the system being used in?
- Has the supplier provided prompt and reliable service?
- Was the training adequate?
- Does the software function as specified?
- Is the speed of the system acceptable?

Analyze All the Information and Select a Supplier

After all of the desired information has been received, the team should meet to make the final decision. The pluses and minuses of each system should be considered from the perspective of each team member. When all issues are resolved, the mutual team decision should be finalized. The unsuccessful suppliers should be notified in a courteous way of the decision, and the successful supplier contacted to arrange for procurement of the system.

Begin the Training and Implementation Process

The team should develop the implementation schedule with the assistance of the software and hardware suppliers. In addition, a professional consulting and education firm, specializing in zero breakdown maintenance training, should be engaged to conduct the required education and training. Critical to the implementation process are performance measurements, including schedule attainment. If properly and aggressively pursued, the new computer-based system can provide the following cost improvements:
- Inventory reduction improvement of 10% to 20%.
- Corrective maintenance improvement of 30% to 60%.
- Labor productivity increase of 25% to 50%.
- Asset utilization improvement of 5% to 8%.
- Quality improvement of 10% to 20%.

Figure 27-1 illustrates the interrelated functions, activities and report generation capability of a good maintenance management system.

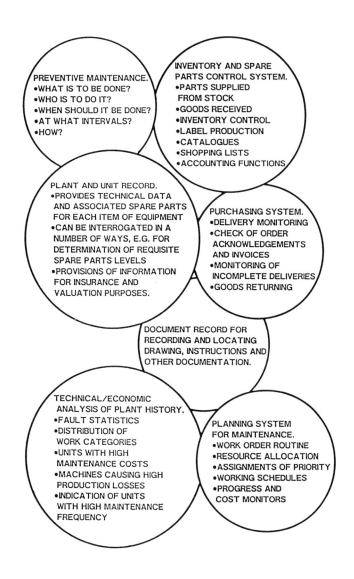

Fig. 27-1. *The interrelated functions, activities and report generation capability of a good maintenance management system.*

TEAM MAINTENANCE MANAGEMENT SYSTEMS NEEDS

A team maintenance management system should include:

Preventive Maintenance Planning and Scheduling
- details planned work schedules; trades tools, resources, and parts.
- lists jobs in order of priority and forecasts workloads.

Work Order Control
- generates work orders.
- controls and manages scheduled and emergency work.
- gives work instructions and inputs data on hours, comments, etc.

Equipment and Manpower Information
- asset register of equipment and facilities.
- data on labor availability.

Job Files and Tasking
- maintains detailed procedures of all jobs, including preventive maintenance and troubleshooting.
- contains parts requirements.

Defect Analysis
- identifies common causes of breakdowns and equipment failures, including mean time to failure.
- leads to remedial action.

Equipment Condition Base
- indicates wear and condition of equipment, e.g. vibration analysis and tonnage waveform analysis.
- predicts service life and failure points.

Plant History
- contains detailed history of technical and financial data on assets.
- establishes cost effectiveness.
- indicates need for repair, modification, and replacement.

Stock Control and Purchasing System
- provides a perpetual inventory system with a full audit trail.
- maintains economical stock holding and controls costs.

Intelligent Query
- permits access to database for customized reports and forms.
- communicates with minicomputers and mainframes.

Figure 27-2 illustrates how many maintenance management tasks operate from a common computerized database.

Report And Screen Features Of a Good Interactive System

The following are important categories for report generation and system monitoring:

Equipment ID—Equipment identification number, name, location, etc. Used to enter or change or display these equipment details for equipment data card, history and PM files.

Data Card Freeform—Used for the equipment data screen or card for

310

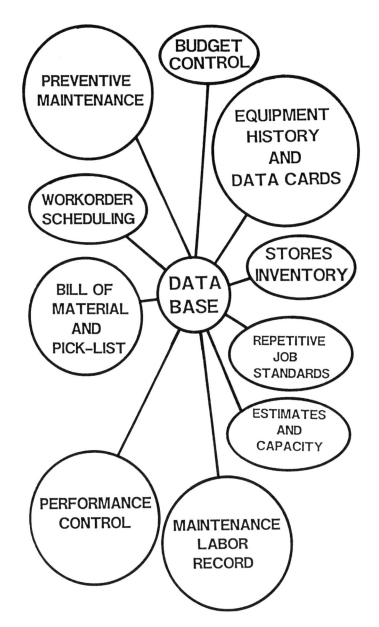

Fig. 27-2. *Many maintenance management tasks operate from a common computerized database.*

additional lines of freeform data for each chosen equipment ID, such as rpm, volts, manufacturer, serial number, cost, warranty, and other important information.

Spares—Used for equipment spare parts data for each chosen piece of equipment.

History—Used for repair history for each chosen piece of equipment ID, including repair date, work order, time, cost, cause of failure, downtime etc.

Vision Display and Printout—Display or print wiring or piping diagram, parts with exploded views of dies and press equipment, etc., all automatically tied into the Equipment Data screen. Also, a video tape library reference for complex maintenance procedures required by specific pieces of equipment is desirable.

Preventive Maintenance by Date—Preventive maintenance running inspection, check sheet or preventive maintenance work order description for given equipment to be issued by date: week, month, quarter, or year.

PM Shutdown—Preventive maintenance work-order requiring shutdown of the specified equipment to carry out the PM task.

PM By Meter—Preventive maintenance inspection or work order to be triggered and issued automatically by the meter when a specified number of strokes, pieces, hours, miles, kilometers, revolutions, etc., have been performed.

PM Replacement—Preventive maintenance replacement of some part of equipment such as a critical punch or filter. The meter will trigger a PM notice.

PM Results by Date—Enter results of PM inspection by date for given equipment.

PM Results by Meter—Enter reading on meter: hours, strokes, miles, etc., and/or results of PM inspection by meter when due.

Work Order (WO) Status Dispatch Log—Display status for any WO, change status, log and WO where extensive pre-planning and pre-scheduling is not warranted, with automatic timestamp and chronological sort. Examples: WOs of relatively short duration, single craft, minor jobs, small service work. Recommends where next job is to be assigned for appropriate craft (skilled-trade), simply on first come, first served basis.

WO Individually Planned—Corrective Repair work order of normal priority, to be planned and scheduled according to present available craft manpower capacity and date needed.

WO Emergency or Critical—Emergency priority one, work order must be done immediately, danger to life or equipment, drop everything and do it first, then write up the details. Critical priority two, work order must be done today, has priority over previously planned normal priority three jobs.

WO Waiting Shutdown—Corrective work order, priority four; waiting for given equipment to be shut down, to be planned and scheduled accordingly.

WO Repetitive—Corrective work order, repetitive job number, reissue and plan the same as a specified previous work order.

Budget Departmental—Monthly maintenance budget, and variances by department or cost center.

Labor Timesheets—For a given employee, enter hours worked, various work orders, regular, overtime and call-in hours.

Employee Rates—Add and delete employees with specified crafts and pay rates to roster.

Material Inventory Status—Display stock items on hand, reserved, on order, location, etc.

Inventory Reserve, Issue and Return—Reserve stock item for planned work order, issue, or return, stock items for a given WO.

Inventory Add, Change or Delete—Add new stock item, change or delete existing one.

Inventory Where Used—For each stock item, show all equipment where it is used.

Inventory Physical Count and Adjustment—Physical count and/or adjustment for stock items.

Non-Stock Material and Expense—Charges to a given work order for direct purchase of materials not carried in inventory, expenses such as contracted work, travel, crane rental, overhead, etc.

Bill of Materials Picklist—Shows all inventory items reserved, issued and/or returned for any work order. The material is billed at the latest averaged prices. Optionally, overhead, general and administrative expense including profit may be added, for billing to customers for field service work.

Completed Repetitive Work Orders—For each type of repetitive work order identified, it shows the labor hours and cost performance for a number of previous repetitive WOs and for estimated hours by crafts.

Performance Daily Reports and Daily Work Order Activity—Shows how much regular and overtime was worked on each job the day before, and how much work still has to be done to complete it.

Stock Reorder List Report—Shows all the stock items that have hit their reorder point, or dropped below it, on a given day.

PM Meter Checksheets—Show all PM tasks to be done, for each craft, for a given equipment ID, triggered by meter, strokes, hours, miles, km, revolutions, etc.

PM Inspection Due Report—Shows all PM inspections done on a given day.

PM Inspection Results Report—Shows results of all PM inspections done on a given day.

PM Inspection Overdue Report—An important fail safe report showing all PM inspections that are overdue, the number of weeks overdue, and by craft and department.

Schedule Backlog and Capacity Reports

Schedule backlog and capacity reports include the following.

Work-order Status Reports—Shows if a work order is waiting for a specific reason (such as a lack of material), is in process, or ready for scheduling. Work orders are automatically scheduled in order of priority and date needed, up to the finite net capacity available by craft.

Net Capacity Report—Automatically determines net available craft capacity for coming week, on a moving average basis, with allowances for average amount overtime, contract labor, absenteeism, vacation, PM, unscheduled emergency, and minor jobs.

Backlog Graphs—Graphs WO backlog trends for each craft in weeks. Shows needed changes in staffing levels, overtime, outside contract labor.

Weekly Performance Reports and Planning Backlog Report

This is needed for authorization and follow-up of work orders in planning stages. Included are:

Work-orders Ready for Scheduling—Shows all planned work-orders ready for scheduling, and number of workers, hours, and crafts involved.

Weekly WO Performance—Shows status of all WOs in process, work done, and backlog manhours to complete them.

Weekly Completed Work-orders—Labor and cost performance report on all completed WOs in a week.

Weekly Labor Report—This is available for each employee. It distributes all the labor costs to the WOs worked on during the week.

Timeslot Averages—Shows the timeslot moving averages for each craft for estimating jobs.

PM Check Sheet—Shows PM tasks triggered by date, that are to be done by each craft, for each equipment ID.

PM Inspection Due Report—Shows all PM inspections due in a week by craft and equipment ID.

PM Results Report—Shows results of all PM inspection done in a given week.

Monthly Reports Examples

Monthly completed work-orders can show actual versus estimated hours, as well as labor and material cost performance of work orders completed during the month.

Equipment History Report—Every completed work-order is automatically transferred to the equipment history file. It shows labor hours and material, down time and cause code for each WO. Also the work order narrative lines can be optionally transferred to an equipment narrative history file.

Monthly Maintenance Budget Control Report—Actual costs are compared to budget to develop variances. The percentage of staff hours worked in different priorities are shown.

Stock Usage and Balances—Shows monthly usage and stock balance for each stock number by warehouse, and year-to-date.

Other Desirable Features

Some other desirable features include the following.

Backup hard disk files—Automatic backup.

Net Capacity Report—Shows net capacity for each craft, in staff hours, to do jobs during the next week.

Restore hard disk—Restores the files in case they were damaged by problems

314

such as a power failure.

Equipment Family Report—Shows associated equipment family, groups, production lines, or assembly components.

Incomplete Work Orders by Time Stamp—Shows all incomplete (open) work orders, sorted by priority, and in order of MM/DD/YY; hrs:min:sec time stamp when received, first come, first served.

Material Inventory Stock Catalog—Prints stock catalog by stock number, by stock location or by warehouses.

Physical Inventory Print—Prints physical count reports for stock removed from inventory and variances.

Stock Catalogue by Equipment ID—For each item of equipment, shows stock number and details of parts carried in inventory.

Warehouse on Hand Quantity Change—Changes on hand inventory reorder to physical count.

PM Schedule for Any Week—Prints preventive maintenance manhours by craft for any week or whole year. This is useful for planning purposes.

PM Outstanding Inspections—Shows all outstanding PM work for each equipment, number including PMs on hold, waiting shutdown, and component replacement.

28

INSTITUTING A TONNAGE METER PROGRAM

MEASUREMENT CONSIDERATIONS FOR MECHANICAL PRESSES[1,2]

Every good program includes a quantification process. Measurements assure repeatability, the reduction of variance, and safe limits for machine operation. In this chapter the importance of measurement cannot be overstated. The following items should be considered:

1. It is necessary to assure that the forces required to make parts do not exceed the capacity of the machine.
2. Every effort should be made to assure that only the *minimum force* is used to make the part. This will not only increase tool life but minimize press component wear as well.
3. Knowledge of the tonnage requirement of a particular tool aids in selecting the proper press size.
4. One important advantage of load measurement is the ability to determine the condition of the press and recognize press problems. *Press-analysis* can be an important part of a preventive maintenance program.
5. Accurate load measurement enables the operator to adjust the stamping process, which assures proper tool and press operations and results in better part quality.
6. The forming of parts in the metalworking process is the result of using the kinetic energy available from the flywheel. Consuming this energy in the working cycle reduces the flywheel speed, hence reducing its energy.
7. Die setup time can be greatly reduced and jobs can be set to standardized optimum conditions of loading and load distribution. Off-center loading can easily be detected.
8. Early detection of changes in stock thickness, die lubrication, or metal characteristics helps maintain quality.
9. Accurate parts counting can be achieved by connecting the counter to the measuring device, allowing it to operate only after the press has reached a pre-determined force.

Emergency Stopping Capability

All tonnage meters are designed to output a signal, usually by relay closure, whenever an overload condition exceeds a preset value. While this is historical information, it can serve to reduce the amount of damage that could occur with multiple mis-hits. A tonnage meter combined with in-die sensing (Chapter 26) can provide enough press and die protection to permit unattended press operation.

The overload signal can initiate either an emergency or top-of-stroke signal. If it is anticipated that an emergency stopping function could result in the press being stuck on the bottom, a top-of-stroke stop may be the best choice.

Hydraulic Overload Tripping[3,4]

Presses with hydraulic overload systems have short-stroke hydraulic cylinders at each press connection. In most cases, the sequence of events during tripping starts when an overload condition causes hydraulic fluid to dump through a relief valve when a preset pressure is exceeded. In the case of presses having multiple connections, a limit switch is actuated and an electrical signal is sent to solenoid-controlled valves to trip the other hydraulic overload cylinders.

It takes several milliseconds for all cylinders to dump their oil when the hydraulic overload system is actuated. During this time, a severe out-of-parallel condition will exist that can cause serious die damage.

The tonnage monitor overload signal can actuate all hydraulic overload cylinder dump valves simultaneously. There are a number of advantages to this system which include:

- A destructive out-of-parallel condition is avoided.
- There is little danger of sticking the press on the bottom.
- The trip point is easily adjusted at the tonnage meter.
- The normal function of the hydraulic overload system is unaffected, which provides desirable redundancy of protection.

Snap-thru

Reverse load forces occur during blanking operations when the punches break through the part. The energy stored as a strain in the die and the press is suddenly released, subjecting the press to a reverse load phenomenon. Chapter 29 has detailed information on dealing with snap-thru problems.

It is important that force-measuring instruments be capable of reading these peak *reverse* forces.

Energy Savings

Checks with a clamp-on ammeter show an increase in current draw as press tonnages increase. Clearly there is an energy savings to be realized by operating at minimum tonnages that will produce good parts. A study of the actual savings should include correction for *power factor*. The power factor of an induction motor is known to change toward unity as the amperage draw increases, resulting in the clamp-on ammeter underestimating the actual savings of current.

A good way to characterize the electrical energy input into the stamping process is in terms of joules or watt seconds per part or stroke.

Tonnage Meter Operating Principles

A tonnage meter provides a readout of tonnage by means of sensors or transducers that measure the slight physical stretch or compression of press members under load. These sensors, nearly all of which are based on the foil strain gage principle, are placed on the press at locations that will stretch or compress in a manner that is representative of actual tonnage.

A foil strain gage is much smaller than a postage stamp. On its surface is a grid-work of very fine conductive foil. When the grid work is stretched the electrical resistance increases, and decreases in like manner if compressed. When affixed to the surface of a press member, its electrical resistance changes in proportion to the actual stretch or compression at the location where it is attached.

To obtain a high output, four gages are used in a Wheatstone Bridge configuration. The nominal resistance of that bridge is 350 ohms.

When a press force is generated, the structure deforms and the resulting strain unbalances the bridge. A minute voltage, proportional to this force, appears at the output terminals. This output is fed via shielded cables (to reduce spurious signals) to the input of the tonnage meter. Once the instrument is calibrated, the entire press will act much like a spring-type weighing scale.

Bolt-on Strain Transducers

Most tonnage meters use strain transducers that can be bolted to the press at locations that exhibit stretch or compression that is representative of press tonnage. Each strain transducer has four strain gages that make up a Wheatstone Bridge.

The bolt-on sensors are produced by bonding the strain gages to an intermediate structure which can then be bolted to the machine structure under test. This method allows for mechanical amplification which increases the measurement accuracy. The sensors are affixed by screws. Pretapped weld pads positioned with a weld jig greatly speed the work. An advantage in the use of bolt-on strain-gage transducers is that the individual units are interchangeable. Thus, once a machine is calibrated, transducers can be interchanged without re-calibration.

Strain Transducer Mounting Locations

There are many places on a press where strain gages or strain transducers can be mounted to obtain readings that equate to actual tonnage. The exact location must be chosen with great care if a good clean gage output is to be obtained.

The press pitmans are a popular location for strain transducers. This works particularly well if transducers are mounted on opposite sides of the pitman and wired in parallel to cancel out errors due to bending.

Signal wires connected to a moving press member can be protected from damage by running the wire through coiled nylon air hose between junction boxes. The transition at the junction box knock-out openings can be made with standard pipe fitting adapters.

On underdriven presses, the pull rods are a popular location for gage placement. To eliminate any error due to bending, it is best to place dual gages or transducers on opposite sides of the rod or link. One manufacturer claims good results by applying a type of metal foil-backed strain gages with a 50-joule capacitive-discharge spot-welder. One half of the bridge is placed on each side of the pull rod or link. This method uses engineering calibration factors based on pull rod cross-sectional area and *Young's Modulus* for the material involved.

An alternative location in underdriven press applications, with similar results, is on the top of the slide near the pull-rod attachment point.[3]

Column-mounted sensors give results that are quite representative of die and press conditions, provided that the mounting locations are chosen with care. Many presses have box-like heavy plate shrouds surrounding the tie-rods with a much lighter fabricated plate to make up the rest of the column structure. This forms a housing for mechanical equipment and provides lateral bracing. A good location for the sensor is on the heavy shroud just below the gibbing.

Locating the sensors on the outside of the columns may result in low signals and poor linearity. The reason for this is that the bed and crown bend or bow under load, which relieves the preload on the inside tie rod shrouds at a much faster rate than occurs on the outside. The bowing of the bed and crown actually tends to drive the outside of the columns into compression. *Figure 29-13* illustrates why this occurs.

Gap and OBI presses are usually gaged near the throat opening on the side of the press. This location is as good as any on the frame, but any location other than the pitman will be affected by die location. The calibration should be done with a load cell directly under the connection. If the die is set toward the rear of the bolster, the tonnage meter will read erroneously *low*. Presses have been damaged because diesetters were not aware of this problem.

Machines having guided plungers can be successfully gaged by installing custom-made load cells between the plunger and its attachment point to the slide.

Sensor locations should be guided by sound mechanical principles, not just for ease of installation. Otherwise the press room personnel will not be able to correlate the results on the meter with actual conditions, and the tonnage meter will fall into disuse.

Calibration

The process of adjusting the force-measurement instrument to agree with the actual load on the press is referred to as *calibration*.

Two common ways to calibrate a mechanical press are dynamic calibration with load cells and static calibration with hydraulic jacks. With either method, the purpose is to apply a known force to the press structure.

320

The sensitivity of the measuring instrument is then adjusted so that the indicated meter-force reading corresponds to the known force applied to the press structure.

Calibration Numbers

The resistance of the Wheatstone Bridge is nearly always a nominal 350 ohms. To verify or re-establish the correct tonnage meter gain setting, an artificial tonnage is created by shunting a high-value resistor across one arm of the bridge. The values range from 50,000 to 1,000,000 ohms. This is usually done immediately after calibration with load cells and the number is recorded inside the instrument cabinet for reference.

If the sensors are carefully located with attention to close symmetry, and the press is in good condition, the calibration numbers should be within 10% of each other. A large scatter indicates that there is a press problem. Extremely high calibration numbers indicate the sensor is mounted in an inactive location. To provide a reading, the tonnage meter must provide a great deal of signal amplification. This can exacerbate any electrical noise problems and result in erratic tonnage meter operation.

Number of Channels

If the pitmans or plungers are gaged, the tonnage meter should have as many channels as there are slide connections. A single channel monitor is sufficient for process control and detecting overloads on an OBI press. The chief advantage of gaging both sides of the throat opening and using a two-channel monitor is that any offset in side-to-side loading can be measured. A major disadvantage is that accurate tonnage values can be measured only if the load is *centered* from front to back exactly under the connection.

When straight-side presses are gaged on the columns, it is normal to install four sensors and use a four-channel monitor. As an economy measure, two sensors are sometimes installed across diagonal corners and a two-channel monitor is used. While this will provide useful process control information, especially if the bed left-to-right dimension is large compared to the front-to-back measurement, it may fail to provide a press stopping alarm in the event of an overload condition.

When a sudden overload occurs due to a mis-hit in one corner of a die, the corresponding column is stretched and the load on the adjacent column on that end of the press may drop to a lower than normal value. This effect is especially pronounced in the case of large dies because the equalizing blocks act as a fulcrum point on the upper die shoe.

A partial solution is to install strain gages on all columns and sum the outputs of the gages on each end of the press by tying the wires in parallel. Generally, the best long-term economy is to install a four-channel monitor early in the planning process.

AVAILABLE FEATURES IN TONNAGE METERS

Tonnage meters should no longer be just a watchdog that protect the press from overloads. The current generation of microprocessor-based meters indeed do much more. Tasks such as counting good hits and indicating deviation from the optimum tonnage values are handled with ease. One of the most important diesetting applications for tonnage meters is to verify a correct dieset as a means to reduce process variability.

Readout

Numerical readouts are usually provided for each channel as well as totals for each slide. Depending on the electronic design, the total reading may be either an analog sum of the peak instantaneous total, or a simple arithmetical sum. Often the analog sum is much lower than the arithmetical sum of the individual channels. This is normal, and is a result of the peak tonnages on the individual channels not occurring simultaneously. For waveform signature analysis work, an analog sum can provide additional useful data such as determining the phase relationship of chatter phenomena.

Communications Capability

Two-way data communication capabilities which permit area-wide press metering and computer-integrated manufacturing (CIM) applications are available from most manufacturers of tonnage meters. This is often done by means of a communications printed circuit board or card that is inserted into an expansion slot within the meter. At least one brand of meter has the capability of exporting waveform signature data for remote analysis.

A very important consideration, when evaluating equipment with this level of sophistication, is to be sure that the data will be used to improve the way that processes are controlled and the way business is managed. Stamping customers are increasingly unimpressed by "showcase" applications of technology.

Automatic Rezeroing Function

The digital signal displayed by tonnage meters is derived by means of an analog to digital (A to D) conversion of the analog DC voltage output of the strain gage. The strain gage output is very small; a few millivolts at most. Considerable amplification is required to get an analog signal level of two to five volts peak for A to D conversion.

Compensation must be made for the temperature changes that affect the DC balance of both the strain gages and DC amplifiers. There must not be a load on the press when the rezeroing function is accomplished. The easiest and best means to establish DC zero balance is by means of a contact closure at the top of the press stroke. This can either be derived from the press cam limit switch or

322

a limit switch actuated by the press slide.

Tonnage meter manufacturers generally produce "camless" tonnage meters in order to simplify installation. The automatic rezeroing is derived by a time delay after the last signal exceeds a fixed threshold. Such meters can be fooled by pressworking operations that produce multiple signals in the same press stroke and exceed the threshold.

Figure 28-1 illustrates two waveform signatures that show an automatic rezeroing problem. The pressworking operation is a combined heavy punching and forming operation. The tonnage meter rezeroing time delay started running at the peak of the punching load and rezeroing to an incorrect value that occurred at the peak of the forming load. This resulted in a very erratic meter operation and false press shutdowns. The solution was to increase the time delay of the rezeroing function. On some brands of meters, the change can be made by entering data inside the meter, while other types require a software change.

The need to start the rezeroing timer usually means that the meter will provide no reading unless the threshold is exceeded. The threshold must be high enough to prevent readings from being generated by normal press movement due to the dynamic mass of the slide. Tonnage meters often fail or give very erratic results on presses that are in bad condition. This is due to the number of signals generated by the thumps and bumps that accompany such problems.

Ease of Use

The most important feature to look for in a tonnage meter is ease of use and maintenance. It is important that the front panel controls used to initialize the meter for each job be easy to set correctly. If resetting of the tonnage limits requires specialized skills, or if the meter is so complicated that it cannot be maintained in house, it is apt to be disabled and provide no useful function.

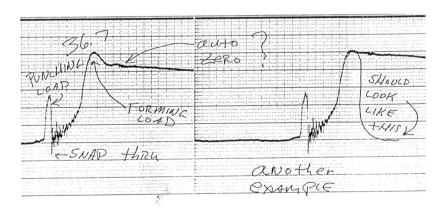

Figure 28-1. *Tonnage signature waveform of a press tonnage meter having an automatic rezeroing timing problem.*

DIESETTING APPLICATIONS FOR TONNAGE METERS

The time required for die change can be reduced in several ways by using tonnage meters. Press shut height can be precisely adjusted to correct values based on the previous run figures. Problems with equipment such as a damaged die or press can be identified. Tonnage meters are an important aid to establishing and maintaining a common shut height, as was discussed in Chapter 11.[5, 6]

Reduction of setup time and improvement of part quality can go hand in hand. To achieve this goal, team members who perform quick die changes should be trained to use the tonnage meter as both a process control and a diagnostic tool.

Standardization of die shut heights is an important aid to flexible stamping capability. Static die and press dimensional measurements alone will not achieve accurate shut heights. Tonnage meters are very useful as a guide to adjust die shut heights to compensate for both die and press deflection.

Duplicating a Previous Run

Common sense teaches us that the only requirement to produce high-quality parts is to exactly duplicate all settings and adjustments of all equipment on the line to values that are known to be correct. Of course, a database of correct values is needed.

There are several important advantages in having a tonnage meter installed on every press even though that press may have a shut height readout. If the die has been reworked, the shut height may have been changed. A slug or other foreign object under the die will not be detected by the shut height readout. Very fine adjustments can be made with the tonnage meter.

Should the die or bolster accidentally be set on some foreign object such as dirt or a slug, the tonnage meter will show a high reading on one side or corner of the press. This is also true of any problem with the press or die that may have caused the slide(s) to be out of parallel with the bed under load. Prompt corrective action can be taken and results verified on the meter.[7]

A quality setup helps to assure high-quality stampings. It is important to exactly duplicate the conditions known to produce a given stamping. Setup reduction objectives cannot be complete if the stamping operation is running below standard pace or producing off-standard parts. A tonnage meter can be used to establish exact shut height adjustment and also as an aid to spot die and press problems.

How Databases are Maintained

Stamping plants often maintain one or more databases of correct tonnage values. When first installing tonnage meters, several ways of maintaining tonnage databases can be tested to determine which is the most cost-effective. If the tool and die department maintains a die maintenance database, the tonnage information can be included in the information about each individual die. In the case of a computerized maintenance management program operating on a plant-wide network, this information can be made available on the shop floor via a data terminal system.

The dieset teams may wish to maintain extensive manual records of tonnages being used and rely upon this data for press adjustment upon die set.

Automated tonnage data gathering from presses equipped with tonnage meters can be transmitted to a central point where the data is analyzed and optimal values determined.

Storage of archival data can be done on a computer diskette for each jobs' tonnage history. Computer software can print graphic displays of trends based upon tonnage history. Any out-of-tolerance condition is printed out for prompt correction.

A simple system that can make use of computing equipment and software prints the correct tonnage values for each job on gummed mailing labels. These labels are then affixed to the presses and/or tonnage meter(s) where the jobs are run.

Figure 28-2 is an example of four gummed mailing labels which may be attached directly to presses, tonnage monitors or a sheet of acrylic plastic attached to the press for that purpose. The labels list the tonnage value considered to be optimum for each job run in a given press.

As part of continuous improvement goals, operating tonnages are reduced to

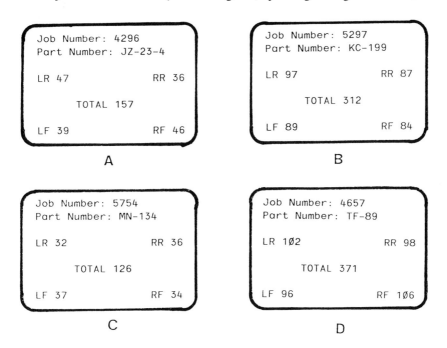

Job Number: 4296
Part Number: JZ-23-4

LR 47   RR 36

TOTAL 157

LF 39   RF 46

A

Job Number: 5297
Part Number: KC-199

LR 97   RR 87

TOTAL 312

LF 89   RF 84

B

Job Number: 5754
Part Number: MN-134

LR 32   RR 36

TOTAL 126

LF 37   RF 34

C

Job Number: 4657
Part Number: TF-89

LR 1Ø2   RR 98

TOTAL 371

LF 96   RF 1Ø6

D

Figure 28-2. *An example of four gummed mailing labels which may be attached directly to presses to display optimum tonnage values.*

the minimum values that will produce a good part. Some methods include eliminating hard marks and unneeded contact areas in the die, leveling the press, and eliminating any skew in the press bed. Chapter 15 has information on how to accomplish this.

Figure 28-3 illustrates the penciled-in corrections made directly on the gummed mailing labels. The person who maintains the database simply notes the corrections and updates the database. *Figure 28-4* illustrates the replacement labels printed from the new data.

If a general purpose database program running on a personal computer is used, archival data is simple to maintain. The file specification under which the file is saved can identify the date on which a given file reflects the then-current records. *Figure 28-5* shows a portion of such a directory printed from the screen of a MS-DOS® machine.

If the database is maintained on the fixed or hard drive of a personal computer, the older files should be periodically moved to diskettes for archival storage.

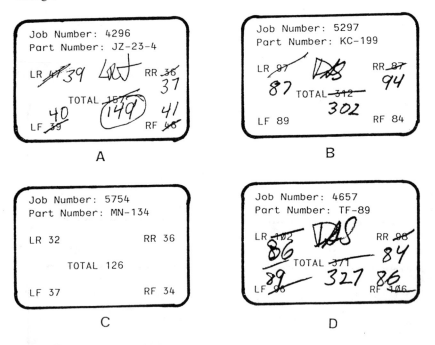

Figure 28-3. *Penciled-in corrections may be made directly on the mailing labels shown in Figure 28-2.*

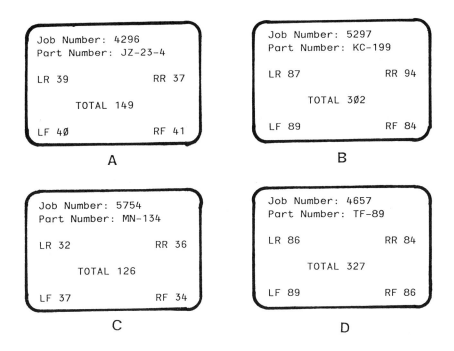

Figure 28-4 *The tonnage database is updated from the penciled-in tonnage values shown in Figure 28-2, and replacement labels are printed from that data.*

```
Directory of C:\TONNAGE

88-3Ø9.DB      53874   11-Ø4-88    9:17A
88-31Ø.DB      539Ø2   11-Ø5-88    8:24A
88-311.DB      53984   11-Ø6-88    9:Ø5A
88-312.DB      53987   11-Ø7-88    9:27A
       4 File(s)       9Ø1Ø274 bytes free
```

Figure 28-5 *A portion of a tonnage database directory printed from the screen of a personal computer: the first two numbers of the file specification indicate the year, with the Julian date or numbered day of the year following the dash.*

INSTITUTING A TONNAGE METER PROGRAM

The Dark Ages

If widespread training in the operating principles and beneficial applications of tonnage meter data is not done, employee cooperation and acceptance cannot be assured. It is a poor idea to use tonnage meters primarily as a tool for employee surveillance and as a basis for disciplinary action.

If the skilled trades' work practices require that only an electrician from the electronics clean room be permitted to adjust and use the equipment, the program will probably fail. This person is not the one who needs the information.

The program has a dim future if detection of an overload condition becomes

327

a subject of controversy between the tool and die department and the plant engineering department.

There should be load cells for calibrating the equipment whenever a suspect reading is noted. This would help settle questions about the accuracy of the readings.

If a proper foundation based upon trust and common goals is not in place at the outset, the system will fall into disuse quickly.

EMPLOYEE TRAINING AND ACCEPTANCE

Ideally, the basic aspects of a plan to install and use tonnage meters should have substantial input from the users. Such a program is an opportunity to get a better understanding of the press/die relationship and to improve cooperative maintenance and setup efforts. Given an opportunity for their input, the acceptance by employee involvement groups and setup work teams is outstanding. The keystone to the success is training.

Sources of Training Instructors

Normally, vendors will provide training in the use of their equipment. When seeking quotes on equipment, it is important to determine how much training is to be provided. Good questions to ask are:
- How much training will be provided?
- Will the training be available for all shifts?
- Will hands-on experience be provided?
- What is the cost, if any, of additional or follow-up training?
- Can the training be videotaped?

Engineering societies, such as SME, are also a good source of instructors.

Training and Trust Go Together

All employees must be expected to be responsible for the correct usage of the meters. Once training has been completed, the student should be issued a certificate of completion and the key needed to set up the tonnage meter controls. Training and trust should go together.

Everyone who is willing should receive training. This will result in a strong grass-roots commitment to using tonnage meters which control the most common parameter of the stamping process—the application of correct tonnage.

Establishing a Pilot Project

Installing tonnage meters on every press in a large shop is an expensive undertaking. To establish cost justification, it may be wise to install several tonnage meters on presses where press and die damage is a problem. An advantage of doing a pilot project is that different brands of meters can be tested under actual production conditions to determine which is the best for the application. This should be determined by analyzing all factors, not just cost alone. The opinions of the users are very important. Setup teams will also want input into deciding where additional tonnage meters are installed.

Employee Involvement and Satisfaction

The tonnage meter will become a focal point for quality circle groups. Employee involvement groups and setup reduction teams can gage the effectiveness of waste reduction and quality improvement efforts. It often is found that a reduction in required tonnage results in an improvement in quality and reduction of scrap.

Setting dies to tonnage meter database figures generally results in parts that achieve quality control approval upon first submission. Delays and scrap generation resulting from trial-and-error slide adjustments are avoided.

WAVEFORM SIGNATURE ANALYSIS

Many tonnage meters have an analog output to permit analysis of the waveform signature. The output voltage ranges from two and one-half to five volts at 100% capacity, depending upon the manufacturer's specifications. This signal is fed to an oscilloscope, strip chart recorder, or digital recorder. Digital recorders have the advantage of permitting computer-aided analysis such as modal analysis, modem transmission and archival storage.

Chapter 29 contains some idealized examples of waveform signatures. The actual signatures, examples of which are found throughout this work, are somewhat ragged due to the nature of the actual forces being measured.

This procedure is excellent for analysis of a number of press and die problems such as snap-thru energy, loose tie rods, counterbalance problems, gib chatter, and floating draw ring impact problems, to name a few.

Tonnage Curve Analysis

The widespread use of inverted-draw and stretch-draw dies in automotive stamping plants has made analysis of forming forces throughout the press stroke a necessity. Attempts to lessen the impact of the blankholder on the draw ring by slowing the press down, or by using compression shock-absorbers or rubber, have made the problem worse in some, but not all, cases.

The kinetic energy of the slide can often be used to advantage in the process. Measured values of up to 10% of slide tonnage have been observed when contacting the work fairly high in the press stroke, without inducing a strain in the press frame. The press is acting much like a drop-hammer in such cases. This phenomenon can be confusing because it doesn't show as a peak when reading data from column-mounted sensors. A normal peak will be seen from in-die sensor data.

To analyze the operation for a problem, a linear transducer that provides a voltage output relative to position can be used with a multiple channel recorder. This will juxtapose slide distance from bottom of stroke with actual instantaneous tonnage. This information can be compared to the tonnage curve supplied by the press manufacturer.

Automatic Tonnage Curve Analysis and Protection

Some tonnage meters can be programmed with the press tonnage curve and are capable of continuously comparing tonnage with crankshaft rotation. An alarm signal is generated if there is a tonnage curve violation.

Draw ring bounce or rebound upon initial contact may occur. This may be a problem.

Correction of measured tonnage curve violations may involve stepping cylinder engagement, lowering the ring, changing the press speed, modifying the press, or specifying a larger press.

Troubleshooting Tonnage Meters

Waveform signature analysis is an invaluable tool for troubleshooting tonnage meter problems. *Figure 28-1* is an example of such an application.

REFERENCES

1. Donald F. Wilhelm: "Measuring Loads On Mechanical Presses", SME Conference Proceeding, Society of Manufacturing Engineers, Dearborn, Michigan, 1988.
2. Donald F. Wilhelm: *Understanding Presses and Press Operations*, Society of Manufacturing Engineers, Dearborn, Michigan, 1981.
3. David A. Smith, *Die Design Handbook*, Section 27, Society of Manufacturing Engineers, Dearborn, Michigan, 1990.
4. C. Wick, J. W. Benedict, and R. F. Veilleux, *Tool and Manufacturing Engineers Handbook*, (Fourth Edition) Volume 2, Chapter 5, Society of Manufacturing Engineers, Dearborn, Michigan, 1984.
5. David A. Smith: "How to Improve Hit-to-hit Time With a Tonnage Monitor.", SME Technical Paper TE88-780, Society of Manufacturing Engineers, Dearborn, Michigan, 1988.
6. David A. Smith: "Adjusting Dies to a Common Shut Height", SME/FMA Technical Paper TE89-565, Society of Manufacturing Engineers, Dearborn, Michigan, 1989.
7. David A. Smith: "Why Press Slide Out of Parallel Problems Affect Part Quality and Available Tonnage", SME Technical Paper TE88-442, Society of Manufacturing Engineers, Dearborn, Michigan, 1988.

29

CONTROL THE PROCESS WITH WAVEFORM SIGNATURE ANALYSIS

ROOT CAUSAL FACTORS OF SNAP-THRU ENERGY RELEASE

The loud boom that characterizes a snap-thru problem when cutting through metal is the sudden release of the potential energy stored in the press and die members as strains or deflection. The deflection is a normal result of the pressure required to cut through the material.[1]

In extreme cases, the energy released can damage the press. The press connection (the pitman attachment point to the slide) is easily damaged by the reverse load generated by snap-thru. As a general rule, presses are not designed to withstand reverse loading of more than 10%. This shock may result in die components working loose.

Mathematical Analysis of the Amount of Energy Stored*[1]

In timing the punch entry or die shear, care must be given to provide for a gradual release of developed tonnage. With the exception of high speed applications, the shock is not normally generated by the impact of the punches on the stock. In fact, when the punches first contact the stock, the initial work is done by the kinetic energy of the slide. To complete the cut, energy must be supplied by the flywheel. As this occurs, the press members deflect. A quantity analysis of the energy involved will show why a gradual reduction in cutting pressure prior to snap-thru is very important.

The magnitude of the energy released increases as the square of the tonnage developed at the moment of final breakthrough, *Figures 29-1* and *29-2*. The actual energy is given by:

$$E = \frac{F \times D}{2}.$$

In this equation: F = Pressure at the moment of breakthrough in short-tons. (lbf $\times$ 2000)

D = Amount of total deflection in inches.

$E \times 166.7$ = Energy in foot-pounds

* Mr. Anthony Rante, P. E., Manager of Mechanical Engineering, Danly Machine, Chicago, Illinois very graciously checked the author's formulas and figures used in this chapter and published in reference 1.

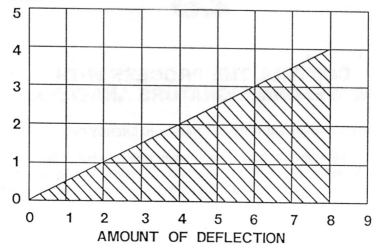

FORCE

Figure 29-1. *Graphic solution to the amount of energy stored.*

or:

F = Pressure at moment of breakthrough in metric-tons (kgf × 1000).

D = Amount of total deflection in millimeters.

E × 9.807 = Energy in Joules or Watt-Seconds

For example, using *English* units, if 400 short-tons (3,560 kN) which resulted in .080 in. (2.03 mm) total deflection was required to cut through a thick steel blank, the energy released at snap-through would be 2667 foot-pounds (3,616 J). This can be seen by the following equation:

$$E = \frac{F \times D}{2} = \frac{400 \text{ tons} \times .080 \text{ in.} \times 166.7}{2} = 2667 \text{ ft-lbs}$$

Note: (1 Foot-Pound = 1.356 Joules or Watt-Seconds)
(1 Joule or Watt-Second = .7375 Foot-Pounds.)
(1 Inch-Ton = 166.7 Foot-Pounds.)

The reduction in shock and noise would be dramatic if the cutting sequences were carefully timed. This would allow a gradual reduction in the tonnage amount at the moment of snap-thru so that only 200 tons (1,780 kN) are released.

This is because half the tonnage would produce half as much deflection or .040 in. (1.02 mm). The resultant snap-thru energy would only be 667 foot-pounds (904 J), or one fourth the former value.

332

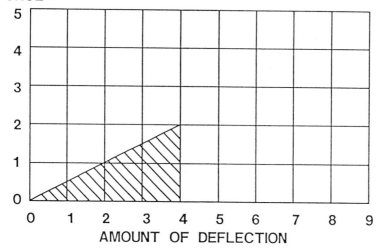

FORCE

Figure 29-2. *Graphic solution showing square law relationship.*

Minimizing Snap-thru Energy

Timing shear and punch entry sequences provides a gradual release of tonnage prior to snap-thru as the most effective way to reduce the shock and noise associated with this problem. Blanking presses should be of robust construction to minimize deflection. The energy released has a direct relationship to the amount of deflection.

Figure 29-3 shows the large reverse load resulting from incorrect punch timing. The result of proper timing to provide a gradual release of tonnage prior to final breakthrough is shown in *Figure 29-4*.

Product Design Factors

A very effective way to use snap-thru energy is to do some forming work in any die that is designed to do heavy cutting. Cooperation between the product designer, process engineer and die designer can avoid press and die damage.[2]

Putting This Theory to Work

The third edition of the SME Die Design Handbook was edited during 1989 and 1990. The die engineering formulas were updated and simplified to better enable users to do die designing and troubleshooting with good mathematical aids. The formula previously presented in this chapter was developed as a simple, but essentially correct means to quantify the amount of energy involved. The most important fact is that snap-thru energy increases in proportion to the amount of tonnage developed at the moment of breakthrough. The basis for quantifying press deflection is contained in references 3, 4, 5 and 6.

FORCE

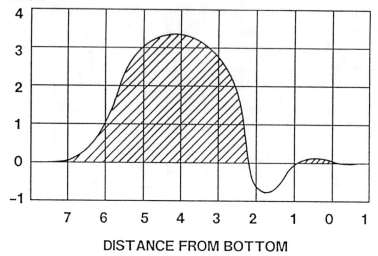

DISTANCE FROM BOTTOM

Figure 29-3. *Reverse load resulting from incorrect punch timing.*

FORCE

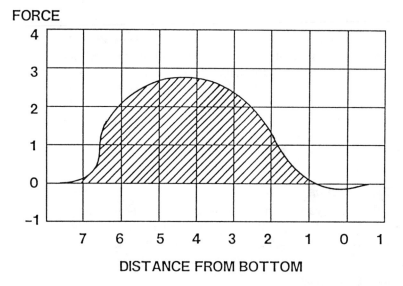

DISTANCE FROM BOTTOM

Figure 29-4. *Correct timing reduces snap-thru.*

The Traditional Approach

Grinding die and/or punch shear together with staggering punch entry has been the approach usually taken to reduce the severity of snap-thru problems. The degree of energy release severity was usually quantified by the occurrence of such problems as:

• The electromechanical relays on the press dropping out.

334

- Electromechanical relays dropping out several presses away.
- Frequent press structural damage, especially screws and pitmans at the slide connection point.
- Motors, flywheel, etc. falling off of the press.
- The need to chain the press to a column like an elephant to prevent it from moving.
- Neighbors complaining about their dishes being rattled one half mile or more away.

While the problem in the case study following involved only an excessive rate of tool steel breakage and press damage, all of these manifestations of a severe snap-thru problem have been documented in the metal stamping industry, and probably still do occur.

Often, the problem has been misunderstood. The perception was that the press required a gradual increase of tonnage rather than a gradual release. The cure to the problem should not be treated as a black art. With the use of a high-speed chart recorder, the tonnage waveform signatures may be obtained, improvements in timing and shear affected, and the results analyzed.

A Practical Application

This case study explains a successful procedure implemented to stop snap-thru related press damage at Webster Manufacturing Company in Tiffin, Ohio. Webster's unique application in the use of waveform signature analysis is used as both a process and quality control tool on every stamping job. This assures both that snap-thru forces are within 10% of press tonnage and that it duplicates a previous setup that produced high-quality parts.

COMPANY BACKGROUND

The origins of Webster Manufacturing Company date back to 1876 when T. K. Webster founded the company to produce elevator buckets. The company has gone through many changes during the past 114 years, most notably when purchased by the management and salaried employees began using an ESOP in 1986.

Under the leadership of President Fredric Spurck and the restructured management team, the emphasis of the business changed to the production of engineering-class chain. This made strategic sense since Webster had a long history of producing a wide variety of specialized chain for use in their custom engineered material handling equipment.

Design for Quality Manufacturing—A Philosophy

With new management came an increased emphasis on value-added quality for the customer. The adage about a chain being only as strong as its weakest link certainly is true. Applying this to quality assurance simply means that quality must be designed into all of the processes required to make chain. This starts with material vendor selection and continues all the way through assuring customer satisfaction in the field, and is followed up by one of the engineering staff. All employees are expected to be the links in a chain which must not fail. As a team, they understand that delivery of dependable value to the customer is the basis for both corporate prosperity and job security.

From a design standpoint, that means value to the customer is measured in terms of functionality, accuracy and longevity of the product. All specifications must be applicable to every link with certainty. Any design change must be evaluated in terms of adding still more value to the customer for each dollar that is spent on chain.

From a process engineering standpoint, all manufacturing processes not only must be in control at all times, they must depend on good process design rather than individual human skill factors to affect product uniformity.

Because of this quality philosophy, when a press damage problem occurred, it was seen as a process control problem that needed analysis and correction.

Types of Presses Used

The majority of the stamping work is done on five straightside presses. A 500 ton (4.448 MN) Minster is the largest. Two 300 ton (2.669 MN) Verson presses, a 250 ton (2.224 MN) Verson press and a 150 ton (1.334 MN) Bliss press are also used. All but one have tonnage meters. The remainder of the presses are of gap frame construction.

Increased Volume Highlighted a Problem

As the stamping volume of chain components increased, the amount of press damage, and consequent downtime, was starting to cause difficulty in manufacturing flexibility. The volume of chain produced each year has increased every year since 1983 when chain accounted for 30 to 35% of the total production. Presently 80% of total volume is engineering-class chain and sales are at an all time high.

The increased production demands pinpointed a need for a good preventive maintenance program starting with the oldest of three plants.

ANALYSIS

Evaluating Total Maintenance Needs

The management hired an engineering firm to determine maintenance needs and set up a preventive maintenance program. All aspects of the physical plant were evaluated.

The author was asked to evaluate and make recommendations to solve the pressworking-related maintenance problems. An important part of the evaluation process was gathering oral data from the hourly employees on their opinions of the root causal factors of all equipment problems. The confidential interviews were conducted by the engineering firm and the author.

The cooperation of all employees interviewed at this facility was outstanding. Upon evaluating the results of the interviews, a group of common employee concerns indicated that:

- The jobs may require more tonnage than is available with existing equipment.
- Problems with equipment reported by diesetters and operators needed better follow-up.
- The tonnage meters did not always provide reliable data.
- Punch head breakage was a problem.
- Setup repeatability was not always assured on first hit, requiring adjustments to produce a quality part.
- Employee commitment to produce a high-quality defect-free product was excellent.
- Training for pressroom employees in pressworking theory was desirable.
- Training in press maintenance and troubleshooting for the maintenance employees was needed.

Evaluation of Employee Interviews

Every item on the above list was promptly evaluated, and action taken. Training for all employees was a top priority with management. The same is true of investigating the cause of any abnormal press performance.

Punch head breakage was a management concern. Many different combinations of tool steels and heat treatments had been tried with little progress toward correcting the breakage problem. The vendor advice was to accept a high rate of tool breakage as inevitable in heavy presswork. Management refused to accept this.

The problems with erratic tonnage meter readings was initially blamed on assembly and metalforming operations that made use of high-power induction heating equipment in the same room.

From the interviews and discussions with management, it was apparent that no one was aware of the role of snap-thru energy release and the damage that had been occurring. A review of invoices for press repair parts revealed that the damage was related to shock loads, especially to the press connection. Because of these factors, the main thrust of the initial recommendations to management was to address the snap-thru problem as a top priority.

INITIAL REPORT OF OPTIONS AND RECOMMENDATIONS

The following report, together with several appendices of supporting documentation, was prepared at the management's request so that the options could be examined and an action plan to solve the identified problems be put into place.

Option One—Do Nothing

This was not an acceptable option. The cost of press repair and attending scheduling difficulties during periods of peak production will not permit this option.

Option Two—Buy Heavier Presses

This was a good long term goal because snap-thru forces are directly proportional to the amount of press deflection that occurs for each ton of load. Used presses may be a good choice because many older presses were built to very conservative design specifications for strain levels under full load, and are available in quantity on the used press market. Look for presses that have very high actual weights in relationship to size and tonnage. Avoid presses fabricated of light-weight steel plate.

Always try to keep snap-thru tonnage below 10% of press capacity. This is easier to do with high-capacity presses.

Option Three—Improve Tooling

The proven approach to reducing snap-thru is to reduce the amount of actual tonnage developed as the last cutting through occurs. This is done by timing punch breakthrough and providing balanced shear where possible.

Reducing the tonnage released at the moment of final breakthrough can have dramatic results because the amount of energy stored in the deflected press increases as the square of the tonnage developed.

A valuable tool that will permit detailed analysis of tooling problems and the effect of improvements is *waveform signature analysis*. A minor modification to the tonnage meters will be required to provide direct access to the analog signal.

A combination of using larger presses (option two) and combining all operations into a single die is an especially attractive strategy. For example, combining form, pierce, shave and cutoff operations would improve productivity and not increase snap-thru. Multiple operations present more timing improvement opportunities. The labor savings could provide an attractive short-term payback. The effect of tumbling to deburr and descale the parts may distort the shaved hole, and must be considered in terms of value to the customer.

The use of punches having a slight taper was suggested by one expert. This has the effect of wedging the punch in the hole requiring high stripping forces. This would require strong punch heads and retainers (pitch blocks). Experimentation and waveform signature analysis are again needed.

Punch breakage problems are separate from the press damage issue and were discussed in an appendix.

Option Four—Shock Arresting Devices

The serious damage that snap-thru energy has caused over the years has caused manufacturers to try many shock arresting devices with variable results.

Both rubber and nitrogen cylinders have been used to attempt to absorb the shock. Some benefits may be realized, but it is not considered a cure-all for a snap-thru problem.

A few hydraulic snap-thru arresters have been used successfully. One design requires bolster modification and very careful height adjustment of the rods that contact the slide. It is effective, but very few are known to be in use.

A second type is configured much like a hydraulic bottle jack. While it is effective, careful adjustment for press shut height is needed because the working stroke is short. A fixed orifice must be sized to provide proper retardation under a snap-thru condition without robbing the press of excessive energy prior to breaking through.

RECOMMENDATIONS

Short-Term Recommendations

The following short-term measurers were advised:
1. Modify all tonnage meters for analog output—the estimated cost is under $100.00 per instrument for parts and one day's labor by a field technician to modify all instruments.
2. Procure a high-speed chart recorder.
3. Train diemakers and diesetters to use waveform signature analysis.
4. Measure reverse loading on all problem jobs in the presses in which they run with a chart recorder. Keep records.
5. Run the worst jobs in the strongest machine (no one can guarantee whether or not it will break).
6. Modify existing dies to the greatest extent possible by means of timing and balanced shear.
7. As an option, experiment with rubber blocks or nitrogen cylinders between the bolster and slide–verify any improvement with waveform signature analysis.

Long-Term Recommendations

1. Purchase larger presses.
2. Choose presses of especially robust construction.
3. Beef up the press connection(s) when down for other repairs–for example, larger pitmans and wristpins where practical.
4. Combine operations in larger presses–for example, to set a joggle, pierce, shave, and separate in one die, there would be more opportunity to reduce snap-thru by timing punch loads than if these operations were run separately.

Management's Action Plan

The consultant's report was accepted and a conservative action plan adopted. It was decided to proceed with a sequential approach, by implementing and

339

determining the results of the short-term recommendations, before proceeding with all of the long-term recommendations such as purchasing larger presses.

The author agreed to provide the required training. Although the procedure has been described in technical papers, no training materials specific to snap-thru reduction existed.[3] Clearly, some unique training materials would need to be developed and assembled into student workbooks.

EXAMPLES OF THE THEORY THAT WAS TAUGHT

Waveform Analysis

Stamping press waveform signature analysis is a tool for determining problems in both presses and dies. Just as an electrocardiogram can reveal heart conditions that cannot be determined with a stethoscope, signature analysis can reveal facts about the stamping process that cannot be determined by feeling or listening alone.

The next few figures are hand-drawn illustrations of the waveforms that we expected to see on the chart recorder . It was very helpful that the diemakers and diesetters were familiar with the interpretation of X-Y charts and graphs because of their training in blueprint reading and multiple axis machine tools. The class had no trouble putting the theory into practice. It is interesting to compare the hand-drawn waveforms with actual examples later in this paper.

Figure 29-5 illustrates a hand-drawn example of the waveform signature of a simple coining operation. Until tonnage is developed, the pen-trace is a flat line *(A)* on the zero axis with slight perturbations caused by mechanical noise within the press.

When the upper die coining steel(s) make contact with the stock, the trace swings sharply upward *(B)* until bottom dead center is reached at *C.* At this point, the maximum deflection of press members has occurred. This deflection is normal and is a requirement in any mechanical press if tonnage is to be developed.

A virtual mirror image of the upward trace *(B)* occurs on the downward trace *(D)*. Usually very little metal is displaced in coining and therefore a symmetrical trace shows the strain (deflection) in the machine as a function of the sinusoidal motion of the crankshaft. The trace is derived from the amplified signal from a strain gage or strain transducer.

Cutting operations are often troubled with a harmful release of energy known as *snap-thru. Figure 29-6* illustrates such an operation. The punches make contact with the stock at *A* and the pressure exerted by the press increases until the force is sufficient to break through the stock. Usually the punches have cut one-third of the way through the stock when this occurs.

Unlike in a coining operation *(Figure 29-5)*, where the compressive force through the stock equals the force exerted by the press, there is nothing to resist the force of the press and the energy stored in the press members as strain

340

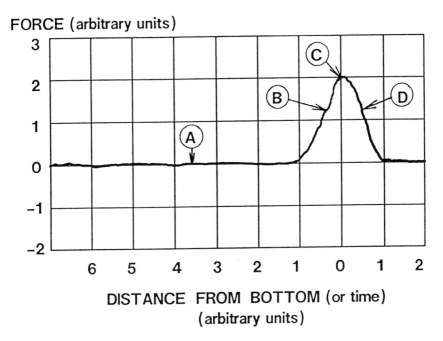

Figure 29-5. *Hand-drawn waveform signature of a typical coining operation.*

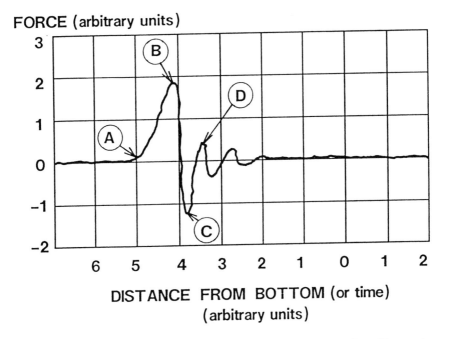

Figure 29-6. *Hand-drawn waveform signature of a cutting operation with snap-thru.*

(deflection) is suddenly released.

The sudden release of energy causes a rebound *(C)* to occur. This release of energy tends to concentrate stress at the press' weakest point in the reverse load mode, which is the press connection (where the pitman attaches to the slide). Continued operation with such reverse loading can cause the press connection to fail.

This energy is finally dissipated as a dampened mechanical oscillation *(D)* within the press.

Timing

The usual solution to the problem of sudden snap-thru energy release is to reduce the amount of energy stored in the press members as strain or deflection. This is usually done by timing the breakthrough of the punch(es) with the timing of engagement, shear angles, or both. Correctly done, this can dramatically reduce the amount of energy released because the amount of energy increases as the square of the tonnage released. *Figure 29-7* illustrates the expected results of applying optimum shear and timing to a cutting operation.

With proper timing and application of balanced shear, the first punches make contact at *A* and the pressure increase begins. As the first peak is reached and breakthrough occurs at *B*, additional punches have engaged the work prevent-

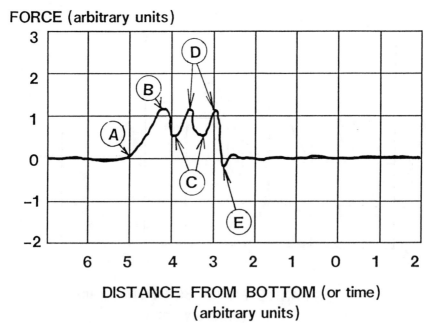

Figure 29-7. *Hand-drawn waveform signature illustrating reduction of snap-thru energy by stepping multiple punches.*

ing a sudden recoil in the press members. Downward excursions of pressure do occur at the two valleys *(C)* but this energy is used to continue the cutting action shown as peaks *(D)*. When final breakthrough occurs, the energy release is not destructive *(E)*.

Figure 29-8 illustrates a combined forming and cutting (piercing) operation. At *A*, the piercing punches make contact and the tonnage increase begins. Breakthrough occurs at *B* resulting in a severe snap-thru phenomenon *(C)* and a dampened mechanical oscillation *(D)*.

Forming then begins, resulting in another tonnage increase at *E*, which peaks at *F* and gradually releases at *G*.

There is an opportunity to reduce the magnitude of the negative load by: (1) timing of punch breakthrough and the use of balanced shear; and (2) using some of the recoil in the forming operation.

Figure 29-9 is a hand-drawn idealized illustration of what is often possible to do to improve a snap-thru problem in a combined operation, such as *Figure 29-8*, through careful timing.

The initial contact at point *(A)* occurs closer to bottom in the press stroke than was the case in *Figure 29-8*. When the first breakthrough occurs *(B)* other punches have engaged the stock to limit the negative excursion *(C)*. Other punches break through at *D* and *E*, but the negative excursion is further limited by the initiation of a heavy forming operation *(F)*. The peak *(G)* and

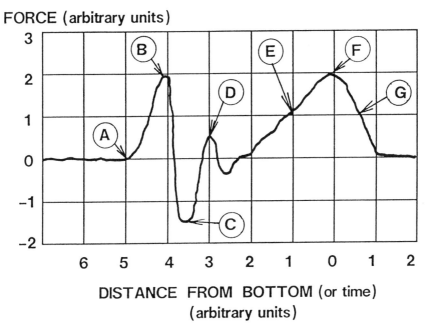

Figure 29-8. *Hand-drawn waveform signature illustrating a combined cutting and forming operation with excessive snap-thru.*

343

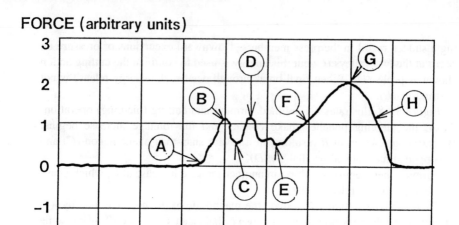

Figure 29-9. *Hand-drawn waveform signature of the theoretical improvement possible when the snap-thru energy is used to do forming work in a combined operation.*

release of energy (*H*) are as nondestructive as that of the coining operation illustrated in *Figure 29-5.*

Limitations of Timing Combined Operations

While some improvement is usually possible, a complete solution may require some modification of the process or combining of processes. Operations where very thick fine-grained hard stock are press worked may result in breakthrough well before one-third penetration is reached. This may mean that any forms or joggles to be made are not started yet. Even so, the effect of individual punch timing and the application of shear can be analyzed and quantified more accurately with waveform signature analysis than by any other method.

MEASUREMENT EQUIPMENT

Modifying Tonnage Meters for Chart Recorder Output

The tonnage meter manufacturer provided instructions for modification of the tonnage meters to obtain the analog signals from each channel, as well as the sum channel. It was explained that the analog direct current (DC) voltage level from zero to 100 percent tonnage was 0 to -4 volts DC. An Amphenol® type connector was recommended for the stamping shop environment.

These were installed in each of the four tonnage meters and a chart recorder ordered. To avoid the need to re-zero the chart recorder each time that it was moved to a different press, a 4.7 microfarad DC blocking capacitor was placed in the signal line from each channel. A larger value of capacitance may be necessary for very slow operations. This can be calculated by using the time constant formula based upon the number of seconds a press cycle takes and the input impedance of the chart recorder.

Chart Recorder Selection

Required bandwidth or frequency response and ease of use are the two most important considerations when selecting a chart recorder for signature analysis. The nominal frequency response of a tonnage meter is at least 1 kHZ.

Electromechanical pen and ink recorders typically have a frequency response that extends to only 125 HZ. This is sufficient for observing slow phenomena such as conventional drawing, embossing, and coining at speeds of up to 100 SPM. For analysis of fast rise-time events such as those generated by snap-thru release as well as cam and draw ring impact, a chart recorder having frequency responses of at least 500 HZ is desirable. Insufficient frequency response will not display the full magnitude of shock and impact problems.

A two-channel recorder is a minimum requirement if comparisons of the coincidence of an event on two different channels are to be done. An important application in press troubleshooting is making sure that all corners of a slide reach bottom dead center at exactly the same time. Timing problems caused by a twisted crankshaft or a partly sheared key can be easily identified by an A to B comparison when peak tonnage was developed on two or more channels. A four channel recorder will permit observation of four channels simultaneously, which often will speed signature analysis work.

The requirements decided upon were:
- Thermal paper to avoid the mess and clogging problems associated with pen and ink recorders.
- At least two channels.
- Automatic identification of voltage range, paper speed, date and time.
- At least 1 kHZ real-time frequency response.
- A wide range of speeds and voltage input levels to permit other uses in the plant such as power line monitoring.
- Portability.
- Battery-powered operation.

An existing oscilloscope with camera was considered, but it was decided that the cost of film to record the amount of data to be gathered would be prohibitive. Further, a chart recorder permits real time recording of a number of sequential events.

Digital signal acquisition and storage done in conjunction with a personal computer was also considered. It was ruled out because it would require the operators to be trained in basic computer skills in addition to signature analysis. Further, the amount of portable equipment required would be greater.

After reviewing the available equipment, a four-channel 25 kHZ real-time chart recorder with all of the required features was selected. An instrument cart with pneumatic tires also was purchased. A protective cover of 0.250 in. (6.0 mm) clear acrylic plastic was fabricated in the tool room. To avoid the need to plug the unit into AC power which could cause ground loop noise pick-up, a 12 volt automotive-type storage battery was placed on the bottom shelf and connected to the recorder by a cable with a quick disconnect plug. At this point, with the classroom training about halfway complete, the theory was going in to practice. Problems must be anticipated.

ANALYSIS

The first waveform signature was made on the 500 ton (4.448 MN) straightside press during a heavy punching and cut-off operation. The entry was not timed: so a signature resembling *Figure 29-6* was expected. *Figure 29-10* illustrates the waveform signature that was actually recorded.

The tonnage increase started at *A* when the punches made initial contact with the stock. Plastic deformation of the stock occurred as the punches penetrated the stock until point *B* was reached, where the punches broke

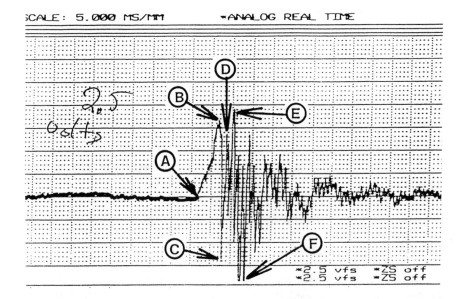

Figure 29-10. *Poor waveform fidelity results from mounting strain sensors in improper locations.*

346

through the stock. The sudden release of energy that occurred when the punches broke through caused a negative load *(C)* to occur. This energy sets up a mechanical oscillation within the press resulting in a positive peak at *D*.

According to accepted theory, the oscillation should decrease in amplitude over a few cycles. This was not the case. A higher peak *(E)* than the force that caused it *(B)* is seen. This is followed by negative peaks *(F)* that exceed the amplitude of the intial snap-thru at *C*.

Analysis of the Problem

Upon comparing the peak voltage levels recorded on the chart with the tonnage values displayed on the tonnage meter, it was found that the chart recorder voltage levels were low by a factor of three. It was found that the press capacity set inside the tonnage meter by the electrical contractor who installed it was 1,500 tons (13.44 MN) rather than 500 tons (4.448 MN). This is sometimes done to get enough strain gage amplification to display correct readings. The root cause of low strain gage output, when measuring loads on mechanical presses, is that the gage or transducer is mounted at a location on the machine that sees little strain under normal press operation.

Figure 29-11 illustrates a horizontal cross section through the press columns. The four tie rods are each surrounded by a shroud made of heavy steel plate. This part of the column structure is designed to withstand the compressive preloading that the tie rods exert on the column. The rest of the vertical steel plate in the column is much lighter. The main design consideration for the lighter plate is to provide enough rigidity to withstand the lateral forces generated during normal press operation, and to provide a housing for mechanical and electrical equipment.

The strain transducers were mounted by the electrical contractor at *L1* shown in *Figure 29-11*. This was probably done because the location was easily accessible. An assumption may have been made that it did not matter where strain transducers are mounted so long as a load cell calibration is done. This assumption is not correct. By mounting the sensor on the light-weight plate, the main measurement was the magnitude of the mechanical resonance or oscillation excited by the snap-thru release. It was not the actual forward and reverse loads.

Correcting the Sensor Location Problem

The tonnage meter manufacturer was contacted for advice on correcting the problem. Even though the installation was done by an independent electrical contractor recommended by a press equipment dealer, and the equipment was out of warranty, the manufacturer was more than willing to provide the needed technical support to correct the problem. This included an on-site evaluation by the president of the company and the manager of the technical support group.

It was clear that a better sensor location was needed. A strain transducer was mounted at location *L2 (Figure 29-11)* and the signal fed into a channel of the

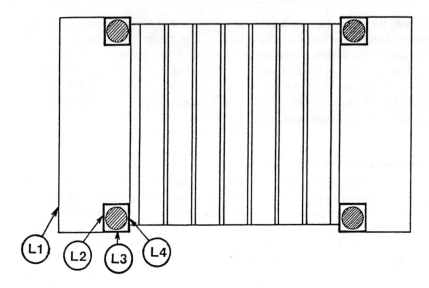

Figure 29-11. *Mounting locations for strain sensors on the column of a Minster 500 ton (4.448 MN) straightside press.*

tonnage meter which was adjusted to the same calibration number or gain setting as the sensor at *L1*.

An A–B comparison of the two side-by-side signals is shown in *Figure 29-12*. The upper trace is from the sensor at *L1* and was made on the 2.5 volts full scale range. The lower trace is from the sensor at *L2* and was made on the 5 volts full-scale range. Note that the lower signature resembles the theoretical wave-form illustrated in *Figure 29-6*.

The improvement in sensitivity measured at the peak load that occurred just before snap-thru is a factor of 3.45. This improvement in sensitivity permitted the tonnage meter to be operated at the correct press capacity setting. Note that the lower trace is much cleaner than the upper trace indicating that the ratio of electrical noise pick-up to signal was also improved.

Location *L4*, shown in *Figure 29-11*, was also tried and the sensor reading approximately doubled over location *L2*. Locations on the inside of press columns are usually much more sensitive than those on the outside of the column. This is because both the press bed and crown deflect. The tie rod nuts act as neutral points. This means that the outside of the columns tend to be driven into compression while the preload is rapidly relieved on the inside of the columns. How this phenomenon occurs is illustrated in *Figure 29-13*.

Sensor Mount Locations on Other Presses

The same problem was encountered on the other three presses that had tonnage meters. Apparently, to simplify the routing of wiring, the contractor had installed the sensors on the outside of the columns. Moving the sensors to the

348

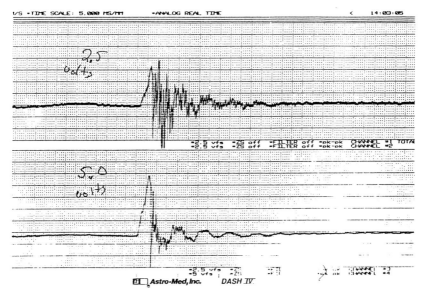

Figure 29-12. *The upper waveform signature was obtained from a strain sensor mounted at L1 in Figure 29-11; the lower waveform signature was from a sensor mounted at L2.*

inside of the columns resulted in the improvements in sensitivity listed in *Table 29-1*.

TABLE 29-1

Press	Percentage Improvement
500 ton Minster	694%
300 ton Verson	294%
300 ton Verson	430%
250 ton Verson	236%

RESULTS

Pressroom Employee Training

Additional training on strain-gage instrumentation was provided as a result of tonnage meter problems. This included coverage of the causes and cures of tonnage meter problems.

As a result, the diesetters have an excellent insight into the physical principles that underlie the successful pressworking of heavy metal. The tonnage meter readings and chart recorder data are now providing reliable process control information to produce high-quality parts while avoiding equipment damage.

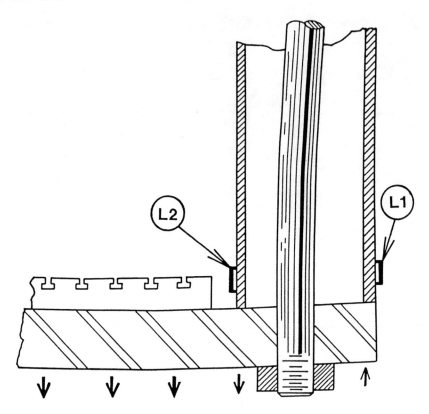

Figure 29-13. *Strain sensors should be mounted on the inside of press columns L2 where possible because bed and crown deflection tends to drive the outside of the column into compression; a factor that introduces waveform distortion and results in low sensor output when mounted on the outside L1.*

To simplify chart interpretation, three-color plastic overlays were made on overhead projector film stock. These overlays *(Figure 29-14)* permit rapid evaluation of peak positive and negative loads.

An Example Snap-thru Reduction by Die Timing

Figure 29-15 illustrates a waveform resulting from an operation to punch two 1.625 in. (41.275 mm) holes and part a side bar from fine-grained AISI-SAE 1039 steel. The steel was 0.500 in. (12.7 mm) thick by 3 in. (76.2 mm) wide.

A 300-ton (2.669-MN) Verson straightside press was used for this operation. The allowable reverse load is 30 tons (.267 MN). Point *A* on *Figure 29-15* illustrates a peak load of 191 tons (1.7 MN) which was also displayed on the tonnage meter. This is well within press capacity.

While the tonnage meter did not display reverse load without accessing a switch located inside the locked box, the reverse load was easily read by using

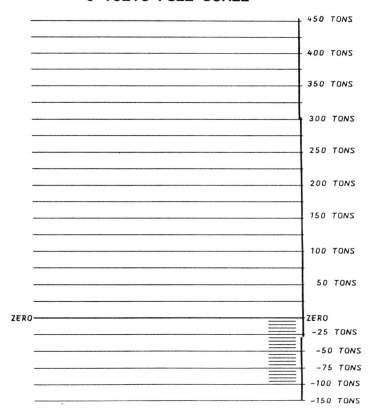

300 TON CHART ANALYSIS OVERLAY GRID
5 VOLTS FULL SCALE

450 TONS
400 TONS
350 TONS
300 TONS
250 TONS
200 TONS
150 TONS
100 TONS
50 TONS
ZERO
-25 TONS
-50 TONS
-75 TONS
-100 TONS
-150 TONS

Figure 29-14. *Plastic overlay made from overhead projector transparency stock for evaluating peak positive and negative loads.*

the plastic overlay. In this case, the reverse load *B* was 87 tons (.774 MN), which is nearly three times the allowable amount. The die was immediately taken to the repair bench and one punch shortened 0.312 in. (7.92 mm). Balanced angular shear was ground on the punches. Balanced shear was also ground on the parting punch.

Figure 26-16 illustrates the improvement achieved by modifying the tool. The peak tonnage was reduced to 82.8 tons (.741 MN) which is less than half the initial value. The reverse load was reduced to 22 tons (.197 MN) or about one fourth the former value. This is keeping with the square law formula.

Balanced Shear and Timing Added to Many Jobs

The one example presented here is with the permission of Webster Manufacturing Company. Webster management shares the opinion that many other press

351

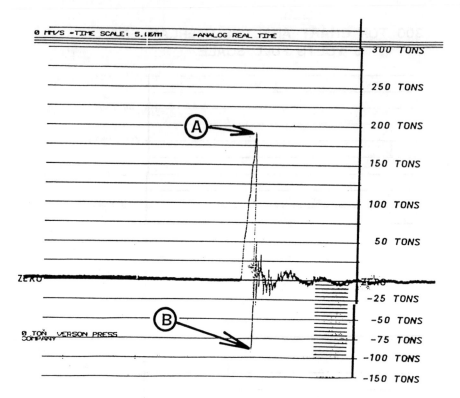

Figure 29-15. *The actual waveform signature of a combined piercing and cut-off operation having excessive snap-thru, or reverse load.*

shops have jobs that have excessive snap-thru.

Further, it is likely that many other tonnage meter installations have been done improperly on the assumption that sensor location is not important provided that a load cell calibration is done.

Literally hundreds of different chain stampings are made at Webster and some of the processes are proprietary.

The application of the principles and procedures outlined in this paper have been applied to all jobs including runs with as few as twenty parts. All jobs are operated at under 10% reverse load with the exception of three that are in the 12% range.

At management's request, a one day hands-on training session in the correct installation and calibration of tonnage meters was conducted for an electrician. This included how to do an accurate load cell tonnage meter calibration. A 250 ton (2.224 MN) load cell was purchased for use with an existing portable tonnage meter for this purpose.

The result is an in-house tonnage meter maintenance and calibration capability. This factor has greatly increased the employees' confidence in the tonnage meter data. Whenever a problem is suspected, the electrician can quickly

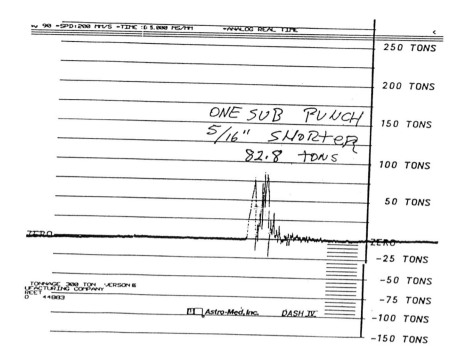

Figure 29-16. *Waveform signature of the job illustrated in Figure 29-15 after adding timing and balanced shear.*

resolve the issue.

In addition, an important part of the consulting engineers' findings and report was that there was a lack of conformance to written maintenance procedures. Too often, repairs appeared to be based upon trial and error troubleshooting rather than problem analysis.

Apart from the obvious cost reduction and the scheduling improvements, preventive maintenance was considered a must from the standpoint of maintaining high standards for employee safety.

Management provided mandatory in-house training for all maintenance employees in the new preventive maintenance procedures. This included training in following proper written maintenance procedures and written report generation.

SPECIAL CONSIDERATIONS

Electromagnetic Interference (EMI) Problem

The common relationship used to quantify EMI as a problem is the ratio of the desired signal to the interfering signal. This is called the *signal to noise ratio*.

Experts who analyze EMI problems agree that there are only two ways to solve an EMI problem. To improve the signal to noise ratio, either there must be more signal or less noise.

The strain sensor signal-to-noise ratio was improved in all cases by the percentage of improvement in mechanical signal achieved by better sensor locations. Moving the sensors effectively solved the noise pick-up problem that was the root cause of erratic tonnage meter operation.

Tool Steel Breakage Problem

Some chain components are cast of malleable iron. The foundry pours two heats of induction furnace malleable iron daily. In addition to casting sprockets, chain buckets, and other chain parts, high-precision custom castings such as pipe wrench handles and diesel engine components are also produced. The malleable iron is made either from malleable scrap of known composition or from AISI-SAE 1010 steel punchings to which metallurgical coke, ferro-silicon and other constituent elements are added. Care in maintaining uniform molten material results in castings that respond correctly to the heat treatment needed to produce the malleable product.

The heavy scrap punchings generated in the press room are not suitable for incorporation into a malleable product because of the alloying elements present. Chromium in particular will cause severe problems if present in malleable iron.

The heavy punchings command a premium price on the scrap market for use as counterweight ballast. The same scrap dealer that buys the heavy punchings also pays a premium price for scrap tool steel. A one-year accumulation of scrap tool steel was stored in a drum in the press shop. The company was very fortunate to have the scrap available because we wanted to know the exact extent of the tool steel breakage problem.

The dieroom employees audited the one-year accumulation and ascribed the failure mode responsible for each detail scrapped. A spreadsheet program helped to determine the percentages of each type of failure and the dollar amount involved.

It was found that breakage due to impact and snap-thru problems accounted for 26.7 percent of the discarded tool steel. An annual expense of $18,045.62 was incurred to replace punches and die blocks broken due to shock and impact problems. Most of this expense was due to head and point breakage.

A slight chamfer was ground on the heads of all punches to stop the flange around the head from flexing under compressive loading. The point configuration was also changed to reduce the snap-thru energy problems. This resulted in tool steel breakage being reduced to negligible levels.

IMPROVEMENT

Productivity Improvement

All of the larger presses have variable speed drives. In an effort to reduce shock and the resultant press damage, many jobs were being operated at reduced press speed.

Once die timing was optimized, it was found that most jobs could be operated at maximum press speed without undue tool wear, noise or excessive snap-thru. This resulted in a productivity improvement of up to 25%.

Buying larger presses was initially an attractive option. However, a typical 1,000 ton (8.896 MN) press operates at a maximum of 24 strokes per minute (SPM). With good die design and careful timing, even the largest jobs can be operated in existing presses that are capable of speeds of over 40 SPM.

A 600 ton (5.338 MN) hydraulic press was sold because of double breakage quality problems on pierced holes. By operating at the maximum allowable cutting speed for the materials being worked both quality and productivity are improved.

Quality Improvement

Quality was improved in several ways, including:
- Freedom from double breakage in pierced holes as a result of faster press speeds.
- Improved setup repeatability resulting from verification of the exact duplication of a previous setup that produced high-quality chain components.
- Optimization of punch-to-die clearance on all pierce and shave operations by means of the waveform signature.
- Enhanced record keeping and analysis of the factors needed to duplicate quality part runs.

Noise Reduction

There is general agreement that the press shop is a quieter place to work now that snap-thru energy is under control. While not an initial consideration in reducing snap-thru energy, it certainly is a side benefit.

Press Damage Reduction

Latent damage that has already occurred is one problem that may show up after a program is in place.

A mechanical press may appear to operate normally even though stress cracks may extend half-way through a pitman or crankshaft. The crack will continue to propagate under normal loading until failure occurs.

To minimize this factor, a program is under way to disassemble all presses and inspect all parts using nondestructive die penetrant and magnetic particle testing. All presses are being reworked to meet or exceed the manufacturer's specifications.

In addition to the improved scheduling flexibility that comes with reduced breakdowns there is a large annual savings in press repair.

355

ANALYSIS OF FACTORS LEADING TO SUCCESS

The President, Vice President, Engineering Manager, and Quality Control Manager all gave their unequivocal support to the recommended changes in maintenance and manufacturing methods. Training was seen as an immediate requirement. Management refused to accept any form of mediocrity in the way that they did business. This absolute support from the top helps insure success.

Other factors insuring success include:

- Analysis of the results of the confidential press room employee interviews and adoption of the recommended action plan of consulting engineers, particularly regarding the need for employee training.
- Management attended the training sessions.
- There was a skilled literate work force to train.
- Attendance of training sessions was mandatory.
- Assignment of an extremely project oriented individual, to act as in-house facilitator for training and project implementation.
- Every employee must follow written procedures detailing how to accomplish every production and maintenance task correctly and safely.
- Support of the labor union for management's training objectives.
- Use of the chart recorder for every setup to insure that previous good setups are duplicated and that there is no excessive snap-thru. This procedure continues to be followed on all jobs to this day.

Employees Rewarded at the Conclusion of Training

Employees were permitted to keep their workbooks for reference, and received the certificate of completion illustrated in *Figure 29-17*. In addition, a letter describing the training completed was placed in each employee's personnel file.

CERTIFICATE OF COMPLETION

This will certify that:

Having completed all requirements by attending twenty-four hours of classroom instruction and having acquired extensive hands-on experience in the pressroom is hereby awarded this certificate of completion of training in using chart recorder data to analyze waveform signatures and reduce snap-thru energy in heavy metal stamping.

SᵌA

David Alkire Smith
President, Smith & Associates
June 11, 1990

Figure 29-17. *Certificate of completion awarded to each employee at the completion of training.*

REFERENCES

1. David A. Smith, *Die Design Handbook*, 3rd Edition, Chapter 4, "Shear Action in Metal Cutting", The Society of Manufacturing Engineers, Dearborn, Michigan, 1990.
2. David A. Smith, "Reducing Die Maintenance Costs Through Product Design", SME Technical Paper MS89-759, Society of Manufacturing Engineers, Dearborn, Michigan, 1989.
3. Donald F. Wilhelm, "Measuring Loads On Mechanical Presses", SME Conference Proceeding, Society of Manufacturing Engineers, Dearborn, Michigan, 1988.
4. D. A. Smith, "Why Press Slide Out of Parallel Problems Affect Part Quality and Available Tonnage", SME Technical Paper TE88-442, Society of Manufacturing Engineers, Dearborn, Michigan, 1988.
5. David A. Smith, "How to Improve Hit-to-hit Time With a Tonnage Monitor", SME Technical Paper TE88-780, Society of Manufacturing Engineers, Dearborn, Michigan, 1988.
6. David A. Smith, "Adjusting Dies to a Common Shut Height", SME/FMA Technical Paper TE89-565, Society of Manufacturing Engineers, Dearborn, Michigan, 1989.
7. David A. Smith, *Die Design Handbook*, 3rd Edition, Chapter 27, "Press Data", Society of Manufacturing Engineers, Dearborn, Michigan, 1990.

INDEX